PURVEYORS of LIGHT and SHADOW

Two Artists Search for Meaning

KATE CALDER KLEIN

Grateful acknowledgment is made to the following for permission to reprint previously published material:

Excerpt from *D. H. Lawrence: An Unprofessional Study* by Anaïs Nin, copyright ©1932, reprinted by Swallow Press 1964. Reprinted here by permission of Ohio University Press.

Excerpt from *Incest: From "A Journal of Love"* by Anaïs Nin, copyright ©1992 by Rupert Pole, as Trustee under the Last Will and Testament of Anaïs Nin. Reprinted by permission of Houghton Mifflin Harcourt Publishing Company. All rights reserved.

Excerpt from *The Places that Scare You* by Pema Cödrön, copyright ©2001 by Pema Cödrön. Reprinted by arrangement with The Permissions Company, LLC, on behalf of Shambhala Publications, Inc., Boulder, Colorado, Shambhala.com.

Referenced or incorporated material is gratefully acknowledged here:

Enchantment and Exploitation: The Life and Hard Times of a New Mexico Mountain Range, Revised and Expanded Edition by William deBuys, copyright ©2015, University of New Mexico Press.

The Heartbeat of Wounded Knee: Native America from 1890 to the Present by David Treuer, copyright ©2019, Riverhead Books.

COVER PAINTING: *Child of Darkness,* by the artist known in this work as Lucy John Yaeger
ANTELOPE GRAPHIC: Nicole Cobb and an ancient rock artist
book design: The Troy Book Makers

Printed in the United States of America

The Troy Book Makers • Troy, New York • thetroybookmakers.com

To order additional copies of this title, contact your favorite local bookstore or visit www.shoptbmbooks.com

ISBN: 978-1-61468-696-5

ACKNOWLEDGMENTS

I AM INDEBTED to Jeanette Wiseman for her close readings through a native New Mexican's eyes and soul; to Judy Eddy for reading from a true friend and fellow writer's perspective; and to Jenny Russell, who knows a little about almost everything and a lot about what good writing looks and feels like. Their readerly scrutiny enabled me to shape this story and bring it forward from its roughest stages. Jane Bernstein dove in early on and helped me find some legs. Thanks to Nina Ryan's sensitive editorial advice, this book came together in texture and depth. Her strong but gentle encouragement and clear-eyed wisdom about story and storytelling helped me understand and hone my role in the narrative. Trista Edwards's keen editing skills guided me through some tricky end-stage fine tuning. Meradith Kill, of The Troy Book Makers, embraced this project unconditionally and brought remarkable care and sensitivity to the task of making a distinctive book. I owe its entry into the world to her artistry and dedication.

I have relied on Michael Lipson for his artful ways of reflecting light back into darkness; on Dave Gould and Monica Bierge for the use of their home as a writing retreat in northern New Mexico; and on the magic of Paradise Pond Casita, where I finished my first draft under Chimayo's October sky. I owe the restoration of my life and voice to the miracle-working of Randolph Ask. The heartfelt support of dear friends Karl Johnson and Mira Goral sustained me from afar, as did the quietly steadying hand lent by Kim Moss. Jeane Weigel, who has taught me precious lessons about friendship and whose trust and generosity made this book possible, has my humblest gratitude. So do my daughters Rachael and Chana and grandchildren Moshe, Emunah, Shaina, David, and Matan, for fueling me with love along the way. To my husband Michael, who remains my truest friend, teacher, and inspiration, I can only express my deepest gratitude as a bundle of love wrapped in wonderment for his unwavering faith in me.

CONTENTS

Your task is not to seek for love.

But merely to seek and find

All the barriers within yourself

That you have built against it.

— RUMI —

PROLOGUE

THIS STORY IS NOT UNUSUAL in beginning as one thing and ending up another. Its inspiration may be traced back nearly fifty years to my early experience of flying unaccompanied to Phoenix, Arizona, a few months before my fourteenth birthday. It was my very first time in an airplane and my first long-distance journey. By a fluke of someone else's last-minute change of heart, I was—with no prior planning or preparation—invited to spend a summer riding and tending horses on a traditional western ranch. Though I knew horses, I knew nothing about the Southwest. The farthest west I had ever been was Philadelphia. All I knew was that on the way from the airport to our destination we would make a required stop in a town called Prescott to buy a western (read: cowboy) hat and boots.

On that adventure I ended up learning a few western magic tricks: turning a piece of cowhide into flower petals, silver and stone into jewelry, cottonwood into Katsinas, tarantulas into pets and (regrettably) paperweights. But the startling desert that met me with a scorching blast when I first arrived—like a hot oven whose door opened directly in my face, and the magical desert I came to know, its extraordinary abundance of life inviting just the kind of close-up lens I had always carried within—changed me forever. It changed the way I see. And something powerful and visceral hidden in its varied landscapes has called me back year after year, partly to be closer to its mysteries and its ghosts, partly to feel more keenly the pull of my spirit toward nature's extremes, and partly to look more deeply into the art and wisdom of its peoples and its complex cultural heritage. The desert in all its forms, and indeed the Southwest more broadly, have given me an appreciation of that land's raw beauty, a sense of geological, natural, and human history that growing up in New England—itself a land of old ways, deep wilds, and mercurial weather—hadn't managed to instill in me before that first of many revelatory adventures in the land of dust devils and endless sky. In one way or another, those experiences carried me through my adolescence into adulthood and inform my telling of this story.

The last two weeks of that first summer in Arizona and the handful of summers that followed were spent on the road with a group of kids from the program. We were piled into the back of a cattle truck padded with our duffel bags (in the days before seatbelt safety was recognized) and driven to scenic and historic sites around the region, passing through places with names like Tuba City, Chinle, Teec Nos Pas (now Teec Nos Pos), Snowflake, and Rattlesnake. At the end of the day we stopped, set up camp in areas wondrously pristine, remote, and untamed, and we slept out in the open. I remember waking up one morning to discover that the ground upon which I had been sleeping was scattered with black and white painted potsherds and remnants of flaked stone older than I could imagine.

I joined the cook crew and was first initiated into the art of building and stoking fires and then mastering campfire cooking—two meals a day for a few dozen people. That crew detail was the first time I'd ever felt part of a tribe. Toughened on grit-laced cowboy coffee, I was emboldened enough by a sense of teamwork to venture out a few strides from the walls of my shyness. Working out in the open at or before dawn and through dusk time, I even overcame an initial fear of bats that filled the skies overhead after sundown and came to love them.

Our caravan of sorts passed through the unearthly Painted Desert of the Navajo Nation, then known and mapped as part of Navajoland, with elegant long-skirted women tending sheep and stringing necklaces of dried corn along otherwise deserted roadsides. I never learned, nor could I even guess, where they found water or how they carried on in this place that appeared so desolate that its other name was "the badlands." We visited one of the mesa-top Hopi villages, still inhabited after more than a thousand years, where I wondered at their way of life and marveled at their stunning pottery. At the same time, I sensed an underlying complicity in something

I didn't understand in our being there at all. That same year, Dee Brown's newly published *Bury My Heart at Wounded Knee* filled in for me the apparent details of a horrific history lesson too enormous and too brutal to fully comprehend. Still, it managed to affirm and shame me in my discomfort and my naïve musings about justice and an unnamed condition in which favor and promise fell to some and not others.

Brown's account came at a time when a wide audience, including my teenage self, was ready to embrace a demystified narrative of genocide in America. A half century later, a pointed counter narrative illustrates the fundamental flaws of that account. *The Heartbeat of Wounded Knee: Native America from 1890 to the Present,* published while I was completing this book, helped me understand that the story I had once accepted uncritically only reinforced another set of myths. David Treuer's much-expanded re-telling of that story celebrates the rich lives and abiding spirit of people and communities whose voices represent a still-evolving vision of themselves. *That* history, thankfully, enables us to see and understand the massacre at Wounded Knee, among other atrocities, betrayals, and injustices, as something other than an ending. For me, this is also a lesson in the danger of falling into mythmaking when the stories we tell are not our own.

On that series of road trips, which for me represented a kind of awakening, I glimpsed the passing of earthtime in my effort to grasp how the rainbow-stone tree trunks of the Petrified Forest came to be. I experienced more uncomfortable gut responses in wandering through the cheap trading posts of Gallup and along the incongruous cliff-shores of Lake Powell, at that time only about midway into the process of being formed not by nature but by the brute resistance of millions of cubic yards of concrete laid downstream, turning long-established ecosystems and even sacred burial grounds into a watery playground for vacationers. Somehow there seemed to be more blue than the sky had to offer up. Yet there it was, stirring doubts and questions for which I found no ready answers.

My small world opened to a universe I never knew existed when we drove through Monument Valley, a place I eventually brought my family and where we enjoyed our most memorable family trip before my parents separated and the universe I thought I knew did, in fact, break apart. My parents never understood or inquired about the lingering melancholy that I brought home with me and couldn't seem to shake after each homecoming. They had yet to grapple with our family's history of depression; so did the culture and the medical establishment in the early '70s, particularly in terms of understanding or even recognizing it in adolescents.

I can't fault my parents for being preoccupied with other troubles, primarily my younger brother's, which abruptly came to their attention when he was caught attempting to sell a bag of marijuana one day on the school playground during recess. He was eleven. He had found the pot in my father's top drawer. These revelations caught me between a natural alliance with my brother, fueled in part by the hypocrisy behind our father's outrage, and my genuine shock and concern over what my little brother was up to.

Through that confusing and lonely time, while I pined for the company of collared lizards and cactus wrens and the stories the desert had yet to reveal, stories it might help me tell, my mother retreated into her bedroom, the hard edges of her disintegrating world blunted by valium. A few years later, during my first semester away at college, she had what they called a nervous breakdown. When I returned, my room had been emptied of nearly all the artifacts of my childhood, everything from my cherished Polaroid photo albums and art books to beetle wings, my tarantula paperweight, and my prolific rock collections. Three things survived: the pair of Katsina dolls I had made, a small box of relics I had picked up off the desert floor, and several sketchbooks tied together with string.

I met the woman I call Lucy at a crossroads, both literally and existentially (though we didn't know it at the time), when my husband and I stopped along the High Road to Taos looking for a piece of art that felt authentic and that we could afford, two things that—for all we knew—were mutually exclusive. After a somewhat quixotic search, we found a small painting of abstracted horse figures in a tiny gallery in a remote village, satisfied that we would have an original piece of New Mexico to hang on our wall back home. But the painting never arrived, having gone missing in transit. After the shipper's customary investigation period of about a week, the painting was officially filed as lost and we were reimbursed for its value. We were informed that once an item is formally designated as lost, the claim is permanently closed. In the event that a lost parcel turns up, it is deemed shipping service property and its contents auctioned off without further notification.

Through this discouraging process and the loss felt on both ends, Lucy and I continued to correspond by email. She graciously offered us a deep discount on another of her paintings, one that I had secretly preferred but that was beyond our budget at the time we made our original purchase. This too was an abstract composition involving horse figures (the same horses, Lucy informed me), but it was larger and more detailed, more finely wrought compositionally, somewhat darker and more subtle in tone and depth. We bought the second painting, and she and I continued our correspondence in earnest after that disappointing "accident." Fairly quickly Lucy and I recognized that we shared a certain animation of spirit, but we could never have imagined the ways our paths would continue to intertwine.

A few months later, though we were still just getting to know each other, I traveled to New Mexico again. Officially, I was taking advantage of the precious narrow sliver of time between semesters; unofficially, I had surrendered to the powerful call of place that was now tied to an address, a face, a particular horizon imprinted upon my imagination as if burned by the sun into my retinal matrix. Unconsciously, I was to realize later, my journey was motivated by an undercurrent of questions about my life choices and a career that had sapped my creative energy and left me broken spirited, burned out, soldiering on, wondering where exactly I had lost my inspiration. Some unacknowledged part of me was looking for answers to questions I was afraid even to ask.

After a few days of talking about our lives, with Lucy doing most of the talking, seemingly determined to draw me out and prod me in a direction I didn't want to go, she asked me to write her story, believing she had a story to tell but not the skill to tell it. Though there was no practical reason for me, beleaguered as I was, to think I could fulfill such a request, I accepted unconditionally.

The next day, on the flight home over a frozen January landscape, I came down with a flu-like illness that lingered an unusually long time and resulted in nerve damage and permanent vocal cord paralysis. The doctors couldn't say with any certainty whether or not I would regain my ability to speak. At the end of a painful and exhausting semester standing in front of class after class managing to produce only an ugly whisper, my teaching career ended, launching me on a journey to reimagine my life's goals and come to terms with a drastic, unforeseen, and frightening change of plan.

Though I had no idea what I was actually taking on when I accepted Lucy's invitation, my lifeline, it turned out, became this project, in all its various incarnations. However, during the following couple of years, as I found my writer's voice and welcomed the gradual return of my speaking voice, Lucy succumbed to a debilitating series of illnesses. Despite a remarkably recovered life, Lucy found herself pushed into another painful period of questioning and rethinking her life and purpose. But instead of surrendering, she began writing herself, while I struggled to write her. In developing her artist's blog, Lucy found she could draw inspiration from her own ability to tell her story—and those of other artists—in her own way. In fact, she too was finding her voice.

Although I remained preoccupied with the unsettling questions Lucy's story presented, I began to see the energy and inspiration she brought to her confessional style of expression as a kind of buffer for her. She thrived in a space where her sharp photographic eye and generosity of spirit, along with her upbeat storytelling, carried her blog pages along each week. Looking back now, it seems we ended up taking complementary tacks: my writerly work directed inward and beholden to the past, hers increasingly public and leaning into the present. That's not to say Lucy had relinquished her past. She was honing her own style of self-reflection in publicly recounting significant events in her life as an artist. Meanwhile, she had given me permission to explore that essential artist's journey as a vehicle for enabling my own. In the process, she allowed me to poke around in the darker corners and make of them what I would. Perhaps this unspoken arrangement freed her to dwell more fully in the beauty she found among the details of everyday life she was living and about which she was writing, tempered with a sense of having survived, if just barely, long stretches when beauty and light had all but forsaken it.

Telling Lucy's story would demand the same degree of earnestness she consistently brought to bear in living, writing, and painting. In overcoming. I resolved to do justice to the work she had done in reflecting on her difficult journey, even when I found I needed to go deeper. So far, charting my own path has depended entirely on finding my way through her story and its various forms, some refracted through memory, others that tendril through our ongoing journey together. In this way our stories amplify one other, alloyed in friendship and impelled by the pursuit of artmaking. The story that follows is a testament to long distances traveled, an indefatigable fighting spirit, and the power of art to bring meaning to the inexplicable circumstances life presents.

PART ONE

1

ART

The High Road
Northern New Mexico
June 2010

Kate

CONTENT IN THE DRIVER'S SEAT and exhilarated about heading south on our little adventure, I nonetheless felt myself tiring of the idea of more gallery stops along the High Road to Santa Fe. I was annoyed and a little ashamed that it hadn't occurred to either of us to pick up a New Mexico road map at the state line when we'd stopped for gas. Navigating south from Denver had been straightforward enough. But being at the mercy of Will's brand new smartphone for the second day in a row, with its jarringly disembodied female voice, gave the whole enterprise a distinctly myopic feel that undermined my otherwise sturdy sense of direction. Was that little GPS all it would take to disable my seasoned internal system? I was rattled and not buying Will's unconditional trust in his new toy, feeling less vindicated than chagrined in the long, lovely stretches of alpine wilderness, where we were completely out of signal range and the device was as moot as a manatee in the high desert.

County Road South presented us with a disorienting ninety-degree right turn at the village of Alces, bending westward before it would return, presumably, to its southerly course. Approaching the turn, I had a vague feeling that I remembered the name from somewhere and wondered if I might have passed through there eight or nine years earlier on a detour up to Taos. I'd flown out to attend a seminar in El Paso which had been little more than excuse to slip into New Mexico for a couple of days. But this time I couldn't be sure that I wasn't just confusing the name with Alamogordo or Alcalde, other place names that registered somewhere in my travel memory. The dusty intersection ahead was flanked by ramshackle adobe buildings in varying stages of decay, some crude but possibly still lived in, some returning in slow motion to their earthly origins in crumbling piles of splintered wood and straw-flecked mud bricks.

A colorful mural announcing the location as Alces covered a long adobe wall that bordered the road leading up to the crossroads. As I pulled to a stop, a gallery sign pointed the way to the left, toward what looked like a small village.

"Want to stop here?" Will asked, an edge of weariness creeping into his otherwise neutral tone.

The tiny dirt parking area directly in front of the low adobe building was empty. I pulled in.

As we entered the gallery, a broad sweep of the scrubland below was visible in slices through three narrow floor-to-ceiling windows along the west wall, which framed the scruffy sagebrush and juniper of the valley running along the High Road toward Santa Fe. Already this fifty-yard detour felt promising. The room, flooded with open sky, seemed poised to vault into the bright space beyond. But the neatly mudded and whitewashed walls and antique wood beams affirmed that the structure was entirely of the earth.

A woman, possibly in her late fifties, stepped out from a back room wearing an oversized smile and a black artist's apron splattered with paint and let us know she was there if we needed any help. Her height, exaggerated somewhat by the heavy, square-heeled boots she was wearing and the way her blunt collar-length hair swung in straight sheets as she moved, suggested a young horse not fully settled into its own skin, willowy but neither awkward nor graceful.

The land was on fire outside in the intensifying bright-white heat of the sun approaching its zenith; inside the white-walled adobe, where centuries-old vigas supported delicate latillas laid across dusty hand-hewn log beams to form a herringbone pattern above, a hushed feeling of relief and protection prevailed.

As we made our way around the east side of the room, where another set of windows had been boarded up to create enough wall space for all of the paintings and still preserve the dramatic westerly view, we moved from mi-cro-realistic oils to bright abstract acrylics, clearly done by a different hand, a different eye. Working past the smooth white kiva fireplace built into the corner, its shelves and bench displaying small block-like oil paintings of soft-ly rendered fruit, we slowed down along the south wall, where the abstract work began to suggest sweeping arcs of landscape, dark outlines of horses, jagged fence posts, muted earth tones and black shapes warmed with umber. The starkness of these pieces struck me, in particular the dreamlike shadow outlines of horses merging with fences and diagonal fracture lines.

To our right, a towering canvas filled the vertical strip of wall space between two of the massive windows. The painting depicted a large, al-most mythical group of black silhouetted animals that resembled cattle, dynamically set on either side of black and white irregular circles within squares of negative space on a mostly white background, complicated by an occasional fleck of red or patch of yellow ochre. Standing captivated below the image, its intensity supplanting my half-awareness of where Will had drifted, I stood there in what must have been an unselfcon-scious pose that presented an opening. The artist approached and stood alongside me.

The price of the huge painting, entitled *Child of Darkness*, was far be-yond anything we could even consider. Not even an option for discussion. The artist's name, printed on the canvas, was Lucy John Yaeger. She and I gazed up from below.

"I'm really struck by the imagery in this painting." I found myself nearly breathless. "Very powerful." I said, savoring an awakened sense of imagina-tion that stirred and held me.

"*Child of Darkness* was one of those painting experiences where I man-aged to disappear and the piece seemed to paint itself," the artist explained. "I think I just had to get out of my own way to let it happen."

She continued while I stood silently, admiring. "When I finished, I was surprised by the symbols. I had this feeling that they were very old symbols of some kind. That inspired me to look into ancient symbolism, and I found these to be quite similar to images appearing in rock art that's believed to be shamanic in nature." She reached out a hand, unburdening me of the stowaway tension that had accompanied me in. "I'm Lucy. So nice to meet you."

We clasped hands firmly. "I'm Kate Klein, and that's my husband Will over there." I wasn't sure exactly what she had meant by "shamanic," but noting the solemn pride in her tone and my own strong response to the piece, I understood it to represent some connection she had—or felt she had—to a world beyond the tangible. Whether newly received by one or rekindled by the other, the dark energy that the painting evoked provided us with a moment we both seemed to seize, one that allowed us to share something subtle and mysterious captured there.

Now that Will and I had viewed the entire collection, Lucy invited us to sit in the gallery's small lounge area for a while. I suddenly realized I was exhausted and surrendered into the taut suspension of a canvas butterfly chair with the open view down the valley outside and the dreamscape cattle above us.

"So how did you end up all the way out here in Alces?" Will asked, taking another vintage chair on the other side of a rough-hewn coffee table. I settled into my chair's deep sling and tried to reorient to a world in which Will and I were engaged in a conversation with someone.

"That's a rather long and complicated story that I doubt you two have time for," Lucy replied.

"Tell us," said Will. I agreed, always impressed by Will's uncanny ability to pose a simple query and draw someone into storytelling.

"Well, I'd been working in Seattle in a corporate job. I hadn't painted in twenty-six years."

Lucy took a chair for herself and paused, as if deciding where to start. Then she told us about seeing and not seeing the signs that she wasn't living the life she was meant to live.

"I was on the wrong path, ignoring all kinds of stress and the fact that I'd been sick for a really long time," she said. "But I didn't know how to stop what I was doing. Eventually the decision was made for me when I had a massive hemorrhage and nearly died."

I audibly drew a breath as Will's complementary "Oh my God!" joined our dual gestures into one expression of grave surprise.

"I had to start listening in ways I didn't understand. That night I saw that I had a choice to leave this life or to change and live," Lucy said, pausing again. "I chose life. But it wasn't until I'd fought my way through months of a very painful and unsteady recovery that I learned what I was supposed to do with it, that I was meant to paint, to live an artist's life. When I finally figured it out, I had to teach myself all over again. It felt like a lifetime since I'd studied painting in college. So I had a lot of doubt to fight through as well."

There I jumped in before thinking through what I wanted to say and immediately began to fumble. "I went to art school, for a while, and then ended up studying—well—several other fields, actually. I've been all over the place professionally, so I guess I understand—to some degree anyway—how it's possible to retreat from art and the roundabout way we sometimes have of finding our path back. Sorry... I didn't mean to interrupt."

"Oh, not at all... And you feel like you *have* found your path," Lucy assured, suggesting less of a question than an invitation.

"I hope so," I said, hearing my own tentativeness and resisting the temptation to shift attention to my own story just as we were beginning Lucy's. "It's taken me long enough to settle onto a path, at least. But I'm still working out how to move forward, now that I'm there—well, not *there*, as in a destination, but—you know—hopefully going in a direction that'll bring me to a healthier and more satisfying place, anyway."

"You're a photographer then?" Lucy persisted. "I've been admiring your camera," she added, referring to the Nikon I was wearing on a strap and cradling protectively in my lap.

"Not professionally. But I do a lot of photography. Will just gave me this beautiful camera two months ago. I'm still getting used to digital, but I'm really enjoying it, so much lighter than the old SLR that I'd been using forever."

"Clearly it was a very special gift," Lucy remarked, looking over at Will with a disarming smile. "So what *do* you do? If you don't mind my asking," Lucy inquired intently as she turned back to me.

"I teach writing and literature at a community college back home in Massachusetts. I've been working on some poetry and doing some preliminary research for a novel," I ventured, feeling the overwhelming chill that always wracks my insides when a meaningful admission is unexpectedly coaxed out of hiding.

Lucy paused again briefly and then continued. "You know, your mention of poetry and the novel you're thinking about brings me back to fourteen years ago when I went to a tarot card reader on a friend's suggestion," Lucy recalled. "I'd been struggling with my recovery and I was still frail and deeply frustrated by that. In the past I'd always just willed myself forward in life, but that approach no longer seemed to be working. Anyway, I walked in and the first thing the woman said to me was, 'What's your art?'

"As I said, I'd been living a corporate life for twenty-six years. I could only see that far. So I just said, 'Oh, I do a little writing and some photography.' And she said, 'No. You're an artist. *What's your art?*' Oh, I've gone and given myself goosebumps. See that?" Lucy said, rubbing an arm with a sense of satisfaction.

"This may sound strange, but I died, you know; I saw a kind of tunnel before me when that choice was presented to me. I chose to live, and the tunnel immediately slammed shut. I came back, but I still wasn't listening. I didn't know how.

"After the tarot card reader asked me that question, refusing to accept my answer, I began to recognize that the self I had denied for so long needed art, needed to create in order to thrive. I mean, until she pushed me to remember, I had actually *forgotten* that I'd studied to be a painter back in college.

"About a month later I gave a year's notice at my job. I taught myself how to paint all over again, eventually got my work represented in a multi-woman show in Utah, did some painful soul searching out there among the red rocks and scorpions and petroglyphs, and then I found this village. A couple years ago I bought two acres of land, sight unseen, out on the edge of a Spanish land grant, and built my little house and studio. I still can't believe I'm here living this life."

I rubbed my own arms. "Now *I* have goose bumps!"

"So you're a writer," Lucy asserted with a satisfied resolve. "That's your art, isn't it?"

"I would like it to be." I searched for a distant point across the valley outside to focus on.

The three of us talked for a while about petroglyphs and pottery shards in Utah, Will's job as an educational technology consultant, and the idiosyncrasies of the artists' community that had settled in Alces. Lucy suggested some other galleries for us to visit in the village, and we eventually roused ourselves to venture back into the heat.

By the time we entered the third gallery we were feeling so dehydrated and I was so peaked that the curator offered us some water and without waiting for a response went to the kitchen, returning with two small green bottles. He and his wife had converted their large adobe home into a gallery. In a central room we came upon several more of Lucy's landscapes, clearly a winter series, softer and in some ways more lyrical than those she had displayed in her own gallery space. I loved them, but the collection was made up of larger pieces, all well out of our price range.

Randolph Markey didn't hide his admiration for Lucy Yaeger, holding her in special regard among the artists whose work filled his home and brought in his commissions. He spoke not as an artist but as a lover of art, a curator of the whimsical and the urbane.

"I like to think of myself as an installation artist," he admitted, the unbroken white of his beard and happily rumpled hair dignifying a trace of mischief around the eyes, and something textured that came across as warmth behind them.

Will and I yielded easily to our host's unhurried affability and passed nearly an hour wandering through a universe in miniature cultivated by an eclectic hand, as the fierce afternoon sun filtered in through a mosaic of green and apricot nasturtium vining along deep-cut window frames that in my mind these years later have taken on the qualities of a delicate stained-glass window.

We politely offered back our empty water bottles and were handed two more as we walked out the back door and said goodbye. The last thing either of us would have expected was to come away from this far-flung village with a couple of new friends.

On our way down the steps Will stopped and gave me one of his earnest looks that generally precedes a big idea. "How would you feel about going back to the Outskirts Studio?"

He had just read my thoughts, bringing me to a stop before leaving the last step. "I would! I really liked that small one of the horses that was part of the triptych on the back wall."

Kate

"So did I. We could go back and buy it," Will suggested, allowing some eagerness into his voice as we headed down the walkway, elbows entwined, a lightly animating crunch of dry earth under our feet.

"Let's go back and have another look," I said, pleased that despite all the other art we had browsed, we had both settled on the same small piece that was actually within our price range. Yet I couldn't bring myself to admit how much more strongly I was drawn to Lucy's larger canvases or that I bore—despite the happy convergences—an unwelcome feeling that we were settling for the smaller one.

As we got into the car and headed back through the jumble of earthen homes clustered along the main road, I found myself wanting to know more about Lucy, about her encounter with death, and the story of how she got to this relic of an outpost community. Her answer to Will's question skimmed the surface of her path to Alces but also hinted at what had to be a much more complicated and nuanced story. Also, her paintings, the large abstracts we'd come upon last, suggested an undercurrent of darkness in her—the strain so clearly visible in the towering work she called *Child of Darkness*.

The power and presence of something hidden or suppressed intrigued and unsettled me. I wanted a glimpse of the story behind the story she wasn't quite telling, the truth of the life she'd led up to that moment of crisis, and the courage I saw in her too. I wanted to find out what made her so quick to share those curious bits with a couple of strangers just passing through. Story-starved in ways I had yet to fully realize or understand, I was primed for a journey, but I would never have imagined that come winter I'd be back in a snow-shrouded Alces, sitting in Lucy's living room. What landed me back there? Partly luck and circumstance, partly my need to know the deeper story of how she came here and came to be the artist who sat before me in this remote high-desert village. And partly the resonance with darkness. I sensed the shadow of trauma and wanted to know how she had gone about making art, and an artist's life, drawing light out of darkness.

2

BLOOD

West Seattle

1996

Lucy

THE VOICE ON THE OTHER end of the line sounded sweet and gentle, soothing: "Talk to me, honey." It had taken more than an hour, but Lucy had managed to drag herself from the bathroom—where more blood than she had ever seen had come out of her—and to slide down the stairs into the kitchen to call 9-1-1.

"Well, I lost a lot of blood, but I'm not sure if I have an emergency," she said tentatively.

"Talk to me. Tell me what you're feeling," the operator coaxed.

"I just feel really odd," Lucy said.

"Where did you lose the blood?"

"In the bathroom upstairs. There was a lot of it. Walls, floor, toilet, everywhere," Lucy muttered, embarrassed.

"Okay, I'm gonna call somebody. You stay on the line. I'm gonna be right here. I'm just making a call," the calm voice assured.

While she lay there against the cold tiles, Lucy clung to that steady gentle voice that had returned as promised, as if it were an embrace. Those floor tiles finally registering through her dim kaleidoscopic sensorium, she realized that in all of the dragging she had done to get there she had lost her bathrobe somewhere along the way.

Lucy

"Oh, no! I've lost my bathrobe!" she groaned.

"Honey, we don't care about that," the voice replied. "They're not gonna care about that."

"Well *I* care!" Lucy complained, letting go of the phone, which swung with a plastic *crack* against the cabinet.

She stung with just enough indignance to make her legs—if they were her legs at all—carry her back to the bottom of the stairs where the blood-stained robe had fallen off. A half-formed image of her slippers faded away as she tried to untangle the robe. It seemed too heavy and complicated to make sense of, so she draped it around her shoulders and shuffled back to the kitchen, stopping to unlock the front door on her way back to the spot by the counter where she had left the phone dangling. Bewildered and too weak to sit in a chair and hold the phone, she sunk back to the floor, aware now of a deep sense of cold spreading through her body from the inside out.

"Honey, they're at the head of your road. You're gonna hear them soon," offered the voice, pulling her back to consciousness.

Wait a minute. Lucy was not about to allow a siren to disturb her neighbors at 3:00 a.m. "Can you tell them to turn the siren off?"

The voice replied, "Yes, I think we can do that for you, honey. Don't you worry about that. We'll take care of it."

True to her word yet again, there were no sirens, just the deep rumbling engine of a fire truck as it pulled into the driveway. Lucy was caught somewhere between fear and relief at this uneasy sound whose source seemed to project from the walls around her. As two men came in, appearing monstrously large from her vantage point on the floor, her Australian shepherd Mackenzie stepped over her in an entirely unprecedented stance, revealed her teeth, and let out a low growl.

"She's fine. She's not gonna hurt you. She's not gonna do anything to you. Please be nice to my dog," she pleaded weakly.

Somehow Mackenzie vanished, and they set to work. Though Lucy drifted in and out of consciousness, her vision impaired by lights pulsing in her head, she was aware of the sharpness of their voices, surprised at the urgency: "We're losing her! We're losing her! We need another unit."

She worked to pull herself back to the movement and sounds of activity going on around her. Somehow, a crowd of people and equipment had materialized in the kitchen. Where had they all come from? She struggled to grasp at meaning from scraps of what she heard, whatever she could hold onto in the confusion of more equipment, more people, more voices: "We're losing her..." "She's gone..." "Is she back?"

Then Lucy was being wheeled across the floor and carried down the winding stairwell to a small landing and out the door. As the dark shape of the house rose before her, she made out the image of Mackenzie's head and upward ears framed in the upstairs window, her distressed posture, a series of quick yelps toward the sky that no one could hear. Lucy felt the accordion of metal legs collapse under her as the gurney to which she was attached slid inside the ambulance. The doors closed with a *thunk* of enforced surrender.

As the ambulance began to move forward, Lucy's weight shifted against the straps that held her in a perverse kind of security.

Someone spoke. The words seemed important, heartfelt, concerned: "I'm afraid your condition is serious enough that we have to take you to the nearest hospital. It's not where we would normally go if we had more time. I'm sorry we've got to take you there."

But Lucy's thoughts weren't clear enough to respond to his implication or to engage with the eddying activity sweeping her from moment to moment. The man hovering over her seemed to understand that and proceeded with a kind of small talk she knew from television. She recognized it, even in her altered state, as a method reserved for keeping a person alert and conscious.

"What do you do for a living? What's your favorite TV show? You look like you're in pretty good shape. Do you work out? Have you read any good novels lately?"

Lucy struggled to answer, yielding to the peculiar lack of substance and urgency of purpose, suspended in the strange incongruity between farawayness and intimacy.

Under the lights of the emergency room entrance a woman in a white coat stood with folded arms to receive the first responders' status report.

Lucy

Her coarseness managed to reach the victim and offend the EMT team at the same time.

Lucy heard her ask, "Did she poop it out?" and through her funneled perception she sensed their disgust and resignation as they turned and walked back to the ambulance.

A vague feeling of abandonment and confusion welled up in her. What is happening here? She had no peripheral vision, though the bright strobe-like flashing that had accompanied the surges of blood had quieted to a raw throb.

It wasn't until someone spread a few layers of heated blankets over her that she realized how cold she was and that the feeling had left her arms and hands. When the blankets cooled and her bones began to quake uncontrollably, she asked a nearby nurse if there were any more warm blankets.

"You know, we *do* have other patients. You can't have *all* the warm blankets!" she snapped.

Lucy felt like a criminal, having dared to ask for that comfort at someone else's expense, and tried to keep from shaking apart, suddenly remembering blood and wondering if shaking too hard might unleash another wave.

She was hooked up to a bag of intravenous fluids and left to herself for what seemed like a very long time. As she lay there, she had the sensation of being herself yet somehow not. Eventually a doctor came in and explained that they were going to observe her for a little while but that she appeared to have a case of food poisoning.

"But I lost a lot of blood…"

"Well, when people are ill and they see blood, they panic and think it's a lot more than it is. You've just had a bout of food poisoning, and I'm going to send you home," he replied.

Alone again with her IV dripping, Lucy desperately needed to empty her bladder, but no one seemed to be available to help her. What else to do but look for a bathroom? She slid off the bed and swam along the edge of the hall, as if under water, pulling the IV rack along with her until shiny porcelain and white incandescent light spilling through a door left ajar announced themselves. Images of the terror she had just experienced in her own bathroom—the blood that had exploded from her bowels, the searing pain—returned as well, but the urgency of over-hydration compelled her in.

She homed back to her bed, where she lay alone for long periods of semi-consciousness. She was able to discern that the man in the next station appeared to be having a heart attack, filling the space with busy movement her eyes could not track and her mind could not process. Temporal sequences collapsed into each other as if in dreamtime. She lay there waiting to grasp something steady, something that made sense.

Mackenzie... Lucy watched the clock, waiting until it would be safe to call Dennis and ask him to come and rescue her imprisoned dog. They both worked at Seymor and Baird and had over the past year pursued an on-and-off relationship. As she lay in that strange bed, her thoughts worked toward a plan: if she called a little before the time Dennis normally woke up—the photo lab opened at least two hours earlier than the rest of the ad company's offices—he could stop by to quickly feed and walk Mackenzie on his way in to work. Despite his occasional reminder that their relationship would never be more than physical, he was a kind soul, and Lucy felt she could rely on him to help, just for the day, until she got home.

As she waited until it was safe to make her call, Lucy became aware of an argument nearby. She heard someone say they needed the bed and he wanted the patient released. A ripple of shame washed through her. She was in the way. They needed the bed, and God she needed to get out of there.

The other voice was emphatic. "This patient can't sit up without losing consciousness! It's not safe to release her."

"I saw her walk down to the bathroom an hour ago. She's ambulatory," the male voice insisted.

"She may have carried herself to the bathroom somehow, but whenever we try to sit her up, she passes out. I can't sign off on a release," the woman maintained.

The voices seemed to float away, as if down a long echoing hall. A figure moved into her field of vision, and Lucy requested a phone.

Dennis agreed to help with Mackenzie. But when the shift change came, the morning nurse who had just come on duty announced that

Lucy

Lucy was being released. Unable to dress herself, which amounted to putting on the bathrobe and slippers that had arrived with her, the new nurse came to her aid. As she helped Lucy into the robe, Lucy looked up at her. "I'm confused," she conceded. "Does food poisoning result in a massive loss of blood?"

"What?" A look of concern came over an otherwise fresh face. "Honey, this doesn't sound right. When you get home, promise me you'll call your doctor. Immediately."

It was late enough now that Lucy could call her friend Ivy to come and get her. Once discharged, she was allowed to lie on top of a made bed for a while, but eventually someone needed it and she was sent out to a reception area, where she lay down on a small couch to wait.

When Ivy finally arrived, she half-jogged across the lobby, out of breath.

"I am so sorry, Lucy! I got really lost trying to find the hospital. I don't know this neighborhood at all."

Advancing, she got a better look at Lucy and exclaimed, "My God! Are you sure you should be going home?"

"The nurse told me to call my doctor when we get there. She also gave me a list of things we need to pick up on the way."

They made their way through intersections and traffic lights, a system that to Lucy seemed foreign and inscrutable. Ivy parked in front of a grocery store and ran in for Gatorade, while Lucy sat quietly in the car, her body buzzing faintly with the memory of the vibrations running through her when the car had been in motion. The cold salt-sugar drink seemed to reinforce the boost she already felt from the fluids that had been pumped into her body for hours, giving her the impression that she was in the process of reviving.

That sensation faded quickly. As they pulled into the driveway and up to the house, Lucy caught Mackenzie's head framed in the window, her anxious posture, and remembered the smell of blood, her own sense of helplessness as the ambulance carried her away into the night. Ivy guided her upstairs one step at a time. Finally reaching the top, Lucy wanted only to collapse in bed, but Ivy insisted that she call her doctor first. "Just for me, so I don't worry," she coaxed, easing Lucy into a chair and handing her the phone.

The familiar voice of her doctor's receptionist pushed back a memory of another voice helping her wait for the emergency crew. This one urged Lucy to come right in while someone was still available to drive her. It seemed impossible to imagine having to gather themselves up and manage the stairs, the car, the traffic again. It was also impossible to challenge the instructions. Ivy took the phone from Lucy and hung it up, then pressed a knuckle to her teeth, thinking out loud. "You know, I'm thinking, let's pack a little bag..." Lucy sat in the kitchen listlessly, her presence, weak as it was, sending Mackenzie into spiraling paroxysms of joy, while Ivy quickly gathered a few things upstairs.

Someone was already waiting with a wheelchair when they arrived at Dr. Carmichael's office. Being rolled past the waiting room fish tanks that she usually stopped to enjoy reminded Lucy of this visit's strangely unfamiliar character. The doctor had already contacted the hospital for her records, so the staff was prepared and kicked into action. Blood was drawn immediately. Lucy's bladder was still responding to all the fluids overloading her system, so when she attempted to stand up to go to the bathroom, Dr. Carmichael reacted quickly, "Hold on! One of my staff will take you. And leave the door **unlocked**! Julie, would you mind helping Lucy to the bathroom and back to my office as soon as she finishes in there," she said, signaling to a young woman in a white smock and casting her chin toward the bathroom door. The nurse obediently changed course and assumed her post until Lucy was ready.

As Lucy returned and was safely seated, Dr. Carmichael excused herself with a folder in hand, briefly leaving her own post to find Ivy waiting anxiously in the reception area.

Reflexively opening the folder though not needing to read it, she explained, "According to Lucy's vitals and a comparison of our blood work with the test results that came over from County ER, she's still bleeding internally. We don't have time to call an ambulance. Can you get her over to Swedish Hospital *right now*, or should I have someone from my staff take her?" Her tone left no room for questions or doubts about her urgency.

"Oh my God! Of course I'll take her," Ivy replied, swallowing a surge of panic.

Lucy

Lucy was wheeled out to Ivy's car, feeling strangely bright and perky from the sports drink but still struggling to grasp what they were doing, dimly aware of the sharp edges of traffic and the shapes of people moving around in the bright morning light. Ivy managed to get to the hospital, fighting the urge to scream at every red light or left turner, refusing space to thoughts of not making it in time.

Dr. Carmichael's office had alerted the hospital staff in advance of their arrival so Lucy would be taken directly to ICU. Her veins had collapsed, which she learned at the same time she learned that she was now in a teaching hospital, where every procedure and decision was announced and discussed as if her sickbed were a round table. She heard someone explain, "She's had a catastrophic hemorrhage and continues to bleed internally; however, the blood loss has been masked by the large amount of fluids that she was given overnight."

In all her forty-six years Lucy had never been hospitalized or even visited someone who was. Lacking this experience, she had assumed that once you're in the hospital all suffering ends. Perhaps her body was coming back to life now, after all that dying she'd done the night before. She had spent long stretches of her life ignoring pain, and along the way she had missed one fairly important survival lesson. Despite many opportunities for practice, she had failed to learn how to pay attention to her body's warning signals and respond to them, instead developing a dangerously high tolerance for pain. Yet over the next twenty-four hours, as she lay there plucked out of time and any recognizable frame of reference, the crushing pain that raged through her body exceeded anything she had ever known or imagined, reducing her to a weltering fetal-shaped bundle.

Lucy now had a diagnosis: Crohn's disease, which, having gone untreated for decades, had ravaged her intestines. Her bleeding and distress had been dismissed so often since their onset in her teens that she had seen no point in going through a colonoscopy just to be told yet again that her symptoms were in her head. Only a couple of months before, she had reluctantly made an appointment to have one and then canceled it at the last minute. Since then she'd been taking aspirin around the clock.

For now, her platelets had been replenished with a transfusion, and the doctors had stabilized the bleeding with prednisone, but she was wracked with agonizing waves of vomiting and diarrhea. Though bouts of intense gastrointestinal pain and vomiting were perversely familiar, she had no frame of reference for what was happening to her now. She didn't even know about the call buttons on the side of the bed that she could have used to contact the nurse's station in her distress.

When she returned home a few days later, Mackenzie outdid herself in a dutiful all-purpose frenzy, but along with the greeting, fear quickly settled into Lucy's bones. The shepherd's vigilance—should her human caretaker attempt another bold and misguided escape—failed to calm the dread. Lucy didn't trust her body, which continued to bind her in pain. Walking into her bedroom felt like returning to the scene of a grisly crime that kept playing itself out in her head. Before the hemorrhage she would never have allowed herself to surrender to any kind of weakness, much less to physical pain. Now fear overwhelmed her, and she was unable to hold it back or even recognize it entirely as her own. It had been her business, her mission, to assure everyone else that everything was fine.

Back in the doctor's office a couple of days after Lucy's release from the hospital, Dr. Carmichael sat her dazed patient down, reached over her desk and firmly clasped her wrist. Leaning as far forward as she could, she explained, "Look, Lucy, you need to get this. There is no medical reason to explain the fact that you are still walking around. I have no idea why you are sitting across this desk from me. It's at the very least a miracle. You need to work through all this to understand what you have gone through, and I think you may need therapy to help you do that."

Exhausted and unable to stop the loop, as if a continuous video kept cycling through her head, Lucy acquiesced. But she remained disconnected from the flow of events, as if the video had captured some particularly horrible scenes of someone else's life.

3

THE LLANO

Alces 2010

Kate

AS SHE FINISHED UP THE paperwork for our purchase and put our painting, *Llano 3*, aside so she could wrap it up for shipping the following day,
Lucy began to tell me about the horses that inspired the painting, part of a
triptych she had done fairly recently, as well as a series of larger paintings
that had been especially meaningful to her during her first winter in New
Mexico a year and a half earlier. She had called it the **Dark Horse Series** and
suggested that those paintings were somehow bound up in an encounter
she had had with one of the village families not long after she had moved
in. Bits and pieces of a story began to unfold around those initial weeks in
her new home. I followed the fragments with interest, despite my light-
headedness, as she recounted those early days getting acquainted with the
land and the herd of horses who arrived in a neighboring pasture not long
after she moved in.

December brought intense storms with bitter wind and heavy snows.
Lucy had arrived in late September 2008 and had spent her first several
weeks walking the rugged dirt road that ran through the land grant abutting her property, exploring the outskirts of the village and taking in as
much as she could of the landscape that lay between her home and the
cluster of stark peaks that rose out beyond her studio windows.

The llano was a broad plateau of pastures large and small, dotted with piecemeal homes and marked with jagged lines of hand-cut juniper fence posts and ancient acequias, communally dug channels where centrally controlled water allotted by the village mayordomo flowed on precise and immutable calendar dates according to the remnants of a centuries-old system of water rights. Lucy had been told somewhere during her land purchase, perhaps at the closing, that these rights would be lost if they weren't used or were otherwise misused. She remembered making a mental note to check into the village records in the spring and find out when the ditches around the perimeter of her property were supposed to open, knowing she would probably need a compelling reason to follow through with that inquiry.

On her morning walks out on the land grant road she had often come upon horses whose lives were hard, receiving as much protection as a hand strung juniper post fence could provide. She photographed these patched and repatched fences, capturing their tangle of reused wire and nylon cord, gnarled branches standing at odd angles—yet standing somehow in this web—in a poignant salute to the resourcefulness of the hard-worn and to the parching climate that could preserve nearly any material for decades. Like the driftwood she found on the shores of Puget Sound as a child, these shapes and textures spoke to her of the lives and deaths of trees, the imprint of wind and weather, sand and dust. They spoke to her of utility and the story of art. She understood too that out here pampering was as foreign as a palm tree. There was honor in the stoicism of the sturdy llano horses. And its people.

She saw the beauty in the hardship and the necessary economy of life in Alces. It must have been sometime in November when she read in one of the local papers about a gang-style execution in a neighboring village. A nineteen-year-old had been found naked in a frozen creek, his throat cut. Drug wars involving black tar heroin were common among the young men of the villages and supported by the same feudal honor system that had served to hold the community together since its inception. Stories of violent deaths, Lucy was learning, occasionally made headlines in the *Santa Fe New Mexican,* and people went about their business of eking out a living off the hard land where well bred horses often marked a family's status, even if their home was pieced together from adobe bricks and resilient desert scrap.

She awoke around dawn one morning, breathless at the sight of several elk browsing out in the field that served as her yard. Startling them when she tried to ease open the screen door, she didn't have time to fully take in their magnificence before they wheeled off in a minor stampede, kicking up clouds of snow powder behind them as they bounded weightlessly through the brush on the south edge of her property.

She was used to silence and generally found it comforting, but she quickly grew accustomed to the nightly staccato of coyotes and accepted, on some level at least, the idea of what had left behind an occasional cat track the size of a softball. She had lived alone amidst the red rock canyons of southern Utah for four years after Sam left, had come to feel that this kind of deep solitude was sacred—a gift of sorts—and the wilderness embracing, despite its obvious dangers, its sometimes unsettling mysteries, and its unforgiving extremes. That blazing red land had been a crucible for her as she struggled to find a way to forgive. She had developed a sturdy independence, close cousin to the street sense she still carried with her from her young life in Tacoma, her solitary unsheltered days, left to her own defenses in the rough neighborhood that echoed with the wails of stray cats tortured by street-gang initiates, a packed dirt landscape where rain collected in puddles of pasty white industrial sludge along the railroad tracks where she played, leaving behind scenes of magical forests scratched in the mud.

The sandstone desert and the streets of Tacoma had taught her about the need for a protective cat enclosure, so here in Alces she had one built off the studio back door with access through a flexible door flap. As long as her cats were safe, she felt she was too. Still, she had more than once brushed off the same uncomfortable question, which suggested that a different kind of assurance was required for a woman living out there alone: "You have a gun, right?"

A small pasture that bordered her two acres and ran alongside her driveway had become home to the herd of five horses and an old, hand-welded water tank standing awkwardly on a rusted steel base. Through the fall the horses spent their time grazing on wild alfalfa and desert grasses and providing a sense of comfort to their new neighbor, whose daily routine began with the welcome sight of the four quiet mares and watchful bay stallion from her second-floor kitchen window as she made her coffee. They were also visible from her spot at the easel if they happened to be standing by the fence along the dirt road.

So when they were visited by a dark figure of a man with a fierce smoldering demeanor bringing an occasional bale of hay and walking around appearing to inspect the grounds, Lucy saw him as an intruder. She was determined to find out who he was—if he had official rights to use her neighbor's empty pasture, or if he had just taken an opportunity to slip his horses in on the far edge where they might not be noticed. Unfamiliar as she still was with the community, she knew very well that Peter, the man who had sold her the land, had moved to Santa Fe, that he still had the adjacent parcel on the market, and that this grim-faced man was unmistakably *not* him.

The visitor made her nervous as he poked around in the pasture, closer to her house than anyone—let alone a stranger—had been since she had arrived. So she walked out one morning to inquire, nearly losing her nerve when she approached and realized he reminded her of Charles Manson—only meaner. But he had already seen her coming; it was too late to turn back.

The man bristled when she asked him what he was doing there. She had surprised herself with her own boldness in approaching him with a what-the-hell-are-you-doing-here tone.

"I may be a stranger to you, walking on the edge of your land, but I'm not a stranger here. I'm Alvin's son-in-law," the man said, his few words at once acknowledging her right to question him and asserting his legitimacy in grazing his horses there.

Alvin Jorge had once owned all the land along the road, and though he had already sold the acreage farthest from County Road, he seemed unable to let go of this last parcel abutting the vast, fairly wild land grant stretching beyond the very end of the winding, deeply rutted, dirt road. His had been one of the original land grant families, awarded a great swath that over the course of the past two centuries had been parceled up and sold off a few acres at a time, including the four acres at the end of the road that Peter had bought, easily making up the price he'd paid Alvin by selling half of it to Lucy.

At the early stages of building, Lucy had received a distressed call in Utah from the site manager in Alces explaining that they had suddenly lost water and that upon further inspection had found the line soldered or welded in such a way as to completely cut off supply to the building site. Alarmed, Lucy called her real estate agent, who informed her that Peter had recently sued Alvin to make repairs to the pipes running through both properties. Apparently, this was Alvin's way of registering that despite her commercially brokered purchase of the two-acre plot, her presence there was illegitimate, that this was no place for a gringo lady from Seattle or Utah or wherever she came from.

His attempts to sabotage her resettlement continued even after she had moved in. Lucy was desperate for her phone line to be installed, her only access to the outside world from her remotely situated new home. A new date was set for the serviceman to come out and complete the work, another in a series of unfulfilled promises. But once again, no one showed. When she called customer service from the village post office, the representative explained, "You'll never believe what happened. Our technician had just installed the box and was running the line when an old man came running down the road screaming and yelling with a hatchet in his hand!"

"Are you kidding me?" Lucy cried.

"No, I'm not," the representative replied. "The man went and hacked through all the cables and chased my guy off the property."

After that the phone company had to go all the way back into the village to reroute the cables from the main road and run them along the land grant road. More of a rocky path than a road at all, it skirted a rough piñon forested canyon that dropped off sharply just beyond the easterly border of Lucy's property.

"I'm checking on my horses," the hard-faced man said.

"I've seen you out here occasionally and wondered what was going on. It was clear to me from the beginning that these aren't Peter's horses," she said, indicating that she was aware of the succession of ownership of the land they were standing on, that both she and the now-absentee landowner had bought the abutting parcels that had once belonged to Alvin. She also knew she had to be careful; Alvin retained a few acres and a house set back from the bend in the road where the first in a series of steel cattle guards was just barely visible from Lucy's kitchen window. His son also lived nearby, his home accessible from County Road by another long driveway. Their ancestors' gravestones, proudly adorned with artificial flowers, stood in the village cemetery.

"Your horses are beautiful, and I've been enjoying their company," Lucy added, as if a note of conciliation would temper her initial challenge. She knew better than to feed enmity in this place. He thanked her without acknowledging any further concord and went about his business, as if having established each other's purpose sufficed to complete the conversation.

Within a day or two Lucy could see from her kitchen window that no hay had been brought out to the horses next door, and the icy snow-blown ground was clean of all but the stubble that managed to cling to it. Water standing in the acequia that skirted the pasture had long frozen through, and the wind continued to drift snow against the fence posts that stood between the dirt road and the irrigation ditch. Lucy could see the distress in the horses' eyes, particularly in the one mare carrying the full weight of a near-term pregnancy. So later that day she bought a bale of hay in Española and returned just before dusk to break it up and heave it in loose sections over the chest-high fence.

Several days later it became clear that her hay delivery was the horses' only remaining source of food. She could little afford to feed them through the winter, but she would continue as long as she could manage it. Spring was a long way off, and so were the summer visitors to the High Road gallery where she hoped to sell enough paintings to continue paying her bills.

On her next visit to the post office, Lucy mentioned the herd to the village postmaster Almarosa Peña, an elderly villager who rented out a no-frills backyard casita to tourists and generally knew everybody's business.

"Oh, Carlos's horses..." she said. "The family's gone over to Las Moradas. You know their oldest son Manny was killed there a few weeks ago. They're not doing so well," she added, squaring a small pile of letters with arthritic fingers and a light tap on the countertop. "I don't know what's going to happen to the horses."

"I read about that horrible murder," Lucy said, "But I had no idea the young man's family lives here. The paper said that it was some kind of drug-related killing."

"That's what they're saying. Carlos has a lot of power. People don't step on his toes," Almarosa explained. "If you want to help those horses you probably should ask him first."

"I'll keep an eye out for Alvin and see what I can find out," Lucy said, deciding that with or without Carlos's permission she wouldn't sit by while those animals starved, as long as she could scrape together the cash for enough hay to keep them alive until the family returned.

A week later Lucy set out for her morning walk. The day was cold but bright, as inviting as it was going to get for a late December stroll. As she headed down her driveway toward the pasture she spotted Carlos walking along the road, head lowered, hands wedged in his pockets. His long wiry hair, which flew out from underneath a red bandana tied flat around his forehead, whipped across his face in the icy wind. Lucy walked up to him, catching him and herself off guard.

"Excuse me, Carlos?" she asked.

Stopping and squinting at her as if searching his memory for a face he must have forgotten, the man replied, "Yes?"

Lucy continued without thinking. "I heard about your son, and I am *so sorry*! Oh, uh—I'm Lucy Yaeger. I don't think I formally introduced myself the last time we spoke. I—I don't know how you're able to get up in the morning, how you're able to breathe and go about your life," she blurted.

Carlos looked down, his hardened face drawing tighter from the pain of revisiting his loss and from the biting cold. He said nothing but didn't back away either as Lucy reached out toward him and put a gloved hand on his shoulder, held it there for a moment, and let go.

"Looks like your horses could use some hay. Would you mind if I brought them some?" Lucy asked, not acknowledging her previous deliveries. "I'd be happy to feed them this winter so you and your family don't have to worry about them on top of everything else you're dealing with. I know grieving takes time—can be all consuming. Caring for these lovely horses is the least I can do."

Carlos looked her in the eye, his own dark eyes deeply shadowed behind taut brow and bones, the line of his jaw sharply drawn, his coarse hair blowing, revealing thick silver strands. He was older than he had originally appeared. She sensed that few knew what it felt like to meet those eyes directly and that those who did were either intimates or underlings.

"You're very kind. That would be a big help to us. Thank you," he said. "Pretty soon we'll be moving the horses over to another pasture on my land over on the llano."

"Oh, I'll check on them over there then," Lucy offered hopefully. "I walk down there fairly regularly," she added. "I'm sure I'll recognize them when I see them," she added, refraining from asking for any more information than was absolutely necessary. "Or maybe they'll recognize *me*."

Carlos nodded, expressionless, looking past her, as if there were nothing but emptiness out beyond the borders of the land that was now hers to claim and defend. Setting his eyes to the ground, he turned to walk back in the direction of Alvin's house, his lean body driving along the weight of his spirit. The wind carried off small eddies of snow that disappeared in horizontal scuds released by his boot-steps. He didn't turn to look at the horses as he passed the pasture fence. The bay stallion snorted twin clouds of frozen breath and nodded anxiously after the figure that trudged on past the crooked water tank and down the road toward the narrowing at the cattle guard that was now just invisible under the snow.

I wasn't sure if we were on the right road as we headed east on County Road until we came to the tall coyote fence where Lucy had indicated the right turn would be and was. Before we had left the gallery, Lucy had given us directions to the llano, the rugged, starkly beautiful stretch of high plains on the outskirts of the village, made up of a patchwork of land grant properties bequeathed to Spanish settlers in the 1700s and cultivated by generations of their descendants, some of whom, over time, intermingled with white settlers, Puebloans, and others, leading to the various shapes, sizes, and cultural heritages of the Euro-indigenous people represented in some part or other by the big-bucket term Mestizo.

I pulled off the road at a pasture that was occupied and began rapidly snapping photographs of the horses, clustered close to each other, tails swishing flies from one other's faces. The bay stallion seemed calm, drowsy, though he swiveled an ear in our direction. The June sky shimmered in shallow puddles left by monsoon rains and spread out around the small island of six horses like shards of pale blue glass. An adolescent filly with markings similar to the stallion's but more striking—uneven white socks and an oblique Vietnam-shaped blaze across her face—stood in the middle, legs splayed like a giraffe's, flanked on either side by her protectresses.

As inspired by the structure across the road as I was by the horses Lucy had sent us out to find, I stole a quick shot of the oddly shaped adobe house, its roundish second story rising above a piecemeal corrugated metal roof fashioned into a porch, under which spread an array of objects indistinguishable in the high contrast cast by the still-white afternoon sun. I stopped before taking another shot, fighting my impulses to feast unrestrained on the crisp outlines displayed before me, in deference to the family whose property I was using for my own artistic benefit. It felt intrusive to stand there wildly snapping photographs of their horses and their home. As I paused to study the house, I noticed the outline of a woman's form, just visible, with long dark braids, sitting deep in the shadow of the porch, looking back at me. I reacted in that awkward moment by waving with cheerful exaggeration, hoping to neutralize any breach of privacy by acknowledging the person whose home and horses I had just photographed without even thinking to ask permission. The silhouette of the woman, hand rising in a polite wave back, relieved my sense of guilt, but not enough for me to steal another photograph.

Later that night when I sat down to download the digital images of the day into my laptop, I was especially eager to take a closer look at the woman's shape, half hidden in shadow, on the single image I had taken of the house. Because I had snapped the shot before realizing the woman was there, I wondered what, if anything, I had captured of her.

But when I scrolled through the images of the horses and came to the photo of the house, I found no sign of the woman sitting on the porch. Incredulous, I downloaded the images from the SD card to my laptop, clicked on the image in question, and immediately opened the editing tool, no longer concerned, as I had been earlier, about the trespass. It would be easy enough to edit out the shadows to explore the obscured shapes on the porch. Once the histogram was open, I slid the shadows bar to the right until the darkness began to vanish from the image. Amidst the clutter of cardboard boxes strewn about under the metal roof, I made out a hot water tank, a collection of miscellaneous auto parts, several truck wheels, a laundry sink, a shovel, and a motorcycle partially covered with a bed sheet, but no human form appeared anywhere in the photograph.

4

WORK

Seattle 1996

Lucy

LUCY'S DETACHMENT FROM HER ILLNESS was complete. She had no concerns about her decision to go back to work in that fragile state. Clients were waiting for her. She had always bounced back before, overriding discomfort whenever necessary. She would bounce back again. Her body may have betrayed her, but she could always fall back on her strength of will to bury any shame and embarrassment over its weakness.

Mid-morning on Lucy's first day back at work, she and Jeffrey met in his office. They had collaborated so well and so long that she was confident the two of them had finally eliminated their boss's concerns about resentments between the production and sales departments. Lucy had been out for not quite a week and a half, and she and Jeffrey were eager to talk over the specs for an upcoming project.

Feeling warm, Lucy unconsciously pushed up her sleeves and was immediately struck by a look of alarm that came over her colleague's face and filled his eyes, stopping him in mid-sentence. She didn't understand at first what he was reacting to until she looked down and saw the deep eggplant wounding that had blossomed over both of her arms, spreading out from where intravenous needles had punctured and repunctured the veins of her forearms and had begun fading to an earthy green around the edges.

In that awkward pause, the muffled sounds of busy people going about their Monday tasks on the other side of the glass wall filtered into the silence between them. Jeffrey's distress briefly and only indirectly drew Lucy's attention to the seriousness of her condition and the gravity that hovered in the air around the long morning's efforts to navigate a world that should have felt perfectly familiar to her. Instead, every step, word, or thought that she struggled to generate had left her feeling less like the confident and creative sales executive she had thought she was and more like a patch of diseased tissue no longer recognized by the body to which it belonged.

The implications of her being there at all that day brushed against the edges of her consciousness but penetrated no further. She looked away and slid her sleeves back down, retreating from the story they concealed to the safety and clarity of the job at hand. Her own sense of caution may have failed to kick in, but the concern in Jeffrey's eyes had registered, and they both knew it. They also knew, on some level, that there was nothing he could say that would force her to accept or fully grasp the danger in returning to work so soon after the hemorrhage.

The daze persisted through a profound and incomprehensible fatigue that she couldn't shake off. All morning, even the briefest glances turned her way suggested the weight of events that had become everyone's business; all the more reason to dismiss them with a show of determination that things were on their way back to normal. She realized only after she had arrived that her brightest pink blouse would highlight rather than offset the gray-blue of her lips and nail beds, the dark hollows around the eyes that nothing could hide.

In the early afternoon Dennis and Lucy met—perhaps by accident, perhaps because he'd been keeping an eye her—on the stairway leading down to the front lobby of the building. He insisted on driving her to the appointment that she had scheduled with the gastroenterologist, offering to leave her car parked outside the medical building and take a cab back to his car in the company lot. In the moment, she couldn't come up with a reason to refuse.

On the way down the stairs the blood suddenly retreated from Lucy's head and gathered itself somewhere apparently more essential in her gut, setting a stumble in motion that would have turned into a crippling fall, had Dennis not been nimble and alert enough to catch her. Drawing upon the impeccable comic timing and soft Texas sweetness Lucy had always found endearing, Dennis made light of the near miss, but even in her wooziness she was aware of his underlying concern. She just wanted to make it all go away and return to life as it had been before. She couldn't understand why that wasn't happening.

After Lucy's appointment, overwhelming fatigue left her unable to drive home. Lacking even the resources to pull out of the parking lot, she remained for several hours helplessly inert, in and out of a fitful sleep in the driver's seat of her car. By the time she roused herself and mustered the strength to find her way home, it was dark. She crept through downtown Seattle along streets that should have been familiar but loomed like a blurry maze, leaving Dennis, who had been calling to see how her appointment had gone, frantic with worry.

Mr. Alliston allowed her to flex her hours, coming in later in the morning on days when she was too sick to get herself there on time and staying later on those days. But he was just as vigilant about expectations as he was about concerns over perceived favoritism. Whether his intentions were philosophical or self-serving, it didn't matter. All she needed to hear was "You're only as good as your next sale, Lucy," and suddenly nothing was as important as closing that sale. Her gut knew that even more than her head did.

Healing, something Lucy's rationale hadn't accounted for, was far from straightforward. The prednisone and transfusion had initially saved her, but long-term steroid use carried serious risks. And without fail, every time the dosage was lowered, she began to bleed again internally.

Such severe intestinal damage had rendered her body unable to absorb the nutrients it needed to function normally. In order to regenerate her intestinal lining, she was put on a strict celiac diet. That meant no sugar, no alcohol, no caffeine, and no grain—not even potatoes. She learned to grind nuts to make a completely unsatisfying bread which filled her up, but in a leaden, saw-dusty way that left her feeling miserably deprived all the time. She was ashamed of her frailty and desperate to wish it away. One day, succumbing to the strain, she closed the door to her office, unsure if she'd even make it a few steps farther to her chair, put her head down on her desk, and sobbed herself into a dizzy semi-consciousness.

Lucy had accumulated some vacation time prior to the hemorrhage, time that she had always coveted but now looked to as a means of survival. Six weeks earlier, she and her assistant had worked out the details of the vacation, which, as it turned out, was on the calendar for the following month. Though she hadn't admitted to Taylor how run down she'd been feeling, in those weeks prior to the hemorrhage the two of them had made all the arrangements and given advance notice to clients to ensure that her absence would be minimally disruptive.

In making those plans Lucy had given herself permission to dream about the Oregon coast. She had been looking forward to that precious downtime at Cannon Beach, just as she had often done over the decade since the end of her marriage to Terry, her second husband. But now she was drawn to her old healing place—her refuge—with a different kind of urgency.

During the early days of that second try at marriage, Terry had brought her to his family's Oregon home and introduced her to some of the most beautiful hiking trails she had ever seen. She had been drawn to the spiritual quiet of the mist-enshrouded beaches surrounding Ecola Park and to Tillamook Head, its dramatic cliffs with their somber spruce canopies and spinning clouds of sea birds. She was so certain a peaceful retreat in a place guaranteed to provide comfort was an idea her doctors would welcome that she was completely stunned by Dr. Carmichael's reaction.

"I don't know any other way to say this, Lucy, but there's more than a good chance you wouldn't survive another bleed."

Her doctor's voice seemed far away as she explained, "Your healing hasn't stabilized, and I absolutely can't allow you to travel to a remote area where emergency care may not be reliable and there are no records of your medical history. And frankly, you've given us plenty of reasons to doubt your ability to judge your level of risk or even to assess your pain levels. Give yourself another three months, and then we'll see."

Lucy bitterly accepted Taylor canceling the reservations, but the persistence of her daily struggle over the weeks that followed made the need to retreat impossible to push aside. She resumed her entreaty with her medical support team, arguing that she could only get the kind of rest she so desperately needed if she escaped to that quiet and familiar setting, less than four hours from Seattle yet removed enough from the intensity of her work life that she could leave the pressures behind for two whole weeks.

Finally, Dr. Carmichael agreed to assess the local emergency response team in the Cannon Beach vicinity. Her official blessing came and with permission to pull a vacation together. Despite Lucy's years of practice getting herself to the coast, gathering herself to be away from home proved more difficult than she had anticipated. But the call to return to a place of comfort, where she could relinquish the daily struggle to bear up gracefully at all times and manage waves of pain and constant activity, was as loud as the clamor in her head, the relentless flurry of expectations, commitments, and demands.

Desperate to be back in the cabin she had returned to so often when she needed to give way to the hush and rush of the salt tide and the long pacific horizon merging with mist and sky, Lucy drew upon every resource she possessed in order to clear her schedule, pack her clothes, dog, essentials, and a couple of good books, and drive herself to the Pacific Ocean. Heading south along Highway 101, Lucy took in the familiar tassels of spruce tops fringing the hillsides, the dense alder thickets, the low mossy tree branches pretending to be green velveted antlers, and began to let go.

At last, there it was: the stretched-out rhythms of the sea and the calls of gulls, a door flung open to a longed-for reverie. There was her old spot. She could settle into a beach chair nestled in her favorite cove, toes dredging warm sand, and be perfectly, perfectly still. She was as close to disappearing as she knew how to be.

5

ALCES

January 2011

Kate

My DECISION TO RETURN TO Alces for a couple of days in January felt right, even though flying back to New Mexico only a few months after a major trip with Will also seemed a little extravagant and—if I thought about it too much—unduly short. By mid-November I'd fully committed to a plan of return.

Almarosa's casita would be available and at much reduced rates. Nobody came through in January, and she would be happy for the business, asking $45 a night. Any friend of Lucy's was welcome, the old woman assured me over the phone. She'd have her grandson check the heater (which, I would discover, was functional enough to produce an orchestra of metallic clanking but little or no heat) and leave out a few pieces of firewood (a single piece, hopelessly wet, and a tiny packaged artificial log that also inexplicably refused to ignite). Her granddaughter would make up the bed and freshen the place up, she said. Sure enough, the cottony quilts I found to be clean and fresh but, boasting summer flowers, hardly adequate for an underheated adobe in sub-zero temperatures. I should have asked for an extra blanket when I found nothing substantial in the closet, but by the time I'd finally settled in that first night, given up on lighting a fire, and tested the hand-made would-be heater, it was too late to bother the elderly lady off in the main house. Winters were long and hard in the high desert. It would be five months before the summer tourists would arrive. I resolved to manage this brief stay as an off-season visitor, reassured that most of my time would be spent with Lucy anyway.

Driving up from Albuquerque just after daybreak that morning presented the desert in a stark winter serenity that I had never witnessed, having spent summers in the southwest as a teenager and stealing three precious days to drive up and back from El Paso one fall seven years earlier following an ill-begotten seminar that turned out to be the death knell for an equally ill-begotten postdoctoral fellowship. Even in October, the intense heat of that 400-mile drive cutting straight up I-25 had left me dangerously parched and disoriented as I wound my way through the back roads north of Taos well after nightfall, finally locating my B & B hours after check-in time. Then, too, an indefensibly abbreviated journey had to suffice.

I was still in a state of disbelief as I navigated my rented SUV north, this time under a low winter sun. The familiar contours of central New Mexico that I had only associated with rising waves of heat were now covered lightly in snow and textured by soft-cast shadows that muted the pinks of the Sandia Mountains and, a little farther on, the faded reds of sage mottled hills outside Santa Fe. Still, my blood quickened as the streaked and gullied badlands announced the dusty climb through the strangely out-of-time villages that would bring me, as a pilgrim or a small bird empowered in heart and bone by an eagle-strong homing mode, to the foot of the Sangre de Cristos.

Here the snow deepened, covering the drive leading from the county road to Lucy's house, requiring me first to guide the large unfamiliar vehicle over a precipitous icy drop-off that conjured visions of careening straight into the even steeper arroyo alongside, and then to maneuver around sharp bends and over ice-encrusted cattle guards barely a pickup truck's width across. I steered into the single set of tire tracks, clenching a little in anticipation of the questions Lucy was likely to ask about how I might change my life in order to establish some creative space. Find my art. Part of me was afraid of how I might answer such questions, not only because I didn't know the answers but also because somewhere deep inside, a part of me knew it was time to try. Another part wanted nothing to do with figuring out, let alone trying to explain, how I'd arrived at this moment.

Lucy's house stood just past a crudely patched-together water tank at the end of the drive, a modest building sitting squarely on a two-acre plot bordered by clumps of tangled juniper. Fields delineated by a network of irregular fence posts' marking otherwise inscrutable boundaries brought to mind the paintings I had admired the previous summer. I immediately recognized the art Lucy had found in the hand-cut juniper sticks strung together with reclaimed barbed wire.

I pulled up to the house, hopped down from the vehicle's unaccustomedly high seat, relieved that I'd sprung for the SUV, and looked out over the blanketed fields, beyond which evergreen covered foothills rose up to a cluster of stark mountains to the east, their snow-enshrouded flanks reflecting so much light as to be almost too bright for fixed eyes. A magpie swiveled on a fencepost and flicked its blue-black swoosh of a tail, rasping in response to a sardonic whistle from somewhere in a shaggy juniper bush. As I stood there in the thin, cold air, the slap of a screen door broke the silence, and Lucy, wearing a heavy red and black plaid lumberjack's shirt and fleece-rimmed work boots, accompanied by a large ivory German

shepherd, ambled down the path to greet me.

"You made it! I am so glad you're here!" she said, reaching to offer me a robust hug. "This is my big boy, Hector. Hector, meet Kate," she said, tussling the dog's thick winter ruff of a neck. He sniffed my leg and boots, squinted back at me with a long-snouted grin, and hopped off toward the drive from which I had just come. I noticed only then that he was missing one of his hind legs, a matted shock of sheep-like winter fleece concealing what might have been a portion of his upper leg.

"Come on in. I have coffee up," Lucy said, ushering me around the side of the house, across a small porch. The entire first floor was wide open, filled with the pleasant smell of acrylics. Two easels stood at the far side of the studio before large north- and east-facing windows that looked out toward the fields and peaks. Next to the doorway a well-stoked wood stove gave off both warmth and a vigorous crackle.

I took in the room, the paintings in progress, the surrounding landscape, the winter quiet, the absolute stillness, the pristine light, and the overwhelming sense of solitude.

"Take off your boots and come on upstairs," Lucy said, quickly slipping out of her own. I removed mine as instructed and placed them next to a long, paint-splattered work table where cans of paint and art books were stacked and then followed Lucy up the stairs to the main living space. The shepherd clamored noisily behind us on the bare hardwood, propelling his weight upward in awkward but practiced movements, as he powered his way to each new step with a determined thrust of his single hind leg and a lurching advance of hips, back, and shoulders.

"Miraculous..." I muttered, breathing hard from the single flight, as the dog reached the top landing and I turned to look around.

The same corner window views were carried through the top level of the house, another open space set off by a dramatic cathedral ceiling and beams trimmed with traditional New Mexico style corbels. A corner kitchen area extended up over towering cabinets tall enough to require a rolling ladder and above which perched an aerie shelf space holding a few pieces of antique Southwestern pottery. Next to the stairway we had just climbed, itself lined with a row of high bright windows through which more sky poured in, a glazed door led to a small south-facing balcony overlooking broad plains, lending a sense of expansiveness to a house whose design belied its relatively small size.

"I would have preferred an adobe home, of course, but since that wasn't an option, I went with something that was as open as I could make it with my limited funds," Lucy offered. "I found the design in a book called *Blueprint Small*. I think the subtitle was something like *Creative Ways to Live with Less*. Believe it or not, the design was originally for someone's pool house. The trick is, it turns out, that a small foundation and a small roof can really cut cost, which is why I built up into two stories."

"The design is extraordinary," I said. "It's so open and comfortable. Are these your paintings too?" I asked, gesturing with my gaze toward some extremely large canvases reaching up to the ceiling depicting nearly photographic images of people in various urban settings.

"They are. From my representational days back in Seattle and Utah. It wasn't until I arrived here in Alces that I began doing fully abstract work."

"Really? Well, from what I've seen of your work so far, you certainly made a smooth transition."

"I'd like to think so, but it's been an incredibly long journey from the life I lived then to the life I'm living and the work I'm doing now." She opened a cabinet over the stove and pulled two coffee mugs out. "May I pour you some coffee?"

"Yes, thank you. I'd love to hear about that journey if it's something you feel comfortable sharing with me at some point... I don't necessarily mean now..." I offered deferentially and reached across the counter for a small cobalt milk pitcher, giving my coffee a good dousing.

"I don't mind talking about it at all, especially if my experience can bring you closer to finding your own art."

"I've got a lot to figure out," I said, turning my mug as if testing its symmetry, hoping Lucy wouldn't press me further on the subject of myself.

"How did you end up in this job then?"

"Will got a job offer that he didn't want to turn down, and I decided to let my tenure-track faculty position go after only a couple of years. We had tried to carry on in a long-distance relationship, but it just didn't work for us living in separate cities, seeing each other on weekends and during busy spells not for two or three weeks at a time. We knew we weren't going to continue down that path. So I left my job in New York City with no expectations of ever getting another one like it. I just had to trust I'd find something that I could live with once we settled in Massachusetts."

"I'd say you took a pretty big leap then."

"I did. While I've taken many turns and had many false starts and recognize that whole swathes of my life have turned out to be horrible mistakes, I'm incredibly lucky to have gotten another full-time college teaching job after that. Tenure track and all. I mean, it practically fell in my lap, after I'd filled in part time for an instructor at our local community college who'd been on medical leave and then was let go. It seemed like a good enough fit. Like it was meant to be." I recalled the deep pleasure I had taken in writing through the interim and then felt the immediate retreat of a tentative antenna-like heartstring at the thought of how I'd talked myself into believing that I'd be able to keep it up after I was in the new job and once again back on the tenure treadmill. This was a small, rural institution where I left a larger footprint and was expected to carry more responsibility. I had hoped, this time, to find the process a little less odious.

Lucy, responding to my faraway gaze, motioned out the window.

"Having this space out here on this land, being part of the energy of this village and the artists' community, it's all about faith that we can make it work somehow, that we will find a way to create and still manage to scrape a living together. Often I don't know how I'm going to survive from one month to the next, but I'm here, I have my solitude, my work hangs in the gallery down the road, and I get to live my life as I choose, even if it's whittled down to the barest essentials—and sometimes I don't even have those."

She stood up and signaled toward the living room area. I picked up my mug and followed—as if I'd all but submitted to blind trust—over to the living room sofa, beneath the massive canvas bridging the sitting space and the vaulted ceiling. Two opposing armchairs were already occupied by an assortment of cats.

"You know, my first winter here I didn't even have the wood-burning stove that's heating the house so nicely today. Somehow—I'm not sure how—I thought I could manage without one. It was so brutally cold all the time for months on end. But I was determined. The following year my mother, who has never been supportive of me until fairly recently, decided to help me with funds she's saved from her and Dad's retirement. She paid for the stove and the installation. Now every morning when I light it up,

I feel a sense of gratitude as well as comfort. And so does Hec!" she said, reaching over to give the grinning shepherd, who had migrated with us out of the kitchen, another rub on the head. He yawned with a contented whine and squinted at me, his ivory lashes lacing espresso eyes, and eased himself into a resting place at our feet.

"He came into my life toward the end of that first winter, but he had known some desperately hard times before that, didn't you, my man." Hector responded to her gushy tone with a huff.

"What happened to him?"

"He'd been living out on the llano for months after his family left him behind. He was so completely loyal to them that he continued to guard their house and their horses through the winter, waiting patiently for the family to return.

"I didn't even know he was there at first. I had started feeding some horses I had gotten to know out in one of the pastures—Oh of course, the horses in your painting. How could I forget!"

"You told us about the llano last summer when we bought the painting, and after we left the gallery we went out to see them. I still can't believe how special it was to actually meet the horses who inspired the piece that's now hanging in our living room." I marveled at the complementary images of the horses along with Lucy's representation of them that I had carried with me home and back to this place from that day Will and I wandered into the gallery and ventured out to the llano.

"I'm so glad that one of my paintings of them is living in your home."

After a pause Lucy continued with her story.

"I'd been bringing hay out to the horses whenever I could after I found out about the death of Carlos's son and the family leaving Alces indefinitely.

"My walking route takes me out to the llano, and one day a few weeks after Carlos had moved the horses from the pasture next to my house to a bigger space across the road from his home, I spotted a white dog. I was checking on the horses, and I noticed this magnificent animal watching me from the porch of the empty house. I remembered seeing him one day when the horses were originally brought to the small pasture out here. But there, half hidden in the shadows of that porch, he looked so much like a spirit that I wasn't sure if he was even real. He just studied me from across the road, perfectly motionless. He was letting me know that he wasn't ready to reveal himself.

"Then one day I caught sight of him slipping back to his hiding place, and I noticed that he wasn't using his hind leg at all. It just hung there, limp, dead. Once I saw how severe his injury was and realized he was completely alone, I became alarmed and wanted him to know I could help. All the same, he didn't come forward for a very long time—too proud and independent," she said in the dog's direction, stretching her last few syllables for his benefit.

"Finally, he presented himself to me, but by then he was in deep trouble. His leg was shattered and had gone untreated for months. He'd been out in the elements during an extremely harsh winter, hunting on three legs for whatever he could catch just to survive. I can't imagine the pain he was in all that time from the injury and from the loss of his people. It wasn't until he had watched me from the shadows and decided he could trust me that he finally came forward—that he finally let me know he was ready to let me help him.

"I'd been calling him Spirit Dog from my first glimpses, but eventually I came to call him Hector," she added, musing.

"That spirit of his must be incredibly strong."

"Oh, terribly strong. He's so strong willed that we often butt heads." Lucy laughed and went on.

"He refused to come inside at first. Even though he had accepted me, he hadn't accepted the confines of being indoors behind four walls, and it took some coaxing to get him to sleep in the studio downstairs. Not long after he had accepted the safety of the house, I came down, noticed a nasty odor, and found him lying in a pool of puss that had begun leaking from his groin. That's when I had to face the decision about amputation, and it was one of the most difficult decisions I've ever made. The surgery saved his life, but the recovery process was so painful, I'm not sure I'd have done it if I had known how much suffering he would have to endure."

"Do you know how he got hurt in the first place?"

"He was shot. This rare white puppy, a sign of high esteem, had been a gift—or some kind of payment—to Carlos. Around here they call people in his line of work bandidos, and he's a big one. His family raised the dog, called him Smoke. Then one day someone wanting some sort of revenge drove by and shot him when Carlos was out working with him in the pasture. The shooters were careful not to kill him—just to damage him—to spoil the rare white symbol of honor he represented. The bullet shattered his leg. Sometime after that he chewed off his own penis, which had been partially severed by the same bullet."

I groaned.

"The family had no means of getting medical attention for him other than an aunt who was a healer, so they relied on her herbs and basically left the leg to heal on its own—or not. Then they left altogether after Manny's murder. It's remarkable that this boy even survived," she said. "Isn't it, mister," her coos eliciting several emphatic licks up the side of her face.

"It's hard to imagine the suffering he's been through." I paused. "At the same time," I said, reaching over, digging my fingers into the thick fur on the back of his neck and running my hand down to where I could feel the bones of his shoulders, "he's so lucky you found him."

"Well, I had to earn his trust—his permission. And I had to get the family's permission to take him, and then to treat him, when it became clear that amputation was the only option to keep him alive. They were grateful—saw that I really cared about the dog. I think they were just so overwhelmed that they couldn't bear the responsibility of caring for him—for anything. And out here dogs aren't treated like family members the way they are in the culture you and I know. They're more like field hands, cast off if they become more of a burden than their perceived worth as heelers, property guards, or—sad to say—fighters," she said. "Hec was a little different because he was a prize, a badge of honor, even though he was a tarnished one.

"I remember that day in January, when Carlos moved the horses from the pasture next door out to the llano. The snow was deep on the ground, at least three feet. He and another man ran with the horses on foot, working them toward my back fence where they'd go through the field gate to access the land grant road that leads down to the llano. The horses galloped round my yard several times before the men were able to get them all through the gate. Those horses running in the deep snow and the two men driving them by sheer muscle was a magnificent sight.

"But it was in the early fall, before the winter had set in—before I had ever introduced myself to Carlos—that I actually saw them bring the horses here in the first place and noticed this dog for the first time. I looked out one day and saw a couple of men and a dog driving five horses through the yard toward the pasture. I had only moved in a few weeks earlier and didn't yet understand how boundaries worked around here. Someone had driven a pickup truck over and parked it on the road, which is actually my drive-way. As they worked the horses into the pasture, I noticed this shepherd limping rather badly along but somehow keeping up with them, darting and circling around the horses' legs with colossal effort. I stood there mar-veling at his strength, the way he fought to move his body, to pivot and accelerate, to shift and heave his weight without the use of that leg and still keep those horses in line.

"The men secured the herd in the pasture and locked the gate. Then they hopped in the truck and drove off, leaving the dog behind to make his way after them. I had no idea where they went or how far the dog had to go. But my heart just fell. However they defined their relationship with him, it was completely foreign, didn't make sense the way I see things. And it hurt. I was haunted by the image of that great-hearted dog running until the truck was out of sight, then continuing on, limping along on his three legs after having done the job of two able-bodied dogs."

Lucy paused in reflection. We sat in silence for a time. I caressed Hector's head, gently tugging a mule-like ear. The dog leaned up into my movement. Tilting his elongated head back, he squinted calmly at me, his teeth, brown with heavy tartar and excessively worn, suggesting a much older dog than he otherwise appeared. I noticed a long, ragged scar on his tongue where it had been badly torn and somehow managed to knit itself back together.

Lucy brought her attention back to me. On some level I must have known I'd been drawn there in the first place to explore how I might find my way back to a creative life, but in that moment, somewhere in the un-dergirding of my awareness, I understood only how unprepared I was to follow Lucy down that path or to do more than acknowledge the equally persistent stirrings I'd neglected for most of my adult life. After all, there had never really been an actual creative life to go "back" to, just formless dreams and longings masquerading as callings of the heart.

"Now that you're here, maybe we can talk about what it would take to open up some space for you to establish more of a connection with your own art," she said.

"Well, it's true that I've been struggling, searching for a way to make time for myself, to work my own writing into my life. I know that's important in ways I hadn't realized before, and I know I've paid a price for not making more of a commitment to solving that problem. I'm not thinking about walking away from teaching and the academic life I've always wanted or anything like that..."

I paused, dangerously close to admitting the one thing I hadn't been able to admit to myself before. Hearing myself make such an obviously conflicted statement out loud galled me because I'd had that job for going on two years and—as much as I'd invested myself in denying it—I'd already reached an alarming state of overwhelm and stress. This wasn't supposed to happen. My determination had been no small thing. With it I'd accepted demands on top of demands that often seemed impossible to meet and that I couldn't seem to rein in no matter what I did or how hard I worked. So I just worked harder, swam deeper.

"Besides," I said, struggling to keep from disappearing altogether, "I can't put Will under that kind of pressure again, just because I'm having a hard time balancing my job and my life—our life. He supported me all through my long years of grad school, and I'm not willing to throw us into that kind of insecurity again. As it is, even if I were to last into my nineties I'd never outlive my student loan payments."

That was all true, but so was the daily fight I seemed to be losing without understanding why. Was there some secret method, some practice of boundary maintenance that forever eluded me but allowed others to disengage in healthy ways and still care? If so, where in my teaching life had I missed that lesson? Did my distress come from my underlying doubts in my own competence or my inability to fully appreciate the context in which I'd allowed that distress to rise unchecked? Not that these were mutually exclusive. My work life had become a constant scramble from one extreme to another, facing a level of student apathy and at times outright hostility I'd never seen before in twenty-five years of teaching and advocating for students with the most dire needs. With every effort to institutionalize the support system they needed, the vision that I thought I'd been hired to implement seemed to be slipping away.

"I'm sure Will wouldn't hesitate to support you in finding fulfillment in what you're pouring so much of your energy into. Seeing you completely stressed all the time couldn't be comfortable for him."

Sinking deeper into the worn leather couch and into myself, I thought perhaps I'd been too naïve, fooling myself into trusting my years of previous administrative experience or thinking that my expectations for change were shared. I'd come in with what I believed to be a mandate to build a program, but I was beginning to see that the tools weren't there, the will wasn't there, and despite my efforts, neither was the meaningful incentive I'd hoped to create among my colleagues. I'd been painfully slow in seeing that my experience didn't substitute for a lack of assertiveness, and that my mission was in fact being undermined by someone in another department whom I'd thought of as a partner but who, it turned out, had been actively working against that collaborative vision all along. Her commitment was to maintaining the small fiefdom she had already built. The blow came, eventually: I'd been an unwelcome threat all along and hadn't even seen the signs that should have been obvious.

My department needed all of me; my students did too; the administration demanded more. I couldn't have been the only faculty member ever to experience that perennial crush of commitment. This wasn't my first time around, but for some reason I wasn't holding up well against the everyday push-pull and the politics. Perhaps the inertia I'd encountered could be traced to the peculiarities of the institution, but I blamed myself for languishing in the murky administrative waters, and I was coming to realize that I was alone, treading water, and growing more and more exhausted following a shoreline that seemed in constant retreat.

My long silence invited Lucy to pick up her line of argument again. She seemed to be working from a well-polished empathy, no less genuine for her effort to follow a careful and deliberate progression in the direction she wanted us to go. As I quietly resisted, she held her position a few steps out front.

"Don't you think he'd want you to follow what your spirit calls you to do? You and I are just getting to know each other, and I've only met Will that one time, but from what I've seen of your relationship, I'm absolutely sure that if you were to take a courageous step in a different direction, no matter how genuinely frightening it might be, the two of you would find a way to make it work. You made a choice to leave what I'm sure was a well-deserved teaching position in order for him to pursue a different—and I assume more lucrative—job opportunity. I doubt that's the only sacrifice you've made, either."

I eyed my mug in admission.

"If you believe in and embrace your truth, if there's something calling, something you need to pursue, then I'm sure the finances would somehow fall into place, even if the way to get there isn't obvious at first—even if it seems totally impossible right now."

This was not a place I could allow myself to go. I didn't trust that too-familiar talk about things just falling conveniently into place if only the intentions were right, even though part of me was almost ready—might even need—to believe it. I shifted forward on the couch, elbows on knees, and squinted out at a row of gleaming pastures bordered with more makeshift fences poking up through the snow, waiting for my eyes to adjust to the brightness. I'd long ago mastered the habit of retreating out the nearest window in a moment of discomfort, finding the horizon, or in its absence even a tree, and staring at it, as if with enough focus that imperfect line between earth-matter and sky would reveal a means of escape. Or an answer.

"It's painful—and frightening, as you say—to admit that I'm feeling disillusioned *again* after landing this faculty position, something I'd given up on ever having another opportunity to claim for my own once we moved to the country, something I hadn't sought out or planned for. I probably shouldn't have, but I dismissed the sense I had at the time that there was something I wasn't listening to in that too-good-to-be-true aura that came along with the invitation to apply for the position, which came out of nowhere—and even more so when they offered me the job."

"Maybe it's time to listen to those feelings, no matter how painful they are. Maybe listening through the discomfort and fear will open up pathways you haven't been able to see before."

Lucy let that thought rest for a moment, as I nodded in a lip-biting sort of way, realizing that my neck had all but collapsed. A signal from that part of me endeavoring to disappear reminded me of the vertical order of things, a turtle's minimalist breach of the water's surface to taste the air from the safety beneath. A barely distinguishable irregularity in a living plane of reflection.

Then a proposal diffused the tension. Surely Lucy had been reading my discomfort all along and left her patient suggestion hovering in the air, waiting to alight on a receptive spot in my consciousness. "I was thinking that we might take a drive out to Ghost Ranch. It's about an hour from here, and I'm ashamed to say that I haven't been there in the two-plus years I've lived here. Have you ever been?"

"I have." I returned from the quilt-like snowy fields, happily exchanging my present uneasiness for the relative clarity of the past. "Will and I went hiking there the first summer we visited New Mexico together. I can't believe it—but it must have been twelve years ago now."

"Let's go then! We can continue this conversation on the way. Or not. I've always felt a connection to Georgia O'Keefe's life and her approach to her work. My time in Utah, when I had first returned to painting and was living and working amidst those canyons, gave me a strong sense of kinship with her.

"And I even have a view of Cerro Pedernal from my balcony!" She motioned for me to join her at the picture window where, on the western horizon, we could see the outline of the modest but iconic tapered formation widely associated with O'Keefe.

"Those are the Jemez Mountains out there. They're not all that spectacular on their own, but the sun sets behind them each night and turns my sky afire. I'll get the map and grab a few snacks, you can put some water in those thermoses over there on the counter, and we'll head up to Abiquiú!" she said, grinning her own oversized grin.

6

VASHON

1954

Lucy

SHE IS TODDLING DOWN THE rocky beach, trailing behind her great-grandmother, who wears funny rubber shoes and a straw hat with a wide flouncy brim. She is three or four years old. The old woman came to the island after a long covered-wagon ride from Kansas. Not much older than Lucy, she arrived in this sheltered green place clutching a buckskin-dressed doll, a gift from a kindly member of a Native American tribe they had met on the way. She later painted landscapes on pieces of the wagon canvas she had saved from that journey.

Several round gems glisten at the child's feet. She collects the deep-water cool jellyfish—transparent, perfect, diamonds in her eyes—and lines them up along a sea-worn beach log. They form jeweled patterns in the sun. A child's free-floating singsong stories bubble out into the air.

Then a hard swat and she is dangling from a wrist held tight above her head. Feet thrown out from under her by the force of the blow to her behind now return to gravity and find their tiptoes. Grandma's face, stern and foreign, drops down low to meet the child's fearful welling eyes.

"These are living creatures, and they deserve our love and kindness!" she says with a never-before-and-never-again harshness that quickly softens. Together they retrace the child's steps, taking each jewel back to the water's edge and gently wetting it so as not to shock its system. The old woman sits down. The child spontaneously follows, plopping down, sandy legs and feet thrust out front, and listens as her great-grandmother explains about the crabs and the fish and even the seaweed, how everything is joined and alive and that as human beings it is our responsibility to respect the life around us.

Until she was thirteen and her great-grandmother died, Lucy came to see herself and her great-grandmother as linked souls. Though her great-grandmother taught her to swim, she never hugged or cuddled the child, never told her she loved her. Still, Lucy was drawn to her. In some ways she saw herself as a girl-child version of the old woman who, despite remarkable hardship, held fast to a sensitivity toward nature and beauty, a love of art, music, and storytelling, and a precious gentleness. Lucy clung to that sense of kinship until her great-grandmother's death. Her earliest memories, which arose from that bond, that feeling of being known, provided Lucy with a comfort that came from the sense—at least while her great-grandmother was alive—that there was someone in this world who was like her, someone who saw the world through similar eyes.

When Lucy was born, her maternal ancestors had been living on the Vashon Island waterfront for four generations. Originally separate islands, Vashon and Maury had been reshaped by early twentieth-century European settlers who began arriving after the forced removal of the Indigenous people from their ancestral lands around Puget Sound. Settlers heading westward from the central and southern plains established small-scale farms there. Not long after the turn of the century, landowners decided to fill in part of the waterway between the two islands, and in 1916 they created a land bridge making Vashon more accessible. At the same time, Japanese farmers and fishermen, many from the Seattle area, arrived and contributed to the success of family-run strawberry farms on Vashon-Maury

Island, at least until they too were removed *en masse* to internment camps during World War II.

Lucy's great-great-grandparents settled near Manzanita Beach sometime in the second half of the nineteenth century, after their own rough journey across the plains, and, following them, her great-grandparents, their siblings, and her grandparents became part of a small island colony that sprung up there. Her great-grandfather worked as a dock master in the early days of the twentieth century, when logging and salmon fishing flourished in the waters around Seattle and Tacoma. In the early 1960s her father built a small cabin on a piece of land barely large enough to hold it, land he had bought from his in-laws. One of Lucy's cousins eventually built a modest cabin on an adjacent parcel.

Grandpa Owen—simply known as Grandpa Owen, even though Owen Hardy was actually her mother's step-grandfather—managed to scrape a rough life together by repairing boat engines, selling gasoline from his floating dock, running a newspaper route, and using his tugboat to coax massive log booms through Puget Sound. As a young child, Lucy was enchanted by the notion that it was his job to light the lanterns on the booms at night to prevent fishing boats from running into them. She would recall those magical lights suspended over the water when, fifty-five years later and nearly fifteen hundred miles inland, the paper farolitos lining the streets of Old Taos on Christmas Eve flickered and glowed.

She spent many childhood hours in Grandpa Owen's workshop, drawn to the equipment and the intoxicating smell of gasoline. She felt at home in the cool dark workshop by the barnacle-encrusted dock where he tended to the fixing of broken things and where, untended, she was left completely to her own imagination.

Lucy's early years were shadowed by a persistent doubt that she had ever been fully accepted by her parents, whose running joke throughout her childhood was that they had brought the wrong baby home from the hospital. Intended or not, their teasing, reinforced by the many opportunities her mother took to remind her how unlike them she was, fostered in Lucy the idea that her parents believed she didn't really belong to them, that she had come to them by mistake. Though her resemblance to her father became more obvious as she grew older, to the extent that her mother noticed it in the younger child, the likeness would only have provided more cause to keep Lucy at a distance.

Mrs. Simkus had made it plain that she didn't consider her husband a handsome man, all the while impressing on both of her daughters the importance of good looks. Over time her views were expressed in comments directed at Lucy's posture ("Stand up straight! You're already too tall for a girl. You'll look even worse if you slouch"), her size ("You'd better stay slim since you're already so tall. You don't want to be seen as *big*!"), or shape ("Your sister has curves in all the right places"). Advice often came as a rebuke: "I sure hope you grow out of that string bean phase you're in or you'll never get yourself a husband, and a girl needs a husband to take care of her."

Among the boat engines and tools, Lucy had found a sanctuary where she was free from judgment, from being told she wasn't pretty or ladylike, from being made to feel that she wasn't really a member of the Simkus tribe. The machinery didn't ask bewildering questions like, "Where did our Lucy go? What happened to the good little Lucy we used to know?"

Grandpa Owen taught her to row, and on summer days he occasionally took her along when he worked the tug. While he was out boom hopping, she remained on the boat, basking in complete freedom to take a swim if she pleased, play with the damp, salty coils of rope, and imagine herself as skipper of the vessel. On these glorious afternoons when she was left to fend for herself, she delighted in their tacit understanding. He trusted her not get into trouble, and leaving her alone proved it, implying that she was capable of avoiding danger, and even more importantly, that she knew what it was in the first place and had the wherewithal to manage safely around it, just as he did. This trust gave her a special—perhaps even illicit—sense of independence. Though in many respects she had become a deeply fearful child, she was confident on the water, whether out in a rowboat watching for the whiskers of the harbor seals watching her or riding along with Grandpa Owen as his unofficial first mate.

7

ABIQUIÙ

January 2011

Kate

LUCY PULLED UP INTO THE gas station in Las Moradas, two old-style pumps in front of a bodega. Despite the January cold and a foot of snow on the ground, the place had a dusty, bleached out, time-warped atmosphere. Decades-old cars, low-slung with amped up engines and pulsing woofers, moved in an odd slowness around us.

"There's a lot of violence in this village." Her matter-of-fact tone made the comment seem less cautionary than observational. "It isn't safe to draw attention in any way, either by appearing to be less than certain about where you're going or by showing any sign of aggressive driving. Try not to make eye contact," she said. Okay, that definitely registered as a warning.

I lowered the map, partially folding it on the way down and letting it fall to the floor by my feet. The woman filling up her tank in front of us had parked her car midway between the two pumps, blocking access to the one closest to us. We waited quietly until she finished and Lucy could pull her Jeep 4 x 4 forward.

After filling up, Lucy hopped back in and continued, "One time I inadvertently pulled up too close to another car and was forced to follow them at a snail's pace from one end of the village to the other. The two men in the car pulled the passive aggressive stunt to provoke me to respond, which of course I knew enough not to do. I just crept along—they drove the whole way at about five miles an hour—as if everything was normal. But I was terrified. Rumors are rampant about people stepping into trouble here without knowing it or getting caught in crossfire. An elderly friend of mine from Alces was once shot at as he drove through Cordova. He's a French national who worked for the resistance during World War II and, as a young man, was actually shot by the Germans at one point. Thirty-some-odd years later he won the Nobel Prize for medicine.

"I can't imagine what being shot at here or nearly killed there would feel like in any case, or what it would be like to come out of occupied France alive and then go on to do such remarkable things. I wonder how one would reconcile this place—today—with that place and time..."

Another unsettling thought occurred to me amidst the otherworldliness of the story and the dark energy of Las Moradas.

"This is where Manny was killed, isn't it?"

"It is. This is sort of the epicenter of family-on-family violence and drug-related violence. Recently there was a manhunt for Stanley Renalda, who supposedly murdered two people he knew in Alces. We were all spooked and uneasy, especially at night, locking our doors as long as he was on the loose, in hiding, somewhere out in the desert. His trailer was burned to the ground. We'll pass what's left of it when we head back up the mountain on our way home."

"Do they know who was responsible?"

"The families of the victims," Lucy answered. "That's the way things work around here. The manhunt went on for several weeks, and then about a month ago they found him dead in an empty home he'd been hiding in."

I sat in silence with these unsettling stories. We passed the façade of a church that I thought I recognized from a brochure I'd seen. The building's two wood framed bell towers, appearing centuries old, stood slightly askew, as if held together by the twining of Christmas lights strung around them. If I was right, this was the shrine made famous by large processions of pilgrims who arrive on foot, on crutches, or on hands and knees every year during Holy Week. They come by the hundreds, often carrying large wooden crosses or tiny ones made of sticks tied with string. They come to pray and often to carry away some of what many believe to be sacred dirt from the floor inside in hopes that they or their loved ones will be cured by it. Perhaps we'd stop there on the way back.

As we continued on toward Georgia O'Keefe's one-time part-time home, I allowed the moving pattern of sage brush, offset by snow and a subtle palette of sculpted pink rock, to wash over me, stirred again by the desert's texture and the powerful way it charged my own spirit. Old longings and remembrances nudged against a creeping awareness of empty space receding into an unvisited corner of my own heart. I opened myself to the land, a solid thing that moved me like a sea swell, setting pieces of myself sliding and clanking around inside. We turned off the main road toward Ghost Ranch and the vast open sky that beckoned above ancient exposed sea beds standing tall and sacred in the painted stone of the Colorado Plateau.

After stopping in the welcome center, we took a leisurely walk along the main path, which the map and signs identified as the Continental Divide Trail, stopping frequently to photograph the surrounding rocks and the view of Pedernal, the closest Lucy had ever been to the wide-necked butte that distinguished her home's far western horizon. From this northeastern vantage point, the snow-reflected mid-day sun cast a film over its sloping rampart and knobby caprock, turning the flint monument into a purple shadow. A transparent half-moon floated above us as we admired a wall of crisp glazed cliffs where gold sandstone had sheared off in arching slabs or had worn away along vertical fissures, leaving behind massive hewn figures standing cloaked and shoulderless above jumbled talus escarpments.

"I don't know about you, but I'm not feeling all that ambitious about hiking into the canyon," Lucy admitted. "I'm quite satisfied following this trail to somewhere we can sit and have a snack, unless you feel strongly about going on a more strenuous hike."

"Oh, I'm very happy walking this trail," I assured her. "I'm not sure exactly where the trail that Will and I took when we were last here begins, or even if we'd want to tackle that with all this snow on the ground. I seem to remember spending most of an afternoon out there," I said, gesturing vaguely ahead of us, "but it was summer, of course, and this map is a little confusing." I scowled at the widely out-of-scale diagram in the photocopy.

As I continued to study the drawing, some details came back to me. "It was a long time ago—at least ten years—but I remember a fairly steep climb somewhere on the far side of those cliffs up there." Reading further, a description sparked my memory of a fairly challenging but impressive hike around the edge of a box canyon. I recalled an overcast sky and a russet canyon spread in a horseshoe-shaped array of cliffs.

"I think it must have been the Kitchen Mesa Trail," I said, pointing to the dotted trail line that began at the top edge of the map but was abruptly cut off at the margin, "because it says there's a '15-foot chimney through a cleft in the cliff.' As a matter of fact, I'm now remembering Will and me poking our way up a fairly steep and narrow crevice in the rocks. That must be it. The climb was worth it because it took us to a cliff-top trail with extraordinary views out across the canyon, one of our more memorable hikes. I can't imagine doing it at this time of year, though. And besides, it says here that it's a three-hour hike."

"I'm definitely not up for that," Lucy said. "Let's find a sheltered spot in the sun where we'll be comfortable sitting."

"I'm just so happy to be here," I added. "I don't really care where we walk to-day. This time it's not so much about exploring... in that way anyway. It's more of an inner journey for me, even though, obviously, I had to travel to get here, and this landscape lends itself to the idea of exploring something important."

"Being here highlights how our paths have crossed on our mutual jour-neys," Lucy said. "And I have a proposal to make to you, in honor of those paths coming together."

"A proposal?"

"Yes. I've felt for a long time that I wanted to tell my story, the story of how I survived, how I found painting again, how I found Alces and made an artist's life here. I think there's a worthwhile story to tell, but I'm not a writ-er. I mean, I can communicate well enough, but I don't have the skills to construct a complicated story and figure out how it would need to be told, to make it compelling and bring in layers of meaning. Make it something others can relate to and find inspirational. But I believe—no, I'm certain—that you have those skills, that you are the person to tell that story. I don't want to put pressure on you, but if you think you'd be interested, that you'd find this type of book worth writing, I can't think of anyone better suited, anyone else I'd want to hand this task over to."

I folded the map, returned it to my coat pocket, and stood there shaking my head, almost afraid to trust another one of those feels-right moments. But there it was, undeniable, unrefusable.

"That is a gracious, *terribly* generous offer. I don't quite know what to say." I paused again, struggling to collect myself and breathe some calm into a swirl of emotion.

"I'm honored that you have that kind of confidence in me, surely more than I've got in myself at the moment. It feels—not to overthink it right now, but—it feels like the right time, the right story, the right place to regain my footing on a creative path, despite all the doubts flying around in here," I said, gesturing to my head, noting how certain I sounded, despite what I was trying to say. "They're definitely there, but for some reason they're not bothering me right now. I can't imagine anyone else I'd want to take that kind of journey with," I said, shrugging off the how-and-when questions before they could neutralize the hope spilling into my heart's lowest swales.

Lucy reached over and slung an arm across my shoulders. "I'm just thrilled that you want to do this! Even though we don't know each other that well yet, I can see us working extremely well together."

"So can I," I added, looking down and taking stock of droplets of snow-melt on my boots and the afternoon sun at our backs. "I like the way things are coming together." Then, needing to move, I pointed along the path ahead of us. "How does that spot by the adobe wall look? Do you want to stop there and sit for a while?"

"Looks perfect," said Lucy.

Treading on our shadows, we made our way toward a sheltered place just off the path.

"I've suddenly got a lot to think about," I said, still shaking my head as I began to take in the scope of the project I had just signed onto. "We'll have to arrange some interviews. I need some time to think through how to begin, how to set the whole thing up. Of course, we'll have to wait until the spring semester ends before we can really get started.

"Oh, there's no rush. We can explore how you want to approach this and then begin in earnest in the summer. Here, we can sit on those stones where the snow has melted," Lucy said, stepping over to several slab-like rocks lining the path, partially sheltered by a rough-mudded half wall. "There's nobody here today but us, it seems, so I don't think they'll mind if we sit here."

"By the time anyone notices we'll be on our way anyway," I agreed, settling down on a smooth gray metate-shaped stone. We enjoyed the quiet and our own private thoughts, passing back and forth between us the bag of fruit and nuts that Lucy had brought along in a small canvas rucksack, our two thermoses propped in the snow between our boots.

8

TRUTH SPEAKERS

January 2011

Kate

As much as I'd hoped to sneak past those two bitter nights in Almarosa's casita without catching a cold, the prolonged chill had done its damage. I started to feel like I was coming down with something that last day, and by the time I stepped out into the clear pre-dawn darkness to head back to Albuquerque, inklings of a sore throat signaled an illness coming on. I pushed away doubts about having just a little over a week to pull myself together for the spring term, but cutting into the desperately short winter break with this trip had been a half-calculated risk wrapped in a sense of urgency. Or was it the other way around?

I boarded the plane carrying a book about life in the Sangre de Cristo Mountains that Lucy had given me at the last minute, its pages filled with marginal stars and underlined passages. Many of the first hundred or so pages were earmarked, the second two hundred, clean. She admired the author so much, she said, that she wanted me to have it, promising she'd get herself another copy. I'd glanced through *Enchantment and Exploitation: The Life and Hard Times of a New Mexico Mountain Range* before I left and was captivated both by the writing itself and by the subject. I liked that the subtitle seemed deliberately ambiguous as to whose story—the mountains' or the people's—the author promised.

Kate

The "Preface," William deBuys's account of a November hike into the Pecos Wilderness, begins with an appealing description of the transitional time in the mountains of Northern New Mexico, just as the winter is poised to blow in but hasn't fully overtaken the land. My own annotations, as if to complement Lucy's, would eventually begin right here, with the author's reference to that moment of seasonal ambiguity. I read the passage both as a paean to the power of the land that had so often spoken to me and as a prelude to a story that explores the bonds between that land and its inhabitants. I've never been a stranger to grand conspiracies spun from written words I could greedily consume as if intended just for me. This felt like one of those, so I followed the author on his late-fall foray in the Sangre de Cristos, held fast by his description of the understated inter-season that arrives "after the dazzling gold of the aspen and all the other autumn colors have faded to dull tones" but before "the deep winter snows that cover the high country with a white mask."

I happily tagged along into the silence and starkness of that canyon as he began his solitary trek into the high country "to enjoy the land and to learn from it." He had me completely hooked by the second paragraph, there by "a clear and ice-hung stream that drains some of the most remote and least visited land in the range." I noted with almost blood-bound fellowship his night spent in twenty-degree weather.

While following some snowshoe hare tracks through the early snow the next morning, he comes upon the grizzly wreckage of a small airplane with four bodies inside. The crash had been recent enough for the bodies to have yet been spared visitation by scavengers but long enough for them to have frozen solid where they lay. An investigation, as deBuys recalls, attributed the travelers' fate to the perils of a poor understanding of the landscape and their plane's limited power to maneuver quickly enough to clear the canyon wall. To inexperienced sightseers such as these unfortunates, he adds, it must have seemed to come out of nowhere.

Two underlined passages announced themselves on the third and final page of the dog-eared "Preface." Lucy's black ballpoint pen indicated that she'd been drawn to the writer's explicit statement of his "deceptively simple" point, which I too took to heart: "...in an unforgiving environment, small errors yield large consequences." Her marks suggested that she had lingered over one particularly self-assured piece of insight: "the trick of living in the mountains begins with understanding the power of the landscape and the limits it imposes." For some reason I've never thought to ask her what special meaning this passage held for her, or what she thought of the imperative that followed, in which the author asserts that the only way this story can begin is by looking at "how people have learned this lesson—or at times forgotten it." Feeling appropriately cautioned, I was eager to launch into the account that I hoped would see me eastward and home.

Once settled into my window seat, I opened the book and prepared for the long flight to Washington, D.C., where I'd catch my connecting flight to Hartford. I'd begun to feel feverish and resigned myself to alternating between studying the landscape below—a strategy I regularly employ to manage my anxiety about flying—and making my way through deBuys's history, though I had no intentions of revisiting the prefatory canyon crash site with him at that point. We lifted off and headed straight up along the I-25 highway from Albuquerque to Santa Fe, the road I'd just traveled in the opposite direction.

A black and white satellite map on page seven caught my eye. The caption read:

North central New Mexico from Skylab. June 1973. Note snow above timberline in the Sangre de Cristo Range and irrigated land along Rio Grande and other rivers. The rounded, dark areas are volcanic formations, the largest of which is Valles Caldera of the Jemez Range in the lower left.

— Courtesy of the Earth Resources Data Center. Sioux Falls, S.D.

As we approached cruising altitude, I recognized Santa Fe below and noticed that the landmarks out ahead of us resembled the image on the recto page open in my lap, though the scale was different and the seasons didn't match. I set about studying the wrinkled wintry earth below, my trusted antidote to the distress of air travel, no more than a trick to stay focused on the ground. But my long-held love of maps suddenly offered me another tool, a useful means of distraction, a puzzle to solve. I resisted the unwelcome irony that we might inadvertently fly over deBuys's canyon and entered further into the Skylab image. There it was, uncanny as any epiphany: a one-to-one correspondence between the photo and the earth's dramatic contours from my otherwise uneasy aerial perch.

Lost in the double images of the Sangres before me, one alive and one colorless, static, and nearly forty years old, I almost forgot the aches beginning to settle into my legs and kidneys, the cottony feeling in my head, and the excitement and bewilderment of everything that had happened in the last few days. There were the peaks I had admired from the ground that morning as I steered along Lucy's snow-covered drive, their austere silhouette just visible along the eastern horizon as I pulled out onto County Road heading south, not long before the dark crystalline sky behind them would begin to soften and warm in advance of the sun.

What lessons were there for me in the topography of this place and my strange and powerful connection to it? Would I even recognize or understand those lessons through the gloss of my own sense of enchantment? How close might I come to fatally clipping one aspiring fir tree with an errant wing tip? And how deep beyond the surface of this terrain would I need to take my untested imagination in order to chart my way to some version of the creative sanctuary I'd glimpsed in Lucy's life?

By the time I got off the plane and the airport shuttle delivered me out to the most distant economy parking lot, the body aches that had begun during the first leg of my trip and the fever that had announced itself during my transfer at Dulles had coalesced into something bone-deep and flu-like. It was midnight, and beyond the immediacy of my symptoms, I found my home world buried in deep snow, the aftermath of a fairly serious storm that had come through. Will had kept me informed about its progress over the past couple of days, with plenty of reassurances from me about getting myself home safely from the airport. At that hour the roads would be empty. The snow had come and gone, and the plows would have been steady at the job throughout past day or two.

I arrived at the snow-encased mound that identified itself in response to my key fob signal with a faint chirp and a brief flash of one partly visible headlamp. Heavy winds had drifted snow, now solidified and chest high, in the spaces between the cars. After one attempt, I realized that even if I could have gotten the door open and climbed inside, the car was partially buried underneath an icy berm the plows had dumped on the parked cars when clearing the main areas of the lot. A snow shovel? At midnight? In single-digit temperatures headed straight for the minuses? I hadn't prepared for that kind of contingency. Without shelter from the fierce wind and cold, and addled by fever, I didn't have the wherewithal to stand up to the elements, open my suitcase, and find my boots and warmer clothing. It wasn't as if I could have peeled down and put on my long underwear.

The overnight checkout clerk boothed in the remote lot had a radio and called for dig-out service. Unfortunately, I had nowhere to go until someone with a shovel worked his way out there. When a truck finally arrived an hour later, I was so cold and despondent that the man on shovel duty invited me to sit in his truck while he removed enough snow for me to get the car door open, start the engine, and pull out. Home was still a wearying ninety minutes away.

The following Monday, after several days on antibiotics, I was back on campus giving make-up exams. I attended to a few administrative tasks, hoping to find a sense of direction by filing and organizing the stray threads of the last semester and getting a start on the one that was about to begin. But even after a second round of antibiotics, the persistent pain in my throat and what seemed like a worsening case of laryngitis dragged along with me as I shuffled through another agonizing week of class.

At night, when I had the strength, I wrote to Lucy and avowed I still held onto the determination she had inspired and urged on, to make significant changes in the balance of my life and work. Her frequent reminders to establish and preserve boundaries and to create space for my personal work sounded reasonable but remained somehow just out of reach, no matter how earnestly I acknowledged the need to block the challenges to that plan. I said it out loud in my messages, trying to make it stick: this space I'd make for the work of writing was neither expendable nor negotiable. At the very same time, though, as my duties piled up, I was powerless to the stop those boundaries from being eroded a little bit more each day.

Kate

A month or so later, an otolaryngologist initiated me into my rather painful first nasopharyngeal endoscopy, a procedure in which a scope tipped with a light and camera is inserted through the nasal cavity and down the back of the throat to the vocal cords housed in the larynx. Even under better circumstances and a gentler hand, this can be an uncomfortable and distressing procedure, though one can, as I was to find out, become more tolerant with repeated practice. That first time, however, it was all about distress when, poking around with the scope somewhere in the approximately five-inch length of my highly irritated vocal tract, the doctor announced, "I'm lost in here." Eventually he did manage to find my larynx and probed it while repeating the "eeee" sounds I was supposed to imitate but which came out sounding more like the ravenous hisses of the living dead than the high vowelly sounds I'd been asked to produce. Whatever was or wasn't going on down there, the doctor had seen enough to make a diagnosis. My right vocal cord was paralyzed. I was sent home with some nasal spray and no explanation for the cause of this condition or the constant throat pain that had begun that day, six weeks earlier, on my flight home from New Mexico.

9

VOICE LESSONS

February 2011

Kate

THE REALITY OF STARTING THE semester without being able to speak hit hard enough to shake some still-sleeping part of me, but not enough to rouse her into a state of wakeful alarm. What good would alarm have done anyway?

The college media department offered me a marginally functional wireless microphone and a portable speaker box. Portable in that it had a handle. I had a total of ten minutes to get the audio equipment across campus, along with my books, papers, and supplies, and set everything up. The mic and amp required even more time to test and tweak repeatedly before class. That left no time for actually collecting my thoughts about the lesson itself. Afterward, the disassembly had to be completed and packed up while students from my own or the following class drifted in or out. Somewhere in there I needed time to talk with students, conversations which I couldn't broadcast from a speaker.

The amount of aid the equipment provided was hardly worth the effort, nor would it serve any purpose in the other contexts of daily life on campus when speaking was required. Advising, committee meetings, telephone calls, and just interacting normally with students and colleagues throughout the day just had to happen. In the end, the inadequate tools and the nature of my work only encouraged me to use my damaged larynx, a painful practice that impeded healing.

Kate

The untenability of all this left me clinging to the aspects of teaching that I had long before internalized and incorporated into part of me that I thought I understood. Over my years as a teacher, I had acquired a certain level of trust in myself, which became an antidote to a stubborn shyness that too often wedged itself between me and the peopled world. Teaching had given me the sense of being totally inside something—as it is in making art—when the body and all other concerns disappear and you're just the thing itself and the thing is you. I had loved that: the adrenaline washing the nerves away, the feeling of being absolutely attuned to the moment, shaping it, folding one step into the next, threading each with a goal, helping others make their own discoveries. In many ways that world no longer existed—or at least my access to it had been lost in my transitions from state university, to graduate school, to city university, to graduate school again, and finally to a rural community college. Despite some disillusionment, I continued to believe I could adapt to the world as I found it and rely on my strengths and experience to help me hang on.

One afternoon, an otherwise reticent student mustered the nerve to speak up. He was one of eight special-needs students from a local area residential program who'd been registered for one of my expository writing classes. I was an English instructor with advanced degrees in literature and linguistics and no expertise in autism whatsoever, let alone an entire group's particular and—as far as I could see—idiosyncratic cognitive and affective needs. I certainly didn't know how to give one full third of the class the attention they needed while simultaneously supporting the other seventeen students on the roster. I raised these concerns to my dean when he first informed me that he'd placed that many special-needs students in one class and returned—finally, fully alarmed—when I better understood the miracle I'd been asked to perform. He maintained that my teaching skills were strong enough for this, and he was confident I could handle it. I wondered if he'd ever been asked to teach that many students with that many unique disabilities he didn't understand while managing a disability of his own.

That one student raised his hand that day as I struggled to reduce the angry static coming from the speaker in the back of the room. "Professor Klein, it's really hard to concentrate on what you're saying when your voice is coming from the back of the room." I could see and feel his agitation. I could see that this was more of a plea for help than a complaint, though it came out as a whine. Maybe it was time to give up the audio "support" altogether. This badly executed form of ventriloquism wasn't working for me any better than it was for him and surely not for anyone else in the room.

Until this crisis, I had seen teaching as an art; but unlike creating other kinds of art, the constant challenge was to make and remake a collaborative act in real time. I had learned to enjoy that performance aspect of it in the domain of my own classroom. I had also learned that the process was uniquely vulnerable to contamination by others' need for approval. Grades, judgment calls, behavioral problems, authority issues, cultural misunderstandings, evaluations. Such things, legitimate or not, could undermine the kind of learning I wanted to nurture and sustain. But I made it work by holding myself open. All channels available for transmission, all the time. Not a recipe for sustainability. Now, in the process of losing that sense of enlivenment and oneness that had once been part of the bargain I'd made, what remained for me, under these circumstances, had narrowed itself down to the constant, irresistible, all-consuming force drawing me into a bottomless well of demands attached to the craft I loved.

If there had ever been a reference or a gauge, I had lost sight of or chosen to ignore it. Somehow I'd never learned how protect myself and establish boundaries that would guard the strengths that had gotten me there in the first place, strengths which, if they couldn't save me, would at least steady me. The cycle broke only when I lost my ability to speak and found myself pondering that reality over several months of distressed silence, not knowing whether my voice would ever return, and if it did, what form it would take.

As if to compound an already painful irony, one day I walked into the classroom to find two strange adults waiting there, presumably for me. They introduced themselves and explained that they were signers who would be working in my class for the rest of the semester on behalf of a hearing-impaired student. They would just do their thing and I would go about teaching my class as I normally did.

Having worked alongside audiologists, speech-language pathologists, otolaryngologists, and linguists as a graduate student, I recognized the student-in-question's cochlear implant, as well as his extremely limited ability to hear or—as might have been the case—to meaningfully process the information his brain perceived. Though of course he understood American Sign Language, some fairly severe and obvious deficits suggested that he had most likely gone through his early childhood without critical exposure to the spoken language in which he was now expected—and expecting—to function at a fairly high level. The most concerning part for me was that he didn't seem to understand or appreciate his own needs and limitations. Perhaps the revelation of the implant opening up a formerly silent world had given him a false sense of confidence. Perhaps the only way to launch into the world with such profound challenges is to deny space for them to establish a hold on one's attitude and expectations, especially for an eighteen-year-old.

My own speculation notwithstanding, I had neither the capacity to assess nor even the permission to inquire about the details of his language learning history, cognitive impairment, or immediate needs. I was supposed to figure out what he needed, how to provide it, and somehow help him and the others get through a demanding college English course without any training. And without my voice.

For the rest of the semester, the signers took turns standing next to me in the front of the room, translating whatever bits and pieces they picked up into something this one student was supposed to be able to understand but—when asked to write or respond—never seemed to comprehend. How much of what I said—or tried to say—did they even capture? How much or how little of the class dialogue was even capturable that way? How accurately did they translate what I said, convey the questions posed or answered in a dynamic setting? The finer points of grammar and mechanics I demonstrated on the board? Small-group activities in which he was supposed to actively participate? How much, if any, of this did he attend to? Did it even matter? I would never know. Still, no amount of effort enabled me to make my own meager sounds entirely audible to the twenty-four hearing students in the room. Neither could I mitigate the confusion and distraction the signers created for the eight students on the autism spectrum, each of whom struggled in different ways to figure out what to focus on and how. As for the rest, I had little chance of reaching them or sustaining their attention. There was no art in this.

10

SILENCE

April 2011

Kate

MY CONVERSATIONS WITH LUCY HAD so far allowed me to imagine something different, but that vision didn't include a feasible way of getting there. Will and I agreed on a tentative plan: over the spring and summer I would actively work in time for writing, if only in small amounts, and make it a priority to limit or curtail administrative and teaching work for as much of the summer as I possibly could. By September we hoped to have gained a slightly better financial footing, which would allow me to take steps to leave my job. Until then, all of my energy would go to finding that elusive balance Lucy and I had talked about and learning how to maintain it, despite the steady build of demands from my students and dean. I had no hope of continuing like this unless I changed my relationship with those demands. I was beginning to understand that if I didn't succeed, something much more drastic would have to happen.

I had our project to think about and a growing impatience to escape and immerse myself in it. The more I struggled with my voice, the more I felt the pull of the work that really mattered to me, the idea that I might be able to clear a path to get there. This inspiration might have felt like empowerment—Lucy called it that—but the struggle to teach, advise, and participate in two simultaneous search committees, among myriad other duties and projects—all without a voice—quickly became anything but empowering. Perhaps if I hadn't been so overwhelmed by the baldly obvious I'd have seen more clearly the irony in these strange circumstances, the bearing out of this moment of transition from one sense of voice to another.

In my nightly messages to Lucy, I wrote of the fear of losing that inspiration in the meantime, but the promises she made served as a framework in which to believe, as if believing that the creative fire wouldn't die served as my singular means of survival. I was in a transitional time, she said. I wasn't alone, she assured. It would be a process of discovery in which we would sustain each other. I had to let old patterns die. Though I softened to it somewhat, I never quite embraced Lucy's belief in a benevolent Universe providing me with encouragement, if only I could recognize the signs. At the same time, I knew there was an important message in her observations about the agonizing process I was going through:

> ...it goes against our survival instincts to let a part of ourselves die. We're built to fight that. So, sometimes the very acts we need to take to grow, change, and become our higher selves go against our innate natures. That's one of the reasons it's so hard to do what you're doing.

I admired her tenacity, her ability to get herself through the scariest uncertainties and find her way to an artful life, so I positioned myself, at least, to believe and to try to hold that idea—supported by some grand invisible advocate or not—in a safe place. Lucy knew what her resources were and seemed to understand them. Might I be ready, finally, to learn how to gauge and nurture my own?

As I continued to languish, I felt part of myself yielding to a deep imperative that I could name but not yet act upon, while other parts stubbornly held to the familiar path, the world to which I'd given so much of myself already. I knew this compromise had cost me the ability to speak and to swallow without effort and pain. I fought the chokehold of anxiety and depression, despite the early signs of spring. Red willow shoots rising through a late spring snow, the birth of a second granddaughter, and a new job for Will stirred some hope, but my deteriorating strength and relentless pain held out, even through a brief round of prednisone. I needed help, a competent specialist of some kind. While I set about searching, Lucy shifted to a tone of concern, gently but unambiguously pressing me to consider the possibility that I might not be able to continue teaching. I might need to make my peace with having no other option.

I took a day off to make the three-hour journey to New York City to see an acupuncturist whom I'd never met before, a friend of a friend, an unlikely expert in treating vocal injuries. Though his practice was closed to new patients, he agreed to see me as a favor to the worried friend who connected us.

In early April the City was already in mid-riot of the daffodils and tulips that hadn't yet made their splash in New England, where so far only a few of the boldest buds graced the most sheltered and sunny spots. Located within the radius of high commotion around the U.N. building, the office was surprisingly tranquil inside. Thick, darkly painted walls and the sound of water streaming toward some welcoming ocean shut out the din as if it had never existed in the first place.

Our session began with Dr. Ronah examining my pulses.

"You're grieving," he said. Not the first words I expected to hear. "Your core has died."

He explained that the adrenals and kidneys, which are the source of the body's energy in traditional Chinese medicine, were so depleted that they had become essentially nonexistent. My Qi had gone completely cold.

"There's no life inside," he said. "Your light is out."

Dr. Ronah went on to say that in this state my body couldn't heal. It couldn't even process nutrients, and if I were to have surgery on my vocal cords, which he thought would likely be recommended, the results would be disastrous. Given my condition, he said, vocal cord surgery, which is very often successful, would be doomed to fail, and I would probably lose my ability to speak permanently.

He recommended intensive Chinese herbal therapy for three months, focusing on my immune system and trying to get my strength back with regular acupuncture treatments to revitalize my core. This required a commitment to making the three-hour trip each way every week for four weeks. Then we would reassess and make a longer-term plan. He also insisted upon complete rest for a minimum of three months. I wasn't even sure what "complete rest" looked like. And there was one problem: the end of the semester was still four weeks away.

Having endured so many tubes and painful probes forced down my throat over the preceding weeks, the needles Dr. Ronah put into my distressed neck and throat muscles, delicate as they were, didn't seem intolerable, even with slightly uncomfortable electro-stim pulsing away. When he turned the lights off and prepared to leave me there with the needles in place, he instructed me to visualize a warm golden light shining on my throat.

The man to whom I suddenly felt connected in an unearthly way half sidestepped, half backed out. Light from the hallway slivered and vanished into the dusk of the room as the door closed. Once I was alone in the dark, the only image that came to mind was the photo of Hector that Lucy had sent a couple of days before. The dog was sitting on the floor of her studio bathed in the early morning sun that made his white coat glow gold and orange pink. He wore that familiar squinty expression of fondness. In that moment, the smiling Spirit Dog reflected the golden sun's light—and maybe, through him, some of its healing—back on me. I envisioned sharing that light with him. Intense flashbacks from my childhood passed through my consciousness in what I can only describe as a dying moment in which I finally understood that my inner light, my core, was gone. I lay there on the table, barely more than a body, but enough of me was still alive enough to cry from a deep dark center and understand what that moment meant.

Reluctantly, I would come to understand that I'd have to find a deeper level of trust, learn to embrace silence as a living, breathing thing. I'd have to examine its dimensions and potential, become intimate with its character, and perhaps, then, neutralize its claim on my courage. If I could just find a comfortable space alongside it, I might have a better vantage point from which to view my own potential, release myself from the unforgiving voices in my head. That constant stream of anxiety about how Will and I would survive without my income. I'd have to turn someone else's words into agency, stop talking about it and let go of the idea that my survival depended on that built-in sense of purpose that came with the job I'd spent twenty-five years mastering. I'd have to stop wondering whether or not I had it in me to stop questioning my capacity to make art that could speak for me or validate my choices. Art that could be bold in ways I hadn't yet learned how to be, art through which I could conjure a voice I hadn't heard before. The only way was to leap across a galaxy of uncertainties, find some vestige of trust, and strive with whatever I had left to make meaning out of so many grand contradictions, real or imagined failures, persistent regrets.

I wanted to believe that somewhere in the process of giving life and breath to Lucy's story, I'd find those other parts of myself I'd lost, dismissed, or never known I had. I was slowly and against my own dark doubts coming to see that like light refracting through a prism, the colors and energy I'd bring to her story originated somewhere, in some other form, in the primacy of my own lived life.

Was it a hallucination or a faint, unsteady patch of light emanating from somewhere within? Real or not, that light I imagined carried the potential to illuminate questions about the part my *un*lived life might play in this process. I hoped it would help me uncover the answers as I set out to understand the choices and compromises Lucy had made and how she'd managed to reconcile with them.

11

....

BREATH

April—May 2011

Kate

FOR ME, THERE WOULD BE no reconciling with the possibility of total voice-lessness, as I sat with the implications of compulsory silence on my work, my art, my identity. In the weeks before I found Dr. Ronah, May's prize of respite remained too painfully out of reach to matter in the daily scheme of things. During that time, I used up my allotted personal days making several trips into New York for evaluations by neurologists and otolaryngologists, none of whom offered any real hope for a positive outcome or even an explanation for why my vocal cord had become permanently paralyzed in the first place. My condition was idiopathic, they said, possibly a result of the otherwise ordinary virus that took hold when I was especially run down on my return from New Mexico.

After four laryngoscopic exams in six weeks, this uniquely unpleasant procedure had practically become routine. I was discouraged and tired, weary of yet one more doctor having to see for himself, refusing to talk to me before scoping me, poking my raw, weeping larynx, and asking for those ghastly sounds. At that point, being lauded as "a pro" would have elicited a gag even without an offending probe's help.

The best news came following a procedure so medieval in nature and execution that I referred to it as *my impalement*. There would be no anesthesia. I was seated in a large vinyl chair—appropriately old school—and a nurse half sat on, half leaned across my body to hold me still. That was body language I understood viscerally from early childhood. I had learned by five or six that adults often choose expediency over preparing a small child for the pain they were about to inflict. That nurse's lean-in signaled pain that would be inescapable and no less real for its being delivered without full disclosure. As if it wouldn't hurt as much without the courtesy of a warning.

With the grim resolve of an executioner, she instructed me not to move and inserted a needle through the front of my throat. I'm not sure how she determined how far to plunge, but the needle, directed between the ribs of the trachea, went deep into the soft, highly sensitive tissue whose eloquent movements allow us to breathe, swallow, and vocalize. These tissues, intelligent as they are, also signal the presence of the tiniest piece of food, dust, or a drop of liquid that shouldn't be there. Even I, who in my youth trained myself to stop hiccups through sheer concentration (and earnestly tried to teach this skill to willing subjects), was unable to stop my body from its natural protective responses.

The Laryngeal Electromyography (LEMG) probe measures the electrical signs of enervation in the muscles of the larynx, not unlike a meat thermometer measuring the temperature deep inside the flesh of a roast. Only unlike a poultry carcass or a cut of beef, the larynx is tender, alive, and primed to react. If I coughed or swallowed—the natural involuntary responses to the presence of a foreign object, in this case, one far more intrusive than a particle of dust or errant droplet—the syringe-like probe was pulled out and the whole process repeated from scratch. When the doctor, facing a screen and seated with his back to us, announced that they had an acceptable reading in one spot, I was skewered again until clean measurements had been recorded in the right, left, front, and back areas of my larynx.

The good news? Ten weeks in, the culprit nerve showed tiny flickers of life. It was damaged but not completely lifeless. The muscle tissue might recover, though the vocal cord would not. That was functionally and permanently dead. The doctor said it could take up to eighteen months to know whether or not my voice would return and to what extent.

Kate

I left the office shaken and disoriented. Rather than make my way to the train station as planned, I followed my instincts. They steered me, wobbly and traumatized, to the Museum of Modern Art, where for a time I lost myself in a luminous clamor of color and the comforting dance of the human imagination, hoping to recover a grain of trust in the world and to process what I'd just experienced.

I continued my painful efforts to swallow, to communicate, and for several more weeks, to teach. Occasionally my throat would spontaneously close up, leaving an opening the size of a cocktail straw. These episodes lasted only two or three minutes—an eternity when one's airway is all but gone, with no certainty that it won't go that tiny bit further to complete closure. Whether or not I succeeded in maintaining composure, which I usually did, my body didn't know that it wasn't choking to death. The distressing sound of my primal, drawn-out struggle to inhale generally frightened others more than it did me when such interruptions came during conversations or meals. I count it as a blessing that this never happened in class.

Under Dr. Ronah's care, a melding of Taoist sensibilities and an uncompromising treatment protocol, my voice gradually returned over a year that would begin—despite my struggle to avoid it—with the resignation I hadn't been able to imagine until I could imagine no alternative. But progress remained fragile and uneven. Accommodating too much stress, fatigue, or even a wave of self-consciousness, could quickly swallow my voice and strangle me into silence. Eating or drinking without full concentration could lead to a harrowing episode of choking, an experience I liken to drowning in slow motion. I was going to have to make survival about a different kind of story in telling someone else's.

PART TWO

12

HERITAGE

June 2011

Kate

I FELT A JITTERY EXCITEMENT at the bubbly sound of the Skype call coming in. We'd had a few of these already, but it still felt fairly new and a little unpredictable. A storm blowing through Alces could easily end an interview. Once I'd clicked the signal open, the channel filled my screen with a welcome view: the bright corner window where Lucy sat at her dining room table, light flooding in signaling a clear sky, the bottom portions of her larger canvases just visible on the wall behind her and across the room. I didn't need to see the front of the canvas just over Lucy's shoulder, or the space that carried the one on the far wall the rest of the way up to the ceiling; those details of Lucy's physical world lived comfortably in my mind's eye. A glimpse of Hector's face swept in and out of view as Lucy cooed invitingly, followed by the sounds of the shepherd settling with a groan and a *humpf* somewhere at her feet. Now we could begin.

My teaching life over, most likely for good, this would be my life now. The jitters were about dipping into the unknown. I wanted to believe that all I didn't know could be bound by no matter how fine a thread to something that felt familiar. That something was story. The biggest leap, it seemed, would be in taking responsibility for telling Lucy's.

I had prepared my questions, feeling fairly confident in my ability to prompt Lucy to drill further down into the details of her childhood, family history, salient events that shaped her personality and emotional landscape. How she learned to navigate her world, cope with doubts, fears, hopes, disappointments, and trauma. The questions wouldn't be easy, despite the invitation Lucy had given me and despite her fearlessness—if it was fearlessness and not acquiescence—in ceding all decision-making to me. In assuming the role of navigator, I was prepared to challenge her and carefully gauge the direction and scope of our journey, keeping one eye on the compass as we moved in and out of safer places and the other on Lucy's comfort level. I knew I could prod her and hoped I could protect her. I couldn't be entirely sure how this would work, but I imagined that Lucy would one way or another discover—or perhaps we would discover together—where and how far she would be able to go, now that the project was no longer an abstract notion.

It began with a basic trust in her capacity to reflect and my capacity to assemble the bits of her life that I could draw out and transform into something larger, something true, something that had shape and resonance, something that felt reasonably whole. A strange romanticized something that each of us would own and at the same time hold out as a gift to the other. At first, I saw myself more or less as a curator, standing on what I thought was fairly solid ground, coaxing my friend along, coaxing my fragile and unreliable voice along, providing support and a sense of direction. The peculiar non-straightforwardness of it all appealed to me.

But as we delved into Lucy's childhood and edged our way into narrower corridors of her past, we entered spaces that challenged my sense of what the past is. Our exploration inspired questions about what happens during the process of reconstructing long unexamined, overlooked, or even over-rehearsed memories. I began to wonder about the trustworthiness of the inner narrative that shapes and colors the stories we tell ourselves, the way we perceive the unfolding of our life's events as our lives skein out and our capacities expand or contract. I began to consider the textures our experiences take on in the act of sharing them, perhaps for the first time, long after they've rested undisturbed under a protective cover of years and layers of emotional sediment.

Kate

The resistances we encountered also began to challenge my assumptions about how to construct Lucy's narrative, assumptions I'd made about giving her space to tell her own story and how I would establish a narrative frame that would carry it along, reveal its nuanced truths, and perhaps, if I got really ambitious, provide a dose of mystery. This didn't strike me as part of the process we'd share; tacitly we understood that figuring out how to tell the story was my puzzle to solve. I'd stepped well into this surprisingly dense landscape before I realized that the project had become something other than an exercise in artful questioning and meticulous recording. It was an experiment in point of view, and I was being tested at least as much as Lucy was, if not more.

I struggled to find ways to work with seemingly unmoored fragments, the inconvenient parts of her story that resisted telling in any way I knew how, at least in the ways I naively imagined at first. Eventually I'd come to see that Lucy's memory, which naturally presented itself as the subject of our mutual exploration, stood to teach me more than I was ready to learn, but not before it had begun to illuminate my own reservoir of resistance. After all, I was still coming to terms with the implications of my vocal injury and slow recovery, uncertainties about what my future would look—and sound—like, and just what it meant to be living in a transitional space of this magnitude.

Once I'd opened Lucy's history up to scrutiny, its gaps and disparities—at first just obstacles to clear away—would eventually push me toward a necessary awakening to the lessons of not telling. While our conversations deepened, I remained a long way from understanding how I would navigate the interspace, and I seemed equally far from understanding how to discern Lucy's expectations, let alone address them. I had yet to see my own way toward understanding what this story was really about and how it needed to be told. I hadn't begun to explore what my role in it would actually be.

The truth is, I didn't know what Lucy's expectations were. In all my exhaustive planning of questions, that was one thing I hadn't thought to ask. In a way, we had entered this project as co-conspirators: she simply believed I was going to write her memoir, and somehow neither of us saw the painfully obvious implausibility of such an idea. I could claim no excuse beyond my eagerness to follow my curiosity, find the art in her story, and dig as deeply as I could. Initially, the challenges only made that part of the journey more interesting, the problem solving more inspiring. The arrangement seemed reasonable enough to keep us moving along a path, for a time anyway. Blind spots and vocal fragility notwithstanding, this was how I approached the early stages of collecting the material I'd need to write Lucy's story. My strength was gradually returning. I'd solve the knottier problems later. In the meantime, I'd supply the prompts and listen to what she had to say about her young life.

"I don't know exactly how we knew that my uncle Phil was a pedophile, but we knew. We just knew."

"How did you know?"

"We just knew. Uncle Phil wasn't the only pedophile in my family, either."

"But if no one talked about it, how... do you remember a conversation in which this came up? Or was it a sense you had?"

"It was more than a sense. It was a knowing that we had acquired long before we had any idea what sex was. There must have been talk of some kind, though not from my parents. There must have been talk among the kids about something dirty going on between Phil and his daughters. Mom and Dad did make passing references to Phil and Martha's boys being beaten... but not to the girls being raped."

"And no one intervened?"

"No. No one did anything about any of it. My parents just told me to stay away from him."

"And they didn't explain why?"

"No."

"Do you remember what they said, how the message was communicated to you?"

"I got the message that he was unsafe. That's all I remember. The two boys ended up in reform school. At some point the girls were expelled from school, and there was some kind of court order blocking them from coming back. I'm not sure what they had done to cause all that.

"We also knew the children stole. When we were younger, I dreaded their visits to our house because they would break my toys—I mean on purpose, not accidentally. So I learned to be wary. They were always rough and desperate and badly behaved, but I felt terribly sorry for them all the same."

Mom's father had a first wife who died during the 1918 flu epidemic, leaving him with five children, one of whom was just a baby. When he married my grandmother, twenty-one years his junior, she raised those four boys and a girl, along with the ten children they went on to have together. Mom was the first of those, born in 1922. Until they went off on their own, the cohort of older half-brothers eventually became a threat to my mother and her sisters. Another unsettling family joke revolves around the story of my mother, as a teenager, throwing a knife at one of her brothers in what I can only imagine was an act of self-defense. The knife missed him and, as the story goes, ended up stuck in the door. Yet she maintained ties with him until he died.

I was aware of my uncles' dark energy from my earliest childhood memories, most of which are fragmentary but suffused with a sense of dread and vulnerability. Somehow I knew that I was surrounded by predators, though growing up among them, I accepted their presence as normal. I learned early on that we were to rely on our own defenses and avoid the particularly dangerous ones. It's possible that I overheard family members whispering about these things on top of making more direct warnings to "Stay away from Uncle Phil," given in the same tone as, say, "Make sure to be home before dark."

Not only did we all know and accept that it was unsafe to be around my mother's older brothers and which ones were more unsafe than others, we also knew that some of her brothers-in-law were dangerous, though perhaps less menacing because my mother and three of her sisters were close and we saw them fairly regularly. I can't say exactly how this information was disclosed to us, but I can say absolutely that there was no doubt about it. We knew that Uncle Phil had done something terrible to his daughters, something we eventually understood as rape; we knew that he regularly beat his sons, that he beat Aunt Martha, and that he was not her first husband. And we knew this was not a fairy tale. Mom simply reminded us to stay away from him. And life went on. The families interacted socially as if nothing were wrong. I knew we weren't like the families on television, but they were so obviously make-believe. We went to large grange picnics filled with playful children and busy wives in the company of the men of the family, and all seemed well and happy enough.

These were the men my mother's sisters married. This was the legacy of silence around the abuse my great-grandparents—and possibly their forebears—passed on and taught their children to tolerate. My great-grandmother chose to spend her life in a small beach cottage instead of in the grand Vashon Island harbor house she had inherited, and it's never been clear why. Perhaps she was driven away by a father or an uncle who had threatened her, or worse. The family history gives us nothing specific to explain her refusal to set foot in the house.

There is one exception to the silence that I know of. Incest was mentioned openly in reference to my grandmother and her stepfather. My maternal grandmother, according to our oddly unreflective family lore, was sent away from Vashon Island as a nineteen-year-old to live with an aunt in Nebraska because the man her mother had taken as a second husband was after her. This stepfather was my very own Grandpa Owen, the man into whose care I was entrusted regularly as a child and who was one of the only people in my young life who offered me unconditional acceptance.

My mother and her sisters, including Martha, remained extremely close, so close that Mom never fully recovered from moving away from them when we left Tacoma and moved to Oregon. The separation left her disconsolate, complaining every December that without them Christmas would never be the same. But during the years we lived in Tacoma, my aunts were part of our extended family, and my parents maintained close and friendly ties with them.

Aunt Joanne and Uncle Donald often came over to play pinochle with my parents, and I cherished those nights with my cousins while our parents were busy at the card table until long after our regular bedtime. When we traveled to their house, I'd eventually get sleepy, no matter how hard I fought it, and often curled up in the mini-fortress of my cousins' bunk bed.

If I felt deprived of physical closeness and comfort, I recognized it and held on tight. I held onto a handful of those memories: sitting on my mother's lap once when she read me a story, something that was never part of our family culture; or being carried into the house half asleep and wrapped in a blanket by my father after a late night with our cousins; or my great-grandma steadying me in the water while teaching me to swim; or my aged grandpa Gene allowing me to sit on his knee while captivating me with a sweet old-timey lick on his mandolin, inspiring me to sing along and to take joy in song. Touch that was benign and loving became precious, so rare that these brushes with it remain in my memory like birthday celebrations.

Tommy was my closest cousin, my age, and we were easy friends, spending cherished weeklong visits at each other's houses during the summer, visits I lived for. But his younger brother Greg was probably my favorite cousin because he was a gentle soul. And maybe that's why my uncle went after him. Greg was just fragile.

One day when I went over to their house, running straight to the bedroom looking for the boys to come and play, I found Greg lying face down on his bunk bed, crying. His shirt was off, and his back looked like hamburger. He'd been beaten with a studded cowboy belt, his flesh torn open and raw.

Mom and Dad generally punished us with their hands, usually not with objects. The idea that this could be considered abuse never occurred to me. They acknowledged that Joanne and Donald used belts and straps and instruments like that to beat their children, and they expressed mild disapproval of that practice. They believed that delivering punishment with the hands was permissible, though Mom occasionally used other means.

I must have been about forty-six. Mom and I float in the late afternoon sun on a raft that lists gently in a light summer breeze off Manzanita Beach. The water laps the underside of the raft battens with a pleasant sloshing that reminds me of being on the water in Grandpa Owen's tugboat with the engine powered off and suddenly the profound quiet of being at anchor or just drifting offshore enveloped me in stillness. I remember marveling at the way the otherwise stiff old man hopped along a massive chain of cedar and Douglas fir logs out in the Sound, the improbable weightlessness of the huge pieces of floating timber, the curiosity of a harbor seal, its bright face breaking the water's surface to investigate.

"My brothers used to rape me," Mom blurted out suddenly, as if she was just describing the spruce trees on the far shoreline.

I responded without thinking. "I was raped too."

Mom asked matter-of-factly, "Was it your uncle Phil?"

"No."

I waited, frozen, suddenly realizing an uncomfortable question had entered my mind. Had it ever occurred to her that something terrible had happened to me the day the babysitter lost track of me and the police found me, hours later, in nothing but a heavily soaked diaper sitting, chilled, exhausted, and frightened, by the side of a four-lane highway? Had she even wondered about my safety before deciding to send me back into that same woman's hands?

Mom broke the awkward pause with a demand for a promise. I was not to share her secret with anyone: "Only Dad knows about this, and I don't want anyone else to know."

I don't know why I didn't ask any questions or try to offer Mom comfort. Nor can I fathom why she didn't ask the obvious questions of me or respond with some form of consternation.

I don't remember exactly what I was doing that day. Perhaps I'd been playing, off somewhere in the lonely-child world of a five- or six-year-old. Suddenly Dad grabbed me—grabbed me hard—and walked me to the back of the house. The screen door slammed as we pushed through and headed to the backyard incinerator. Gripping my arm with an enormous hand, Dad raised his other one over the fire, dangling my cat Jake, curled into a ball, frozen in fear. Jake hung by his nape, fur and skin squeezed tight between Dad's powerful man fingers, legs curled in front, tail pinned to his belly. Dad glowered down at me. I felt the heat of the fire, shame burning in my cheeks.

Sensing Dad's attention turned to me, Jake let out a half-swallowed yowl, his eyes bulging like large, white-rimmed marbles. Dad's fingers hurt my arm. My hands went tingly, my legs rubbery, as if my knees had stopped working. I heard each word, pronounced with deliberate slowness: "If you are ever... *ever*... a bad... girl... again... I will take this cat... throw him in the fire... and make... you... listen... to him howl... until... he's... dead."

I couldn't make it make sense. What had I done? I swallowed tears down inside, sure if one were to fall Dad would let go. *Jake, I won't cry, I promise*. Dad might as well have had *me* by the throat, it was so tight. My mouth tasted funny, like blood or something dry and bitter that I couldn't name. I could barely swallow, choking tears down into a deep gut place. He held us there for what seemed like a long time. I was certain that moving or breathing or speaking would be the end of Jake, dangling there, so still, both of us waiting in the strange stillness of fear, the nearness of death. I tried to imagine the transgression I so badly wanted never to repeat, but I could only see flashes of Jake falling and burning. And Dad's pinched not-Dad face. He had always been kind to Jake and the cat loved him... I tried desperately to understand.

Then as inexplicably as his anger had exploded, Dad let go of my arm and released Jake, who leapt to safety in a border hedge. I watched the stiff wings of my father's shoulders as he strode back to the house. The screen door slapped its frame. Tears came now, with a flood of confusion. Had he asked me to be quiet? Had I been playing wildly? Daydreaming? Had I not heard him call me? Why would Dad want to hurt us? I would never have thought to disobey him. How would I know how not to do the terrible unknowable thing again? I waited and watched, terrified that I would somehow make him throw Jake into the incinerator, and I tried to be a good girl. I had to show them that I was a good girl.

Dalco Passage separates the southernmost beaches of Vashon-Maury Island from Point Defiance Park, the semi-wild northern tip of the peninsula that extends up from the city of Tacoma and out into the lower basin of Puget Sound. This narrow waterway, just a fifteen-minute ferry ride across, could have stretched a thousand miles between my paradise on the island and my life in Tacoma.

Joy never found a place in our home. It seemed our parents had never learned to recognize it or embrace it. They kept us at a distance, though they acknowledged Christina, four years older than I, at least as their own. In the years to come they would attend her choir concerts and other school events but inexplicably never mine.

Christina never recovered from the wounds of being stigmatized by our poverty. She had never been a loving or affectionate child to begin with. But during high school she grew increasingly bitter and angry, remaining so into her adult life, long after financial success had come to her, and only softening toward me after Mom's death at ninety-three. The million-dollar lifestyle Christina and her husband enjoyed never freed her from the sense of being marked, of being broken by the resignation that paralyzed our parents, who remained unable or unwilling to help us dream about something better than what they could provide. Dreaming, it turned out, was forbidden. But stamping it out of me proved more of a problem than either of them was prepared for.

Dad nearly had the life beaten out of him by his father when he was about twelve, resulting in injuries serious enough to send him to the hospital, one of many visits, according to the stories Mom told. As a boy he often ventured out to the highway, hitchhiking to the farms outside of his hometown of Worcester, Massachusetts, to glean roadside fields of whatever he could find to take home for his family.

Kate

I knew him to be a gentle man, despite the incident with Jake, often at the mercy of Mom's casual insults and offhand criticism. I often got the sense that his distance, and even his reluctance to show affection, came from a fear of hurting us the way he'd been hurt. But it was no secret that he adored Mom, often expressing an almost innocent wonder at her beauty and at her having chosen him. On one occasion when Mom and Dad pushed the furniture out of the way on a Saturday night to polka gracefully around the center of the living room, I too imagined an abiding love between them, imagined it filling and warming our home. For decades I held onto this single memory as if it might have had the power to lift the dark spirit of that house.

Dad also had a sketchbook. As a young child I would sit with him admiring the drawings he had made when he was a young man, mostly sketches of people's faces. He had always been private, reserved, reluctant to speak, especially about himself. But his drawings spoke for him. And they spoke directly to me. They expressed a sensitivity that he never openly shared.

Those sketches gave me a tiny window into his imagination, along with the sense of beauty that never found a place in his daily life and which he would never feel he deserved. To him, artistic creativity was a form of personal indulgence rather than a valuable skill. It wasn't something worthy of admiration. The beauty I saw in his drawings was completely at odds with my experience of our lives, the joylessness that shadowed everything we did, the starkness of the poverty that seemed as much of the spirit as of our material world. It spoke of something beyond the superficial attention devoted to lace and frills, my sister's blonde hair, the comeliness Mom worshipped in others at the expense of qualities like kindness, intelligence, and curiosity, despite the fact that the man she had chosen to marry was a plain man. His face and lanky body—and eventually the artistic soul that neither one of them had the capacity to understand or appreciate—would continue to be reflected back at her through their restive younger daughter.

The first book that came into our home other than the Bible was a book on mythology that I won in a poster contest in third grade. I wasn't sure if my parents knew what to make of it, but I did. I was nine years old, and someone had chosen *my* poster as the winner. I loved that book as much for the reason it came to me as for what was in it, the dreams and wonder it inspired. A book filled with heroes.

The same year my teacher recommended that my parents enroll me in a free art class for children at the Tacoma Art Museum. That summer my Saturdays were filled with projects about light, shape, and color, with weekly exercises to do at home. Mom had to drive Dad to work early so she could take me to class, a commitment they took seriously. At first I did my shadow studies with pleasure, drawing crumpled pieces of paper with a bright light bulb shining on them. But under my parents' supervision it became an almost painful chore, a stultifying drill.

Though my art exercises were enforced with misguided severity, Dad maintained that I should experience art. So he occasionally took me to the state capitol building in Olympia to look at the Winged Victory memorial to World War I. We walked around in the rotunda with its fancy chandelier and dome. We admired the lamps and the bust of George Washington. It wasn't until I was older that I got to walk through a real museum or to see Dad's sketchbook, and much older still that I understood the aspirations he never allowed himself to have—let alone fulfill—in his own life.

But there were glimmers that I recognized. Dad loved to show slides on Saturday nights. Often, after our once-weekly baths, Mom would make popcorn and we'd hang a bed sheet on the wall and look at the big-screen images of the places we had been: Mount Rainier, the cabin on Vashon Island where we spent weekends and summer vacations with our great-grandparents. Mom made a point of complaining about Dad's pictures, believing that good pictures should always have people in them. But Dad couldn't resist the scene of a stream running through a grove of trees or the mountains along the horizon, in which case Mom always let him know he'd come up short.

13

EXPLORATION

Tacoma, 1955

Lucy

MY FIRST FRIEND WENT OFF to school a year before I did. At five I wasn't ready to lose my best friend for a reason I didn't understand: that once Ricky began attending school, he could no longer be friends with a girl. This cruel change of allegiance was my first heartbreak. But before Ricky's decision to end our friendship, we spent much of our time exploring our immediate neighborhood for interesting things to eat, the most memorable of which were toothpaste and chocolate chips and something lush and fabulously green and tasty—what I have since preferred to think of as mint—growing in a neighbors' side garden. Whatever our delightful and happily nontoxic discovery was, it offered immeasurable satisfaction in that primal and almost fairy-tale way small children experience feeding themselves, imagining a world where they are the providers and caregivers rather than the seekers of protection. Sampling weeds with Ricky was the closest I would ever come to a tea party.

My second friendship, with a boy named Louis, began in infancy and lasted until he and I were twelve, when my family left Tacoma for a different kind of railroad tracks in a Portland suburb and I watched him run down the street, trailing behind our car as we drove away.

Our mothers had been friends during their pregnancies. As toddlers we had learned to play, share, and explore the world together, and as we got older our bikes took us out in ever-larger concentric circles into that world. Our seemingly vast playground included the mud puddles that bordered the railroad tracks, puddles that grew into lakes along our sidewalkless neighborhood streets; the concrete pools of the electrical substation around the corner where lush manicured turf lured us through child-size gaps in the chain-link fence; and our very own racetrack, the blacktop fields surrounding the Catholic church and its dormitory complex. Someone must have paved right over rocks and natural irregularities because the tarry blacktop retained rounded hills and swales that formed a perfect obstacle course. One ill-conceived race, in which Louis and I rode at top speed in opposite directions around the church, left me unconscious after we crashed head on, sending me high into the air along with the bike, and sending him racing home to find my mother. By the time they returned I was coming to, badly scraped and bruised but remarkably whole, pinned underneath my bike, which had landed directly on top of me.

We spent our summer days on private adventures, some intimate and embarrassing explorations that we will take to our graves, others a companionable unfolding of hours in long unselfconscious stretches of quiet. But most often we inhabited a dimension outside earthly time, turning puddles into village-destroying tidal waves, coming home wet, shivering, and blue after riding our bikes back and forth through the ponds that had formed by the tracks, oblivious to the rain. In drier weather these industrially enhanced ponds sometimes congealed into a pasty white residue ideal for creating spectacular designs by drawing a stick through it or patting it into castles surrounded with elaborate moats and access roads.

Louis managed to track down my parents and turned up at our house in Parkson, Oregon, one day when I was away during my freshman year in college. When my mother told me that he had visited, my first question was, "You told him where I was and how to get in touch with me, didn't you?" She hadn't.

And when I asked her why not, she replied in a chirpy voice with not a hint of irony in it, "I didn't think of it." I searched for Louis several times but failed to find the man who had once been the artful, loving companion whom I saw less as a boy and more as a soul-friend, closer than a brother or sister, someone who just loved me as I was and whose love I returned in full measure.

Lucy

One of my youthful haunts was a scrubby hill topped with a swamp that Louis and I knew only as "the big hill." Though it couldn't have been more than a half-mile from home, it felt remote, a secret world, removed, rarefied, and just wild enough to be wondrous. This was a place I sought out on my own, drawn to the universe of small creatures that had somehow found a hidden oasis amidst the otherwise lifeless landscape.

In spring the hill was mostly wet and swampy, and by mid-summer shrinking pools that had sheltered polliwogs through the spring had all but disappeared. This seemed wrong to me, so I began setting up containers as crude aquariums in our back yard. Anything that would hold water suited my purpose, and as they grew, I transferred the polliwogs I saved to terrariums I made from pots and pans. As they emerged from the water and began to appear more landworthy, I even tried to catch flies to feed them, but with minimal success. Miraculously, quite a few managed to reach froghood.

I'm not sure why my parents left me to freely pursue this mission, but as my amphibians developed, so grew my secondary project: a frog stand. I had heard of Kool-Aid stands, so why not sell frogs? They're good for the garden, which was the pitch that helped me make a few sales. My customers were probably the same handful of people who bought Kool-Aid on some other block. Despite my efforts, most of my frogs ended up making their home in our garden and keeping Jake entertained. It never occurred to me that they would need to return to a vernal pool or a pond in order to lay their eggs.

When I got a little older, I discovered a church several blocks from home. Hearing music through the open window one day, I peered in and was mesmerized by ecstatic music, people's voices and vigorous clapping, ladies and men falling down on the floor as they were taken over by the Holy Spirit, their prayer language sometimes incomprehensible. Their energy was like a warm spell cast over me. Knowing nothing about Pentecostals, I later heard my parents refer to them as "holy rollers."

At times when I was feeling particularly down and lonely, I returned to watch this strange and joyful celebration through a narrow window next to the steps leading to the back door of the church, watching unnoticed and feeling my own spirit lifted by their jubilation.

My parents were involved in our own church, and we attended services every Sunday. My father was a deacon and sang in the church choir, one of the few sources of pleasure in his life. My mother worked as a secretary, and one of her duties was to organize the communion. I loved to watch her prepare the wafers and wine before the service. I loved the hectic activity of the community's potluck suppers, when a host of women would cook and cheerfully fuss over a communal event that they all seemed to care about. I was held in awe by the ceremonial aspects of the church, the pleasant taste of the wafer in my mouth, seeing my mother dressed up so stylishly in her best wool suit, and exploring the vast subterranean space of the church building, a miracle of riches unto itself, it seemed to me.

Our years in Tacoma, where we lived until the summer before sixth grade, were often a bleak exercise in resignation. I learned—though it was never spoken of directly until I was in junior high school—that we weren't supposed to hope or strive for anything beyond what we had. That hope led to disappointment, and the worst kind of failure came from seeking what wasn't deserved, what was intended for someone else. Yet the bitterness that filled our home, sucked the life out of it and suffocated my parents' lives, seemed to come from their unwillingness to believe in hope, their incapacity for inspiration, their fear of the danger posed by imagination. This compound affliction, along with the ever-present expectation of betrayal, was what I have to believe they had learned in their young lives, and what, in turn, they had to teach. Life was a trial full of injury and disappointment. There was no protection they could offer me. So they didn't try.

The more I resisted the undercurrent of these teachings, the heavier my parents' burden, and the harder it must have been for them to love me. Perhaps their own experience of violence—their powerlessness in the face of unprovoked harm—destroyed whatever instincts they might have had to protect and nurture, leaving them without the capacity to act upon a gut sense of danger and intervene on a child's behalf. Perhaps neither of them had the opportunity to know a flesh-and-blood protector or mentor. Perhaps their families, inhospitable to the growth of such a soul, simply didn't produce any.

The first time Mom made me fetch a piece of oak flooring from Dad's workshop in the basement for my beating, I didn't fully comprehend the task I was being sent to do. Perhaps she was planning to use it as a straight-edge or to prop up her sewing machine, which sometimes slipped on the older floorboards. When the smack came across my bottom, all the air left my lungs. My hands flew involuntarily behind me to the burning welting place. Tears welled, black spots floating across my eyes like dark fireworks. Who made that strange laughing sound? Then another voice came from Mom's mouth, vaguely cheerful, patient, almost instructive, "We're not finished yet. Turn around. Hands to your side. I can wait. But you're not going anywhere until we're finished." I remember a second slap coming, this time sharper, gathered with more precision, sending a bolt of electricity through my center and slicing through my flesh. A thin breath, and a plea gathered inside me, but I realized I didn't know my own voice or what to ask for. I had been bad again, and this was my punishment. I stood silently until she said she was finished and the beating stopped.

The next time Mom ordered me down into the basement to find my whipping stick, she made it clear in that same almost cheerily admonishing tone that I didn't have to rush: "You can stay down there all day if you want. But at some point you're going to come up, and you're going to bring a piece of wood, and I'm going to beat you. It doesn't matter how long you stay down there because you're going to get a beating, and dawdling won't make me forget to give it to you."

The stairway leading down the basement was the dirtiest place in the house. I hated the stairs for the grime covered walls leading down into the darkness, and though I knew my father's workshop was his special place where in some ways he found shelter, I hated the basement for the cold and the piles of boxes stacked there, silent witnesses to my miserable errand. Whatever crimes I had committed to provoke my mother on these occasions, I can't remember them, though I do recall specific acts of misbehavior for which I was scolded and even punished at other times. One of those was breaking the glass on the back door after my father had nailed the kitchen window closed to prevent me from entering that way when I forgot my house keys, something I was prone to do. I never knew when Mom would send me on another of these trips downstairs, why she did it, if the laugh reserved especially for my beatings was involuntary or an expression of some cruel impulse. Perhaps it was a nervous laugh, but I couldn't guess at its meaning.

14

CATS

Tacoma, 1956

Lucy

JAKE AND I HAD OUR own language. On days when I came home from school and had to wait until my mother got home, we would hide behind my parents' old upright piano, the two of us snuggled in a squeezed-up kind of way into the spaces in the back of the piano's heavy wooden frame. I made up words and signs that only Jake understood, and he kept me company, listening to my secrets until Mom arrived, his calm gaze affirming that I was heard and recognized. As soon as the sound of the kitchen door signaled Mom's arrival, we slipped out of our hiding place. In some ways, I was more of a shy cat than Jake was, wary of divulging my daytime refuges, my invisible comings and goings. I had to keep us out of harm's way.

Our neighborhood was the turf of a gang known as the Cats. In their white T-shirts, straight-leg jeans, and perfectly sculpted ducktails, these hard boys and the bold girls who followed them around inspired our curiosity, awe, and fear. We were much too young to know irony. Their fights brought flashes of switchblades and chains, coveys of wide-eyed children like us watching from an alleyway or scrub hedge, and muscular cops breaking up their battles with rivals from other neighborhoods. The fights that I witnessed never resulted in fatal stabbings. Instead, they appeared as chaotic and unchoreographed flares of activity punctuated by sudden lunges and bodies darting in great animal waves, scurries, and scuffles; the loud drama and adrenaline bursting from tight circles of taunting figures; the particular meanness of girls on girls. And always there was the threat of violence, putting an end to my ambitions of pitching a tent in the back-yard and camping out, a prohibition that I found profoundly discouraging. An aura of tension followed the gang members, even when they were just standing around practicing their posture, squinting at each other through drifting cigarette smoke, anticipating a challenge or an opportunity, a con-quest of one sort or another always in the ante.

But the real terror came quietly and unexpectedly to my street corner. The first time I witnessed what was to become the telltale mark of our neighborhood gang's signature, I was on my way to school, a three-block walk from home, past rows of insipid two-bedroom homes like ours and two or three tumbledown Victorians, their inhabitants far poorer than we were. We knew that because the children who lived there were dirtier and regularly scorned by my parents.

I left the house that morning feeling the eager pull toward the happy mixed-up energy of a new school day ahead. While waiting to cross the street at the corner in front of our house, I noticed a gnarled blackened shape hang-ing from the telephone pole above my head. Legs charred, a visible set of small claws and a long twisted tail still holding onto a few tufts of fur—though there were no whiskers left, the small teeth and the shape of the head were clearly recognizable as those of a cat, its face twisted in agony, its torment a message broadcasting doom. It made no difference whether this gruesome signpost was meant for the gang or for some potential usurpers. That morning the burnt corpse was a message for *me*. The terrors long dwell-ing in my imagination were now given tangible form, like furies in pursuit of vengeance. My shame now had a face, a form, a smell. It also had a sound. In that moment I remembered the howling that had sent chills through me during the night, at first not sure if I had dreamed it, now certain I hadn't.

The occasional tortured cat nailed to a telephone pole became an almost normalized sight in our neighborhood that nobody seemed to notice or be troubled by as they went about their business. The accepted explanation was that the killings were part of gang initiations, but to me they represented a strange and vicious reality that I saw and felt but could not understand. In the desperate logic of my own heart, they validated my deepest fears. They were reminders of my covenant with Jake and the tenuousness of my ability to protect him from the consequences of my own misbehavior. Encountering these hideous apparitions—visible even from our kitchen window—would send me ducking and shrinking in fear, fraught with distress over my incapacity to grasp what I had done or was capable of doing wrong without knowing it. I understood only that I was implicated in these animals' suffering, suffering that wrenched me out of sleep with agonized howls that told me I couldn't escape my wrongs or my parents' wrath.

15

....

COMFORT

Pierce County, Washington, 1958

Lucy

MERCY CAME IN THE FORM of a discovery, a window into another kind of life that I found when I went to stay with my mother's older half-sister, Eileen. She lived on the dairy farm that she and her husband Franz had built with their own hands in the lush Washington State countryside. Though Eileen, my mother, and their thirteen other siblings and half-siblings had been raised by a Nebraska dirt farmer barely able to eke out enough income from his few acres and some livestock to feed them all, Eileen married a farmer. Starting from absolutely nothing, she and her German husband, along with a brother-in-law and their own three sons, created and maintained an extremely successful dairy that won the honored Dairy Farmer of Washington award year after year.

By virtue of her own character and integrity, Eileen managed to escape the cycle of dysfunction. I saw her family members' lives, filled as they were with hard work and purpose and yet with commensurate rewards, as idyllic beyond anything I could have imagined. I saw the coherence of their family, the fullness of their lives, and I admired the things she and Franz made or built with their hands, the joy they took in being good stewards of their land, their animals, and their children. They never took a vacation because they couldn't afford to leave their livestock, but I saw how they were sustained by the fruits of the kindness they gave the living creatures in their care, their pride in their home, and the freshness of the food they ate.

But most striking to me were the family's shared values and goals. They all worked together, respected each other, and treated each other with a kind of love I hadn't seen before. Ever. The common purpose arising from a nurturing environment captivated me. Even the land they tended embraced me with its rolling hills, deep welcoming fields, and a set of railroad tracks that ran through the farm, as if the familiar steel rails had been laid there just for me. I was safe and grounded there. On this land I was somehow forgiven. I was free.

Theirs was a foreign existence, the lives my aunt and uncle lived and the ethic that guided them. It all felt clean and honest to me. I never grew close to them as people, but by letting me share in their bounty without judgment or obligation, they gave me the gift of safety. On their farm I was allowed to watch, explore, and wonder. There it was possible for me to play, to savor tastes, textures, and smells otherwise unknown to me. And all these riches came to me by virtue of what Eileen and Franz had made all by themselves, cutting down virgin timber, milling cedar for their home, erecting barns and dome covered silos, and through some means far beyond my imagination, building a magnificent stone icehouse, a marvel of their enterprise that only deepened my enchantment with it.

The noon-day meal that Eileen served up every day was an enormous farm dinner with a glistening jug of cream-topped milk standing in the middle of the oil-clothed table, slabs of home baked bread with butter that I had watched her churn, vegetables we had gathered in a basket each morning from the garden. One year during our morning garden rounds we were regularly trailed through the pea patch by a small, orphaned calf whom Eileen had, for all intents and purposes, adopted.

Enthralled, I would sit when the boys and men came in from the fields to join us at the table, listening as they spoke of their concerns, of how the season was unfolding and what needed attention or repair of one sort or another. If a round of guffaws broke out, somehow it never seemed to be at anyone's expense. I delighted in witnessing the praise offered, playful exchanges welcomed, misfortune recognized, and comfort bestowed among them.

As a witness to their daily cycles, I learned to understand the rhythm of seasons and how farm life derived from them: when the barn would be piled high with fragrant bales of fresh hay that we could jump into from a rafters-high loft, when the silos would be emptied, releasing the smell of fermenting grain as I poked my head into the deep echoing column. But by far, my favorite place was inside the icehouse, its cool stone walls and pristine stainless steel milk tanks filling me with a sense of otherworldliness. Lifting the lid of a magically chilled tank and peering in, I could take in the grassy animal sweet-sugar smell of milk and feel in my soul the meadows with their generously preserved evergreen borders, the wet-nosed cows wearing sunshine on their backs, the barn cats idling in the afternoon, and the dusktime swallows dipping in the yard. I must have seemed a complete alien to them all, but even as the untutored guest in Eileen and Franz's home, I learned not to be a stranger to the nurturing that happened there, and in that protective space the weight of my existence was briefly lifted.

16

WIDER CIRCLES

Tacoma, 1960

Lucy

THE McKAYS LIVED A COUPLE of houses down from us, but theirs was much older and larger than ours. Their yard was dirt, while ours had grass, a garden with a plum tree and a pear tree that my father had planted. We had baths once a week, part of our Saturday-night ritual in which, in sequence from Dad down to me, we used the same tubful of water with a little hot added in between. The McKay children were always dirty.

But Mrs. McKay was mysterious and artful. She didn't work and was always home. She must have had a previous life that was very different from the one she ended up living, and the evidence of that life was stored in several large trunks in their dusty fourth-floor attic. Just being in an attic perched on top of an old house was new to me. I was accustomed to living in our small four-room main floor with just the basement and an unfinished upstairs floor.

Mrs. McKay's trunks were filled with costumes. Sequins and lace, feathers and gold, hats and shoes. Any time Louis and I knocked on the door and asked to play in the attic, we were allowed to go up and get lost in the extravagant contents of the trunks, imagining we were king and queen parading about with a train of fancy ladies who must have worn these clothes. I never learned where they actually came from, how Mrs. McKay came to own a trove of fantastical garments and accessories, or what they meant to her, but she was kind and easy about giving the children of our neighborhood a magical world to play in almost any time we wanted.

One day Louis and I knocked on their door and heard the trill of Mrs. McKay's voice beckon, "Come on in!" As we entered the kitchen, we saw that the bathroom door was open. There she was in their old claw-foot tub, hair pulled up regally into a big knot on top of her head, cigarette between her fingers. We were stupefied. She waved us on in with a smile, "Go on up, kids," and we slipped up the stairs, abashed at having seen her bare shoulders and arms, at the idea of her nakedness behind the deep sided tub, at the drama, the beautiful drama of her gesture.

Somewhere, I still have a photograph of a motley group of neighborhood children sitting on a patchwork blanket laid out on the pack-dirt of their back yard. My sister and all of the McKay children are squinting in the sun, along with Louis and me. And on the head of one of the younger McKay boys, slightly askew, sits a large golden crown.

During our final year in Tacoma, Dad built us twin beds. I was eleven, and Christina was fifteen. We had slept in the same bed all our lives, me clinging to her every night with my thumb in my mouth, her vigorously pushing me away. The empty existence in our home didn't bring us close as sisters. My presence in almost any context was a source of annoyance to her, often leading to surreptitious attacks of pinching, the kind intended to cause pain without drawing attention. Despite her cruelty, I looked up to her, admired her, impressed by the notion that she was pretty like Mom, and charmed by the way she was always surrounded by a tight coterie of friends. Sisters are supposed to love each other, I believed, and I vigorously held onto to that precept. Though our parents were no more loving with her than they were with me, they treated her as if she were real to them in a way that I wasn't, as if she possessed some value that they recognized or to them was at least a known quantity. She wanted nothing to do with me; she was the queen of the neighborhood. But I was prepared to wait for things to change, for my family to see and know me as the loving sister-daughter I was.

17

MARKED

Parkson, 1962

Lucy

WHEN WE MOVED TO OREGON and Christina's world collapsed, I was devastated for her, indignant at her loss of social cachet and her marginalization in what was supposed to be the bright new world we had entered. In Tacoma almost everyone we knew was poor or very close to it. So while the contrasts may have meant little to us, distinctions based upon whether or not one had grass growing in the back yard or how frequently one bathed, in Parkson High School the pecking order went all the way up to children of lawyers and lawmakers who lived in million-dollar homes which, at that time, represented a kind of affluence we had never seen or imagined. Suddenly we—and Christina in particular—faced a completely new set of rules, the first of which, we quickly learned, was exclusion.

In Parkson, the contrasts between those who wore hand-me-downs or dresses sewn badly by their mothers and those who wore the fashion of the day were stark. The high school had just gone regional, so unlike Tacoma, the student body Christina encountered brought together kids from the wealthiest and poorest neighborhoods. In the still-rural Portland suburbs of the early 60s, where my twelve-year-old world was in some respects opened up by riding my bike past sprawling, sweet-smelling horse farms instead of up and down railroad tracks and alleys or around electrical substations, Christina, who defined herself solely by her friends, was shunned and therefore completely lost. Where she had once been secure in her popularity and swatted me away like a small dark spot marring the sunshine of her existence, rejection made her bitter, and like our mother, perennially soured to life for the misfortune it had dealt her. She came home from that first day as a freshman at Parkson High, threw herself on her bed, inconsolable over being scorned by some mean girls, marked by our circumstances in ways that had been obscured by the faithful clan of Tacoma slum kids who had always surrounded her.

We finally had separate bedrooms, which was supposed to be a good thing. I wanted to believe that, but I often found myself sneaking into Christina's room, crawling into her bed, and trying to curl up alongside her when I thought she was asleep, only to be shooed away if she was still awake enough to realize I was there. In Tacoma I had been able to watch her get settled and gauge when she had drifted off to sleep. Now I had to guess—based on the sounds across the hall—when it was safe to make my move, and I often failed in my estimations, drawing my sister's ire and a shriek of *"Get out!"* This was a scene we were to repeat, even in her visits home during her freshman year of college, and it always ended the same way. As determined as I was to be loved, or at least to reach for a form of comfort that might stand in for love, Christina sought it elsewhere, only to fail as miserably as I did, though on a grander, more public scale. But where I could only dream of being noticed, the drama of her anguish, as I observed, succeeded in capturing a measure of our parents' attention and sympathy, one of the few things she had left to hold onto.

Fairly quickly I discovered that my invisibility granted me a certain freedom, which I embraced by taking longer and longer excursions into outlying fields and orchards on the far reaches of our neighborhood and beyond. But I didn't have to travel great distances to feel far away. Just down the street were hayfields into which I could walk chest-deep in grass and stamp down a clearing all to myself, a cave of solitude, not unlike the space behind the piano or the couch where I once hid from the world's view, and breathe at ease in stolen safety. It was a revelation to nestle into a soft, sweet smelling fortress in the middle of a field, disappear into the flowered canopy of an almond orchard or the golden leaves of an autumn filbert tree, listen to the satisfying echo of my footsteps on the deep walls of the town gravel pit or the decisive *plunk* of tossed stones sailing far below into a jade green pool.

Eventually, when I had saved some spending money from my after-school job, I combined that with my allowance and went trail riding from a horse stable a few miles away. I had never been around horses before, but these semi-retired quarter horses were gentle and forgiving. They accepted me on their backs—absolutely untrained as I was—and carried me along the well-worn trails that they navigated in a state of sleepy semi-consciousness, attuned to little more than swatting flies with their tails or nipping half-heartedly at a cheek or a flank that brushed too close as they ambled along through the trees. On these rides I entered a daydream state, lost in the stream of quiet thoughts, lulled by the comforting rhythm of the horses' slow strides and the creaking tack leather, the pleasantly sharp-sweet smells rising from their hides and from their digested grasses mingling with sun-warmed earth, browning acorns, and fir tree balsam.

I realized in my early days as a sixth grader that I was starting with a clean slate and—just as importantly—that this was an opportunity my sister didn't have as a ninth grader. I couldn't improve my family's lot or erase the outward signs that broadcast our station to our new schoolmates, but I sensed that I could strive to achieve the social and academic markers that were—as I saw in the aftermath of that painful first day—require-ments for earning acceptance.

I decided to study every detail of every advantage that could be gained without the benefit of wealth, and to do whatever was necessary to at-tain those markers. Surely this path, excavated with whatever merit and congeniality I could muster, would open the doors that everyone around me assumed closed to kids who didn't come with a birthright pass to the land of popularity. Emboldened by the injustice of my sister's snubbing, I resolved, through what began as a secret personal militancy, to change myself, despite my social misfititude, into a girl who would fit in by the time I got to high school. I had time to make this right. And in the process, surely I would win my parents' love and recognition, as well as my sister's.

But in the beginning, I had yet to fully recognize my own awkwardness or to shed the leap-and-tumble of the boy-play that Tacoma had given me. So my quest began with an inauspicious start. That fall my teacher called my mother in for a conference. Mrs. Mills reported gravely that I had been wearing cut-off shorts to school underneath my proper clothing and that I had been seen "repeatedly" taking off my skirt and playing football and baseball and basketball with the boys during recess. She explained that she had no choice but to assign me a C in citizenship for the first quarter, that it was time for me to become a lady, and that she had every hope that these problems could be corrected if they were addressed promptly. She cautioned my mother of the need for me to wear ruffles and be a girl.

I had never gotten a C in anything before. The utility I had discovered in my easy-off skirts with their handy elastic waistbands had suddenly become a liability. So the next day I left my skirt on, along with my modesty-preserving shorts, and hung upside down from the uneven bars to calm my nerves and meditate on my predicament.

18

MISSION

Parkson, 1963

Lucy

THOUGH I WAS SLOW TO recalibrate my passions, which remained stronger on the ball field than in front of a mirror, a neighbor briefly took me on as a girl in training. Anita dedicated herself to her project and continued to invite me to take on new challenges of friendship, efforts that worked against my natural proclivities toward solitude and unconditional trust. But my innocence and gullibility allowed me to persevere under her instruction and to believe that she and I were girlfriends traveling the same path, that our shared expectations applied equally to both of us, that I was—though perhaps a little less graceful—keeping step, heading toward the same goals she was.

But I didn't take the same kind of pleasure in this effort as I did when out on my own, moving around in a world of my own making, or at least in the one that was familiar. I had no instincts for cultivating friendship based on social conventions like being stylish or socially adept. But I was buoyed by the mystique of discovering the secrets of girlhood, cheered on by Anita's ministrations and the belief that I could learn the skills necessary if I paid close enough attention and followed her advice. Unfortunately, even the most assiduous obedience would not hasten the onset of my period or the necessity of wearing a bra. Still, I observed and dutifully embraced the rites of girlhood, despite some ill-fitting trappings. I still loved playing ball, running track and field, and—in private—mulling things over while hanging upside down on the uneven bars.

When cheerleading tryouts approached in the spring, Anita and I were ready. We had practiced our moves together after school for weeks. I had begun to envision myself as a member of the squad, one of the elite girls holding a coveted place in junior high school society. My handspring wasn't perfect. Actually, it was all legs and odd angles. But Anita encouraged me, and we remained hopeful that I could smooth out the rough spots in the more difficult elements.

But I was completely unprepared for the truth when my name failed to appear on the final list, which meant I hadn't made the cut. This outcome was not part of the plan. Neither was Anita's announcement that we could no longer be friends or sit together on the bus. She was moving on, and I failed the test that would have allowed me to move on with her. Not long after that we learned that Anita's family would be moving to a better neighborhood at the end of the school year. Her parents' goal was clear: to eliminate any shadow of poverty—and the people associated with it—from their daughter's life. My mother, on the other hand, admonished me, brushing my disappointment off as a perfect example of how I would only get hurt if I tried for things that were sure to end in failure and if I wasn't more careful in picking my friends.

Though my awkwardness was a constant and somehow managed to get worse before it got better, by eighth grade I was beginning to find that my school world might open some doors and allow me to discover nascent talents and new interests. Being a joiner was the ticket, and I needed to learn how to mingle and make friends. Lots of them.

It was all there in my sister's annuals. She was already a junior, and her yearbooks proved instructive. I could tick off everything the successful kids did to become successful over the course of their high school years. Aside from being well liked and getting good grades, of course, the ones who finished on top had started early, running for class office and participating in clubs, chorus, and sports. They organized special events, acted in school plays, played in the school band. Popular girls, in particular, all seemed to be on fashion boards. I'd need to learn more about those. The big winners, though, were selected for the biggest prizes, Homecoming Princess and Homecoming Queen. Their path to royalty was laid out before me in photos and captions.

My first step then, having lost my chances at cheerleading, was to run for student office. As soon as my mother caught me making fliers to give out and post in the halls and discovered that I was writing blurbs to introduce myself to the junior high school populace, she sat me down and demanded to know why in the world I would continue to punish myself, insisting that I accept my station and not try for things or put myself out there because I would be disappointed. I would lose. I shouldn't hope for such things because those hopes would most surely be dashed. Look at what had already happened with cheerleading.

Unable to find the fortitude to resist or rebel against Mom's edict, I put the fliers in a box and slid the box under my bed. I still had time to figure this whole popularity thing out, get to know people, make more friends. How could Mom find fault with that?

In the meantime, I remained an easy target. The school bus was one place where rules of conduct were few and opportunities for mischief abundant. The socially challenged were on our own to fend off the worst of the bullies as well as the opportunistic small-time teasers. Shy and achingly gullible, if I didn't simply walk straight into an ambush, I could easily be drawn into one unawares.

A vague dread followed me into social encounters, a sense that at any time I might become the butt of a joke that I might not even know was being played. One day I climbed onto the bus, walked about halfway toward the back to the first completely empty seat, sat down, and with books clutched tight to my chest, slipped in against the window, as far from anyone's attention as I could get. Some boy was in the process of telling a joke amidst a cluster of kids in the back. It was one of those jokes that could send kids who had little understanding of adults and the thing called sex—kids who didn't yet know how far from complete their understanding was—into a frenzy.

This time it was something about a man who asks for advice about what to do with his wife on his wedding night and is told to put his "longest thing where she goes to the bathroom." The punch line, in which the man can't quite figure out why sticking his foot in the toilet doesn't bring about the desired result, left me bewildered. My effort to conceal my confused embarrassment only seemed to broadcast it and amplify the response: an explosion of laughter. I thought I heard my name and a fragment about being "too much of a prude to get the joke." Now the laughter really *was* at my expense, and as usual I had no idea where I had made my false step. I focused on the blur of trees going by, but the muffled taunts continued.

A girl who had friends in the crowd, a girl whom I saw as belonging to the tough kids' clan, a girl whom Anita had ruled unequivocally, "someone we would absolutely *never* be friends with," got up out of her seat farther back. As she walked forward, she shouted, "Cut it out, you guys! I mean it!" I immediately turned to face the front as the order was given, wary and unsure of what was happening or what trap might ensnare me if I let myself watch. She slid in next to me, and when one of the boys teased, "Oooh! Watch out for Janey! Who made *her* the boss?" she turned around and snapped, "Who made *you* the biggest jerk ever *born*?" A girl in the way back hooted in mock surprise. Snickers bubbled up, breaking the tension, and the bus fell quiet. Janey Wilcox threw a half-serious scowl toward the back, then turned to me and smiled, gently nudging my shoulder with hers.

"I swear! Isn't that the worst joke you've ever heard? It's not even funny, is it?" she said, the temperature and noise in the bus returning to baseline. I just looked down at my knees and shook my head in baffled agreement, grateful for an ally.

I'd begun to notice Janey in sixth grade, initially for her athletic ability, the ease with which she met physical challenges, and the charm she brought to the conventional team warfare we were encouraged to wage during gym class and then, perhaps with less direct approval, carried forward in recess. She was always on the other team, connecting with the ball to bat runs in, delivering a mean softball pitch without any meanness. I liked her fun-loving style, her friendliness, her striking red hair, and the easy smiles and shrieks of enthusiasm that burst out of her when she secured another point for her team or someone else needed a boost of confidence in a critical moment.

During the previous year I'd watched Janey and her two best friends, Gina and Sherri. They stuck together during recess but never clung to each other. Gina was bold enough to wear nylons, which were always impressively tight, squeezing her kneecaps white when she sat in a chair, something I admired and thought unimaginably beautiful. I wanted bloodless kneecaps like that.

No longer under Anita's scrutiny, I was free to return Janey's friendship after her brave rescue. On the face of it I trusted her, but deep inside I remained protected, never fully opening up. Friendship had proven itself dangerous, and eighth grade provided countless opportunities for that idea to be reinforced.

The Wilcoxes lived in the same neighborhood, our families dwelling on the margins of the suburban lifestyle that was supposed to be about upward mobility. Their mother seemed loving and attentive compared to mine, but their house was dirty and always smelled as if something had gone bad somewhere. Janey's clothing carried the faint odor of her home wherever she went. But to me she had untold riches in her sociability and in her two handsome and popular big brothers. The older of the two played football and in his senior year was crowned Homecoming King. In the world that was taking shape around me, this signified the absolute height of social achievement and acceptance. If there was hope for a boy from our neighborhood rising to that pinnacle, there had to be hope for me too.

Under everyone's radar including mine, my buoyant friend had been caught up in a kind of familial darkness I should have known about. Janey told no one. There I was taking in her sunshine and allowing it to add a little light to my world, while she was suffering totally alone.

I only learned about her history of abuse after her husband Thomas died twenty-five years later. I was still in the very early stages of my own recovery when I called her.

"Janey, you'll never believe what's happened."

"Oh, no! What is it?"

"Three weeks ago, I had a massive hemorrhage and nearly died, *did* die, in fact, but pulled through, just barely," I explained. "I've had a terrible time getting back on my feet."

"That's *horrible*, Lucy! I'm so sorry, but thankfully you've pulled through. You'll never believe what's happened *here*! While you were having your hemorrhage, Thomas was diagnosed with inoperable brain cancer, and he's..." She paused, struggling to speak through the emotion. "He's dying. I feel absolutely terrible about the way I've been complaining all these months about how he's been acting." She started sobbing and struggled to continue. "I thought he was just being difficult—couldn't understand why, and now I know it wasn't his fault, that all this time it was the cancer affecting his brain, his personality, causing him to do and say strange things all the time. I should have been more supportive, but the way he was acting got on my nerves. And now I don't know what we're going to do. The boys don't really get what this means, and I don't have the heart to tell them the whole truth. They know he's very sick, but I haven't been able to tell them he's going to die. The doctors say he's only got days or, at best, maybe weeks. He can't even walk or speak anymore!" She broke off. I could only urge her not to beat herself up for something she had no way of understanding.

Thomas died barely a week later, and I went back to Portland for the funeral. Still shaken and overwhelmed with grief over the loss of the man she had trusted, the man with whom she had been happily raising their two boys, Janey told me about the helplessness she had lived with all those years before and how helpless she felt once again. Fumbling for a throw-back kind of comfort, she and I lay next to each other in the same bed where Thomas had died just days earlier, exchanging secret stories stirred up by loss. I thought about the oddness of that. And to make it worse, the sheets were rumpled in a way that felt like they hadn't been changed since his body had been carried out. I too felt helpless and guilty in the face of Janey's despair and the awful knowledge that as a teen she had suffered silently in our midst, despite the genuine exuberance she presented to the world. The pain and the strangeness of the moment, combined with my own uncomfortable family history, left me feeling like an accomplice. I had never guessed at the time, but I, of all people, should have seen the signs.

But where were they? Janey was the one blithely and unselfconsciously modeling for me how to be an outgoing person, a part of the world rather than apart from it. We sang together in chorus and quickly made it into the elite girl's chorus. In ninth grade we formed a trio with Sherri, the three of us singing a cappella, winning a coveted spot in the high school variety show, and eventually making regular appearances on stage doing comedy skits and singing popular songs. We performed Peter, Paul, and Mary's "The Cruel War" and drew hearty laughs from our rendition of the Smothers Brothers' "Crabs Walk Sideways" routine in which we acted out the mismatched lovers' dilemma of Herman and Sally in our homemade oceanic costumes. Janey's comic timing found a perfect outlet, and so did my love of music, which had begun with the reels my grandfather played on his mandolin and the songs my great-grandma had written and perpetually hummed as she puttered around the cottage on Vashon Island.

I always invited my parents to our shows and choral concerts, but their impeccable record of absence from my performances kept my self-esteem in check, arresting it before its tiny roots could take firmer hold. Yet those roots held, somehow, undernourished as they were, and by ninth grade I had regained enough confidence and a sense of purpose—emboldened by singing in front of an audience and feeling like I was becoming a known quantity—to make my run for student office.

19

MIRACLES
2012

Kate

"You're a little pixilated, but I can hear you fine," I encouraged. "It's inspiring to see you there in your living room and imagine sitting there with you with a cup of tea and the peaks out in the distance. Is the signal clear enough on your end?"

"Yes. And it's nice to see your face and imagine you here. There's some weather blowing in from the east, and that may force us to stop at some point, but we'll see how far we get. Storms often appear threatening and then just skirt around us. You never know," Lucy added. "We should probably get right to it though. Where do you want to start today?"

I knew where I wanted to start, but I had only a gestural idea where we would ultimately go. The collector in me hungrily turned long conversations about Lucy's young life into weeks of tedious transcription. There was satisfaction to be found in filling notebooks with more detail than I would probably ever use and hope in testing the usefulness of multi-colored post-its. The satisfaction, it turned out, was mostly tactile. Over and over again I returned to places where those seemingly dense pages yielded an odd lack of solidity in the particulars of the experiences we explored. It wasn't for any lack of enthusiasm or cooperation or effort on Lucy's part. But along with her earnestness came a recurring feeling that we were hovering over rather than striking the core elements of her experience. At times I wasn't sure where shortcomings of memory began and ended or whether I had, so far, simply failed to look in the right places and therefore failed to spot less squishy patches of ground.

"Well, I've been thinking quite a bit about your school experience in Parkson, based on what you've described in our last couple of Skype sessions, and a few questions came up that I'd like to focus on a little more."

"Sure."

"I'm trying to get a clearer sense of the kind of student you were in junior high school. At least for me, middle school was a gut-wrenching time. It left me with strong—and often painful—memories around social challenges, all kinds of challenges, really. You know, a couple of friends, but mostly overwhelming feelings of exclusion and not fitting in, all that highlighted by a backdrop of distressing world events and a difficult family, these are the things that I remember most vividly. But I don't want to make any assumptions about your experience based on my own, even though I had more than my share of insecurities and can relate to that. So let me ask you directly: once you reached a point where the content of what you were learning was becoming more challenging because it involved memorization, which you've told me was a problem, did school take on a different character to you?"

"Yes. I definitely became more anxious, but I still loved school. And in an effort to continue loving school and to embrace the concept of learning as much as I could, I worked out systems to get around how my brain was wired and the kinds of learning that weren't working for me."

"Right. You were saying you had a system of tapping underneath your desk, one of the tricks you used to help you remember," I continued. "But as the challenges grew, did you find new ways to compensate? I guess what I'm trying to do here is look at your transition into the junior high school experience and explore the positives and negatives of your school life, the issues that were new, challenges that you figured out or didn't figure out how to master."

Lucy considered this while taking a sip from a tall glass of water and then went on. "Well, in Tacoma—and it's interesting really to think about this—I think I had already begun learning how to dissociate. Then, as a young child, I had nightmares about not being able to learn, almost like everyone was speaking a language I didn't understand, and I was compelled to run from that, both in my dreams and in daily life. But moving into junior high school, I don't think I was conscious of feeling inadequate or threatened in the classroom. I had a solve-it kind of personality, which probably saved me. It wasn't as if I could go to my teachers or my parents and say, 'Look, I'm having this problem.'

"When we started having to rely on memorization, I recognized this as a challenge. It was important to me—everything, in fact—to find ways to remain within the culture of learning. I couldn't let this nurturing place become dangerous. I needed to belong there. It was my safe harbor. Fitting into that world and not drawing attention to my difficulties required that I figure out my own little systems for getting through the lessons. I had to bury my anxiety and focus on staying with the thread. And that was how I managed to maintain a positive experience in grade school and into junior high. As I got older, I had to devise more complicated ways to keep up, to remember, and this eventually required untold extra hours of studying before tests, with late nights and little sleep.

"Of course I had Vashon Island too, which was a world unto itself, completely independent of life in or out of school, a place I could escape to." Lucy lifted her glass again, drew from it, exhaled with a whisper of "Sorry," and continued.

"Somewhere in our conversations you described me as living on my bike, and I did. In Tacoma I rode down alleys and searched for rocks and got myself out into places where nature poked itself through the cityscape. I suppose I was always a pretty solitary kid, but I wasn't lonely in my solitude. I lived a really full life, filled with imagination and wonder. I collected my feathers and my rocks and wandered toward whatever gave me a sense of wilderness. And so I had this positive but mainly solitary life outside of my own house."

For a moment I followed the younger Lucy in my mind, the sound of the girl's bicycle skidding to a wrap-around stop in an unpaved Tacoma alley as she makes a quick scan for treasures. I saw a girl's dirty bruised shins, then returned to the graying bespectacled woman's pixilated face in the computer monitor.

"In Parkson, though, you still spent quite a lot of time alone, riding your bike out to fields and orchards and horse farms, seeking out nature in whatever form you found it there too. But now I imagine school—and social life—taking on a more prominent role in your life. And that's where I'm going with this. What we're trying to tease out here is how that took shape in your psyche, your school life, your academic life, and your friends, and whatever issues you had with learning, the fact that you were so devoted and dedicated while at the same time you had some learning challenges that you worked your way around without any help. I guess I'm trying to get a sense of the landscape of your inner life as your social and academic world took on more importance in junior high school."

"Well, you know, you're bringing up an interesting set of questions and thoughts, and I'm seeing this for the first time—that moving to Parkson was more challenging for me than I remembered initially. I mean, my friendship with Louis was old, if it's possible to think of a friendship between twelve-year-olds as old, but it was. To me he was like family. He was the closest thing I had to a brother, and he just *was* in the same way that family is a given. With him there was never any thought of betrayal. We were connected in some deep and important way in which we were both completely comfortable and accepting of each other. But moving to Parkson, I became aware of a new concept of friendship, of girlfriends and back biting and needing to nurture friendships, needing to actively hold onto them to keep them. With Louis that wasn't an issue. We just *were*; we were just friends who had never not known each other. Until I moved away, we thought we'd be friends for life.

"So yes, I think this sort of theme that you're touching on has carried through my entire life. I'm a loner. I really and truly am a loner, and I'm most at ease when I'm living in the protection of a world that I have created for myself with my own beauties and fascinations and wilderness." She paused to collect the thought. "You know, even through high school, when I became popular, when I became *the girl*, I didn't have friends that came home with me. There were rare occasions when people came to our house, but these were meetings, and Mom's unpredictability discouraged me from holding them at our house. Janey was a friend because we sang together and we lived near each other. For me our friendship was based upon learning songs together and performing more than anything else.

"It's not that I ran screaming from friendship, but in answering your questions I'm beginning to realize that I was a pretty self-contained unit. I found my pleasures on my own, by myself. And I started feeling uncomfortable when that equation had to include others." Then, as if seeing this part of herself for the first time, she added, "I realize that all through my life, on a personal level, I've felt uncomfortable within friendships and maybe even within love relationships.

"Even when I went to work as a buyer at Meier and Frank, I sunk myself into work. Turns out I was *really* good with corporate relationships. Yet at one point my assistant at the time insisted that I go to a party with her because she thought I didn't know how to be social. And I didn't. I went with her to the party, and I didn't even last a half hour." Half smiling at herself, Lucy conceded, "Most of my life I've struggled with friendship. Even here in Alces I've tried to create a protected space for myself, buying my piece of land outside of town where I could just be left alone."

"And creating your little world with nature and a few friends, your animals, and everything that is meaningful to you—especially your art," I added. "I think I understand this because I have to some degree been a loner too. So this is another part of your story that resonates with me. This isn't about me, of course, but I just want to say that I understand, to some degree, based on my own childhood experience, which was very different from yours. I tended to and still can be that kind of person, inclined to build my little world and just leave the rest at arm's length. All I'm saying is I understand your need to embrace solitude. Though I did—and this is about to lead to another question—I did have one or two friends as a kid—I guess you could call them buddies—and we would tramp through the woods and go on adventures together, you know, I never really had more than one close friend at a time, and I think you were, perhaps, less inclined toward even one buddy than I was. It sounds to me like you're saying that negotiating a friendship was effortful, risky, and not something that you naturally understood how to do."

"It was downright uncomfortable for me," Lucy said. "I felt uneasy and out of whack. And yes, it was absolutely much easier to have a relationship with myself than it was to deal with the complexity of others."

But what kind of relationship was that? I was still stuck on trying to reconcile Lucy's admission of discomfort, a response to the world that at least felt familiar, with the utterly alien process of becoming *the girl*. I went with the safer question. "And do you have any sense, now that we're bringing this to the surface, of what was so hard about friendship? What was so uncomfortable? Can you put your finger on it?"

"I felt inadequate. I felt clumsy. I felt that I wasn't good enough. And so if I just dwelled in a world by myself I could be okay just being who I was, the little girl that my parents were always disappointed in. I could just dwell within myself and not feel exposed. But as soon as there was someone else in my life, I felt like I was being seen for the loser that I was."

"It sounds to me like as soon as you started to become friends with your neighbor Anita, you became aware that there's a kind of cultivating that needs to happen with this thing called friendship. Is that true?"

"No, not exactly," Lucy said. "I just was uncomfortable within it. I don't think I reasoned it out further than that, and I'm just beginning, in talking to you, to realize the extent of my discomfort with friendship."

"Did you feel judged by Anita the way you might have felt judged by your parents, or that perhaps you picked up that feeling from them and then projected it onto her?"

"Yes, I think I did. I mean at least the potential was there for her to see me up close and then to discover that I was inadequate."

There they were, just barely tangible pieces, somehow misaligned. Limbs detached from body. Something to grasp and somehow draw together. "So how did your friendship move along then with this kind of underlying expectation? Because you remained friendly with her for at least a couple of years, didn't you?"

"Well, I think it moved along because she came into my life unsought and because I passively engaged with that until she decided that I wasn't good enough to be her friend. By then she had become someone important in my life, and suddenly she was exiting my life, like Louis did, and even

Ricky before him, but the difference was, she was leaving my life because I wasn't good enough. So the truth, as I believed it internally, was being borne out.

"I had exposed myself, and just as my parents said, I came up lacking. Anita left. And so for the first time in my life I felt lonely because I had allowed a friend in. I had risen above my fears of inadequacy, and then within a couple of years I was seen for who I was. Yet despite my underlying expectations, I was stunned by it, completely shocked. I felt a tremendous loss. But I realize in talking about this now that Louis and Anita were the friends that I actually let in. And after Anita I shut myself down. I think my friendships with Janey and all the people that came after were about something other than being friends, whether it was singing or organizing a school event or being a member of an after-school club. I never fully opened up after that, though I enjoyed Janey and appreciated her joyfulness and charisma. I put myself out there, but I never really opened up."

Unsettled by the questions this might have raised about *our* friendship, I asked, "Do you remember your relationship with your parents changing during those junior high years? You were saying that your parents started bickering and fighting more when you were in Parkson, but the more your school ambitions started to gel, even though your self-confidence didn't grow in kind, your school life—which had begun to take on a life of its own—did. How did that play out in your family life?"

"Well, even in grade school my school life had a life of its own," Lucy said. "So that was just a continuation."

"Yes, but did anything change at home during this period?"

"Yes."

"What kinds of things were different?"

"Mom became a monster. Of course she had her monsteresque sides when we were in Tacoma. But in Parkson it was no longer underground. In Tacoma and even when we were new in Parkson, little kids would knock on the door and ask if Mrs. Simkus was home. She'd initially welcomed that, been the kind of mom who fried donuts for neighborhood kids on a Saturday afternoon."

"I expected you to tell me that they'd run away from her," I said.

"They did. There came a point when they stopped coming to the house and started to avoid her. For the first few months in Parkson she was the mom that the kids came to see. Then that changed. These were little kids, younger than I. They must have picked up on the mood, the volatility, and it scared them. It was like her anger just came to the surface, was palpable. She yelled constantly, and they must have heard her voice in passing, enough to sense her lack of control and the rage that was coming out of her.

"Dad blamed it on menopause, saying she was 'in the change.' I think she was grieving the move because she had lost her sisters. But I don't think Mom was ever conscious enough or reflective enough to have any sense of her own behavior or its impact on others. I think Dad was searching for a plausible explanation, so he latched onto that. And so whether she was going through menopause or not, this is clearly what they used as an excuse. It was the only framework that allowed Dad to make any sense of what was happening. She had always been an angry human being without ever knowing or acknowledging it. I think in those years her anger just boiled over, and she made no effort to hide it."

Perhaps I might have paused to consider what the phrase "angry human being" might mean, or at least the relative nature of its potency, given the many ways anger can reveal itself. But even if the moment had contained space in which to interrogate our respective frames of reference, I probably wouldn't have seen it. "In thinking of suppressed anger, I'm reminded of what she did to you, sending you down into the basement. It feels to me that her strange behavior might have arisen from anger that had been pushed down and from her allowing it to erupt in these private episodes with you in which you would get physically punished for something and not even know what it was. It seems, from what you've described, that there was something sinister and deeply injured inside of her that came out, for whatever reason, in these episodes, and then later, when she was so intensely miserable after you moved to Parkson, perhaps it was all unleashed."

"And Dad started spending more time in his workshop," Lucy continued, "which left us in her clutches. At first I thought he was almost trying to compensate for her outbursts. One day during my freshman year in high school, he presented me with a beautiful lap-style drawing table that he had made from leftover scraps of wood, and it meant the world to me. I thought the lap desk was an effort to show his support, to show that he appreciated, on some level, how seriously I was applying myself at school. But eventually I had to question that too."

"It's sad that even such a lovely gesture didn't hold. Was your mother's anger directed toward one person more than anyone else?"

"I think her anger was just directed out into the house. She filled the house with it. Certainly, as I got older and made choices she didn't like, it intensified. She was a control freak, and her power had purchase as long as she could devise ways to wield control over us. Part of that control came from the excessive chores she made us do as we got older. The other kids could be outside on the weekend or going places, and we'd be in the house doing chores all day Saturday and on Sunday afternoon after church, using toothbrushes to scrub the floor and all that.

"And when I got to the place where I was saying no to her, starting to rebel, or just making my own choices, she exploded. I remember her hitting me in the face, slapping me hard, shaking me by the shoulders, and saying something about how I 'had changed' and 'needed to snap back into shape.' I don't honestly remember what initiated this because she yelled constantly about pretty much everything. But I remember her yelling at me, and I just walked away, something that I started doing as I got older and a little bolder. At some point I stopped being willing to tolerate the anger. I didn't want to engage with it, and I didn't know what to do other than walk away. Of course that would infuriate her even more. She couldn't stand that I'd dare to walk out of a room while she was yelling, whether at me or at someone else.

"This time I think she was screaming specifically at me. I remember that we were in the kitchen, but I can't recall what I had done. I remember walking away from her into my bedroom and slamming the door. She followed me in and grabbed me by the shoulders and said something like 'What are you thinking! Who have you become!' I threw it back at her and said, 'You're yelling at me, asking me who I've become, but why don't you stop for a minute and look at yourself!' And that's when she hit me."

"Do you remember how old you were when this happened?"

"I was a senior, seventeen."

I sensed a shift, space for an opportunity to better understand what I was learning here. "Since this came up, I'd like to ask a question that I've had in my notebook for a couple of months. I've wanted to ask how you responded inwardly and outwardly to your mother telling you not to do the things that were important to you because you would inevitably get hurt by not achieving them. You told me that there was a conversation, but I'm not sure if it was said explicitly or if that was a message she communicated to you in some other way. But you got the message, one way or another. That has been a lingering question for me, which seems relevant to this time when you were sixteen or seventeen and you finally began to stand up to her."

"Actually, you're not jumping as much as you think because I believe she said that to me in seventh grade. And it wasn't just implied. She said it right out loud.

"I told you about what happened in seventh grade after I had lost cheerleader and Anita was no longer my friend. When I mentioned to Mom that I was considering running for student office and she just asked why I would continue to punish myself like that. She couldn't understand why I would put myself out there when obviously I was going to lose. When she told me I needed to accept my station and not try for things like that because I would be disappointed, the immediate effect was that it made me very sad. I felt almost desperate, crushed, and unable to pull myself together to go out for that office. After that it took two years for me to muster enough courage to actually run."

As it took shape, I couldn't fully process the picture of monsterhood Lucy was presenting, the words, the intent, or the child's response. But I had to press through the interview. "Do you remember when you decided to go for it and how you thought about what that might mean? Were you doing it out of spite, or did you come to some realization that you weren't going to listen to your mother about these things? How did you get to the point in ninth grade when you were able to say, 'You know what, I *am* going to do that'?"

"I'm sure she was still counseling me not to do it," Lucy continued. "That was an underlying thread through my whole school career. But in freshman year that became—I mean even if it wasn't written on a spread-sheet or laid out with an absolute plan, it represented the beginning—my mission to vindicate my sister and change the rulebook. I had to begin. I had four years to become popular. And I was very aware that even in the eighth grade I wasn't yet there. By high school I felt that the building blocks were almost in place, and I kind of knew what they were. People who were popular were class officers. It was all laid out in Christina's annuals. They were my guidebooks. My sister would point out who was popular and what they were doing. From that I learned what I needed to do. I knew I wasn't even on the radar screen yet. And then we mixed with all the rich kids with their expensive cars and expensive clothes and vacations in the Bahamas and Europe.

"It was mortifying when I first ran for office because I was such a goof-ball. I had absolutely no sense of humor, I had intense stage fright, and I was writing my own speeches. I would get up on the stage a complete fool. People would laugh at me, but I would just go back and do the same things over and over again."

"What exactly are you referring to that you see as foolish? Was it your speech writing? Was it your—"

"Yes."

"Trying to make jokes?" I offered.

"Yes. It was my ineptness, my total ineptness, my total lack of cool. I didn't know the game. I didn't know the politics. I didn't know how to be anything but what I was on the surface. I just put my little goofy self out there and didn't see that I was in a shark pool. I really didn't. And I didn't understand the rules. I didn't understand the sharks, and I don't think I ever really understood that."

"But you still stayed in the tank. You didn't give up. That was part of your mission too, wasn't it—to withstand the torture?"

"Yes," Lucy continued, "to break through. The way I finally did it was in senior year, when it all came together and I became the popular one—I did that by a pure, innocent kind of outgoingness that wasn't really me. I didn't have any truly close friends. I'm sure that to the friends I had we probably *seemed* close, even though I didn't allow them all the way in."

I hung back, waiting for Lucy to elaborate.

"But here's the thing: I befriended everybody. I befriended the entire student body—not the other grades; that would have taken too much effort. But I reached out to my entire class, kids from every walk of life. I learned people's names; I walked down the hall and said hello to everyone, rich, poor, those with friends, those without; and this was by design, this was my agenda. This was finally my strategy," Lucy added, "to believe—in a hostile environment that I didn't fully understand—that I had a chance of winning.

"But it didn't happen overnight." She continued. "I mean you can't just go from being the awkward kid that everyone picks fun at to being *the girl*. It took three years, three years of work that finally came to fruition my senior year."

Another opening presented itself. "This might be a strange question, but do you think your determination was also, in some ways, an act of rebellion against your parents?"

"Probably," Lucy said. "By that time, I understood how different I was from my parents, and for the first time I began to feel grateful for the difference. But I was still figuring out exactly who I was. I wanted fiercely to *be* that other person I had envisioned myself being. It wasn't so much an act of rebellion against them as a fierce desire to believe that the world worked a different way. I didn't want to accept their way. I had grown enough and seen enough to grasp that they were wrong, wrong about *me*. So it wasn't as much an act of rebellion as it was an announcement: 'This is who I am. I don't buy this program you're selling. My worldview is not your worldview.' It was almost like a cry of survival, a proclamation of my existence, an act of validating myself."

Necessary, yes, but a validation of which contrast, exactly, I wondered. "Okay. Yes," I said. "Yet on one level I can't help but see that your self-validation completely contradicts everything your parents were about. It goes against everything they taught you, which was nothing good. But all the terrible things that you learned from them about self-hatred and about never having dreams, all that, to me, is about denying them the satisfaction of having you carry that burden they placed on your shoulders. You—"

"Well, no," Lucy interrupted. "I want to be really clear about this, even if it's a fine line. That's not quite it. I wasn't rising up and trying to prove them wrong. I was rising up and grasping for a world I prayed existed."

"Ah. So it wasn't an active assault on everything they stood for."

"No. That was not the energy behind it. It was more an act of hope, a leap of faith. It was me saying 'This is what I believe.' It wasn't me saying, 'You're wrong.' It was a plea: 'Please, God, show me that this thing that I believe in really is true.'" Lucy reached for her water and took a deep breath, then a long drink.

"Still, it's also the case that standing up for yourself and believing that—whether with God's help or not—somehow you were going to be able to achieve your dream, stands in complete conflict with your parents' expectations for you, doesn't it?"

"Yes. The conflict for me was exactly what you're saying because I was still sensitive to my parents. And for all the hurt that living with them wrought, especially from Mom, I was very careful to avoid hurting their feelings."

"The ever-compassionate girl."

"I truly was not doing this to show them up or prove them wrong, even if my internal framework needed to rest on that idea," Lucy explained. "In fact, I worked exceptionally hard to shelter them from what I was doing, precisely because I *didn't* want to hurt their feelings. I *didn't* want to throw it in their face.

"At home I tried to minimize everything that I was doing. I avoided talking about what I was doing at school. They knew I regularly stayed late for activities and projects and meetings, and they knew I was up until 1:00 a.m. on a regular basis doing homework. But I purposely didn't share the details with them. I suppose I was protecting them."

"So the result of that was they never showed up for any of the things that you would have liked them to see because you didn't—"

"Well, I *did* invite them," Lucy asserted. "I didn't tell them I was running for office and going out for this and that club, but when there was a girls' chorus concert or a choir concert or variety show night, I always invited them, and no, they never came. Not a single time."

"But it sounds like you gave them opportunities in such a way as to be respectful and not to present the invitations in a way that would antagonize or provoke them. That's a really interesting dynamic, your determination clashing with who they were, and you trying so hard to follow your ambitions so carefully as not to offend them, and at the same time, making those achievements absolutely and inexorably what your whole life was about."

"And," Lucy added, "it's interesting that the summer between junior and senior year I had my first major Crohn's event. I hadn't thought about this until now, as you and I are talking about it, but I think the conflict that went on for three years with my working so hard, even putting myself out there for ridicule, and fighting to achieve popularity for a specific goal—to show that the social order could be changed—and actively hiding that from my parents so as not to hurt them, I mean, I think I paid a high price for that internally."

"What you were doing couldn't be anything *but* at odds with your family *and* your own internal system, the body that absorbed all the distress. Your family, your conscience, and your dreams—they couldn't coexist." There, I'd at least glanced the deeper question.

"At home I was pretending to be their daughter, you know, pretending to be the product of their upbringing. And in school I was ambitious, focused, working toward goals. But at home I was trying to be the girl they wanted me to be."

"And who was that girl?"

"I was submissive. I did chores and I didn't outwardly question the order of things."

"So where in all this is the person who always questions, who challenges what she sees in the world?"

"I don't think I came out to my parents with that until senior year. I was always questioning—that was my internal life that you're talking about. I was always questioning within. And I think that created the conflict—when I was living in an environment where everything was just as it was stated, the simplest form, living life on the surface, asking no questions, and accepting a norm that had been laid out. That was the culture of my family, and that was not who I was. I was hiding who I was in an effort to try to fit into that world as defined by my family. And I think probably that desire to fit while being incompatible with them tore my guts apart.

"The first event, which happened in the summer between junior and senior year brought it all to a head. I could no longer hide what I was doing from my family.

"At the end of junior year, I applied to be on a fashion board at Meier and Frank, one of a handful of major department stores that participated in this program. Fashion board members were important and conspicuous people in the context of school life, and I had had my eye on them from my very first days in ninth grade. Every year, one girl, a senior, was chosen from each school to represent the store on its fashion board, a Hi-Board, as it was called. The girls were given beautiful uniforms, fabulous outfits from the top brands at the stores, and every Friday they wore their outfits to school, modeling the fashion of the day and advertising the fact that they were members of an elite few. They were celebrities. And this was something I'd dreamed of for three years, wanting desperately to believe I could be on a fashion board and not quite believing I could. Still, I was encouraged by the steps I'd taken and the progress I'd made to become popular.

"I put all of myself into my application to represent Meier and Frank. And then the big day came. The extravagant event included a fashion show all its own, celebrating the outgoing Hi-Board members and announcing the new ones. It was held on a Saturday at the Paramount Theater in downtown Portland, with a band playing in the orchestra, a stage with velvet curtains, and a hall with ornate balconies and exclusive boxes. Kids and families from all the regional schools were there, but my family was not. I sat in the balcony with a group of girls, all of them atwitter with hopes of me winning. We were completely dazzled by the fanfare and the glittering fashion show going on under the lights down below.

"Then the department store announced its chosen school representatives for the following year. The winner for my school was announced, and it wasn't me. I shrank into my seat, devastated, my biggest dream shattered. I have a vague memory of someone on stage stepping up to the microphone and explaining something about a brand new award they were giving this year. I barely heard what the woman was saying, but I sensed a building anticipation in the audience and began to tune into the speaker's voice as she continued, '... *Seventeen Magazine* has asked us to select one girl who, among 600 other talented and creative teens from around the nation, will represent all the high schools of the Portland metropolitan region. This girl will be featured in a profile of the lives of this very special group of girls who stand out among their peers, are exemplary students, community members, and, of course, connoisseurs of style. We are happy to announce that we have found just the girl, one worthy of *Seventeen*'s recognition... and her name is Lucy Simkus!'

"The band strikes. I am engulfed by the sound of applause and my companions' wild shrieks of joy. I am whisked down to the brightly lit stage in a state of tearful disbelief, then escorted to a reception area flooded with flashing camera bulbs, parents, and celebratory interviews. We're told that a bus would later transport the winners to the corporate offices of Meier and Frank, the state's largest department store at that time, where we would meet with our executive hosts.

"I follow the crowd of girls down the hallway toward another reception room where refreshments await us and am suddenly overcome with a strange and painful sensation in my belly. I stop as the crowd continues on. Without warning, my bowels empty violently and uncontrollably. I duck around the corner and into a ladies room, horrified to discover how badly soiled my clothes are. Using the pay phone on the bathroom wall I call Mom, imploring her to bring a clean outfit so I can participate in an important meeting. I do my best to clean myself up while desperately awaiting a dubious rescue. Miraculously, Mom delivers a clean outfit, and as soon as I've changed, she leaves without inquiring further about either the occasion or the illness. I rejoin the group that has now spread out in the buzzing reception room. White-jacketed servers are walking around with plates of hors d'oeuvres. I slip into a leather chair next to a large punch bowl and carry on as if nothing has happened."

"That is just incredible! Was anyone aware that you had disappeared?"

"I don't think so because there was so much hubbub with the outgoing people, the incoming people, and the novelty of someone being selected as the *Seventeen* representative. Somehow, in the chaos, I wasn't missed—enough for anyone to become alarmed, at least."

"And your mom actually came through for you. Did she understand what was happening, what was at stake for you?"

"No. How could she? It was the first time I had to come out to them. But on some vague level I knew it was coming. When they announced my name, I had the sense that I was being unveiled to my family, that even though they weren't present at the event, I wouldn't be able to hide this."

"So that revelation contributed to the internal—"

"Distress." Lucy finished the sentence and went on. "Yes, I think so. I've never thought about that before now, but yes. After that day my parents knew something was wrong with me, so we started going to doctors."

"Clearly this was the first of many episodes of something serious going on with your digestive system," I said. "That must have been extremely painful and frightening. Were the initial symptoms more of the same, explosive moments in which your gut just gave out on you like it did that day?"

"I was *really* sick, all the time, throwing up night after night, not sleeping, and steadily losing weight. My parents rarely sought advice from doctors, but this was bad enough that they took me anyway."

"Did they even know what Crohn's disease was back then?"

"I believe it had been identified as an illness," Lucy replied, "but it was very hard to diagnose. I didn't find out until I was in my forties that the doctors had told Mom and Dad that I was dying and that they should prepare for that. So for a while, despite Mom's outbursts, they were gentler on me, to some degree, with Mom offering a little softness here and there.

"The greatest compassion she gave me was when she'd wake up in the middle of the night hearing me in the bathroom throwing up, and she would come in, hold my hair back, and then lie across the foot of my bed. Those times were her one show of care and comfort giving, but even with that there was a catch. I became afraid that I would forever associate being sick with being loved, that I would remain sick because I wanted love so badly."

"And this came up when you were talking about the aftermath of your hemorrhage, having memories of your mother sitting with you at night during your senior year and that fear of having love and illness inextricably tangled up together."

"Yes, it's all related, isn't it? I see that this all goes back to the seventh grade. It's so clear now—that when we started this conversation and you intuitively asked how I came to know that the things I strove for in school stood in direct opposition to my parents' lives and their expectations for me, you weren't jumping ahead, you were just seeing the connection that was there."

20

CATALYSTS

Parkson. 1967

Lucy

By THE TIME LUCY APPLIED for Hi-Board in the spring of junior year, she was already past the point of no return. She had worked assiduously to befriend kids from among the rich and poor. Her outreach campaign had brought her to their homes; she saw how they lived. She relied on a sense of creative flair, and putting forward that style and spirit helped her get onto school committees and clubs, gained her some social capital. But if royalty was her goal, she not only had to have social recognition, she also had to secure academic recognition from the National Honors Society. She studied through the night to compensate for her limited ability to memorize and hold onto facts. Reading was slow and laborious. Her after-school time, going well into the evenings, was consumed with event planning, designing fliers for bake sales, and organizing committee meetings. There was no respite from the relentless to-do lists, the endless chapters to read, reports to write, tests to prepare for, calls to make.

Lucy generally turned down requests to host committee meetings at her house, but one time she let her guard down and agreed to it, knowing full well that the group included kids from Sprucewood Hills, the most affluent and exclusive community in the area. Her biggest worry was her mother's unpredictability, but mercifully, the afternoon passed without incident other than an attack of Lucy's anxious stomach, nothing that would stop her from feeling that she had broken through.

A few nights later, long after the school busses had delivered kids to their far-flung neighborhoods, she left the empty school building to walk the two miles she had grown accustomed to walking when she stayed late, which was nearly all the time. Stepping down the stairs with a chin-high stack of books, Lucy recognized their car and her father's figure in the driver's seat. Nobody ever picked her up at school. Shifting her load to free one hand, she opened the door and immediately saw distress darkening his face. Cold vinyl pulled against the bare backs of her legs as she slid in, shuffling her books into loose order.

"Dad? What's wrong?"

"I need to talk to you, Lucy."

"What about?"

"I've been watching what you're doing," he said.

Lucy waited, frozen, dumbfounded. Her father never spoke like this.

"I see that you're not happy with your family," he continued, his heavy hands gripping the steering wheel as if there was nowhere else for them to go.

Lucy sat in silence, until she managed to blurt out something like "Dad, I don't understand…"

As he pulled the car out of the school drive he said, "Going places with those rich kids and bringing them to our house shows us that you're trying to be one of them."

"Dad, I'm not—" A shard of guilt began to cut its way into her alarm.

"Don't you think I can see that you're ashamed of us, that you don't accept who you are? Bringing those kids from Sprucewood to our home and acting as if you're not one of us?"

"I'm not ashamed of my family!" Her mouth twisted against the words. "Dad! That's just not true! I'm not trying—"

"I don't want to hear another word from you about this," he interrupted. "You are who you are, and so are we, even if you don't like it. I learned in a hard way that people don't get to rise above their station. You were born to us. We've given you a good home. We've done right by you, but instead of appreciating the things we've given you you're still grabbing for something better. You've really hurt your mother with this highfalutin act you've been putting on, and it's got to stop. You have to accept your place and that's it. Your social climbing ends now."

What does the heart do with what it feels, the eyes make of what they perceive, when the world stops making sense? The once familiar shapes of the trees along a road we have walked in seasons both kind and cruel loom silent and inscrutable, as if under a different sky than the one under which we have so often passed, thinking we've learned all of its moods. How well we suppress our inklings that pain will come of a dangerous and desperate enterprise and yet find ourselves broadsided when it does. When Lucy's defenses collapsed, torn through by her father's reproach, perhaps part of her knew that his words had come from a place of hurt and mis-understanding too big for her to reason through, a wounding too deep for explanation, argument, or healing. Perhaps that was the part that held so stubbornly onto some vestige of love, even if she couldn't figure out how to make her father understand that she loved him.

But something else had changed. Lucy had begun to feel what it would be like if she were actually part of a broader world, the world beyond her family, and that feeling couldn't be undone. The sense of being known there had made that world a kind of refuge. There were inklings that she could have agency in her own life. She had allowed herself to believe in possibilities that she didn't know how to unbelieve.

"Lucy, I've called you to my office, first to congratulate you, now that the National Honors Society members have chosen you as their president, and second because I wanted to waste no time in inviting you into a con-versation that I've been waiting to have with you."

"Thanks, Mr. Gedelman."

"You must be excited about taking the seat as president for the fall."

"Well, it's something I hoped for all year."

"And you certainly deserve it, even though you've taken a slightly out-of-the-ordinary route getting there. It's been gratifying for me to get to know you a little bit this year through your contributions to the Society's activities, even though it's a little unusual that I haven't had you as a student in any of my AP classes, which is how I normally get acquainted with NHS students. But now, thankfully, we'll have a chance to work together more closely. Truth be told, I have a plan I want to share with you, Lucy. And this is the main reason I've asked you to come in today."

"A plan?"

"Well, I've been waiting for just the right student to lead this group of kids—kids who are considered the most outstanding and talented individuals at Parkson—in a community initiative to bring the arts to less fortunate kids who would otherwise have no access to art, dance, and music in school. I've been looking for a catalyst, Lucy, and I believe you could be that catalyst."

"What's a catalyst, and how am I that?"

"A catalyst is someone who sets things in motion, sets off a spark. The kind of catalyst I've been looking for, though, is more than that. It's a person who also knows what to do once things are moving and how to keep them moving, someone who can not only organize but lead, someone who has vision. And I have a feeling you are those things, just based on the glimpses I've had of your activity in this school over the past couple of years. But you also have another quality that I haven't seen enough of around here: you are someone who is completely open and never judges others. That's remarkable, and it's why you could very well be the person I've been waiting to come along and help me create the arts program that I've been dreaming about."

"An... arts program? I'm not sure I understand."

"I've been working with honors students for a long time. They're always smart and they're usually pretty conscientious. They're achievers. Doing well matters to them. It's what they know. It's what they do. But they're not always inspired to do *good* in the world or to think about others. They don't necessarily stick their necks out and take risks. I've seen a whole lot of potential walk in and out of my classroom, potential that just needs the right kind of inspiration, a spark. My dream has been to find a student who also has big dreams, who can inspire this group of talented and capable people to take an active role in the community, to see beyond their own four walls, their familiar friends, and even their school.

"And the problems that this group can address are right in our very own back yard, in one of the most hard-hit neighborhoods in Portland. Albina is a tough place to grow up, Lucy. I don't know how much you've read in the papers or seen on the news lately, but what passes for education in the Northeast district is not fit for human consumption. Those schools hardly function as places of learning. And the unrest that's been brewing around the nation as a result of failed efforts to combat poverty and neglect is spreading there too. Those students need to know that other kids—that people in our community—care about them and are willing to share our best and brightest, our most prized resources. To brighten up their world and help them find their talents. While we're pretty good at showing our top students off academically, we're not always as good at showing them ways to make the world a better place."

"But how can a few high school students make that kind of difference?"

"That's just the thing, Lucy. It's about bringing love of learning together with the arts. A basic recipe. With the right ingredients, everybody wins.

"I have some contacts who can work with us, and I believe we can get the powers that be to help us in the name of good will and old-fashioned community building. It's about kids teaching kids and bringing passion for learning right to the doorstep of those who have been left behind by society, and in the process building bridges and a sense of brotherhood, bringing joy and music and painting and dance to those who don't have easy access to such things and whose lives could very well be changed if they did."

"This sounds kind of like the Peace Corps."

"Well, you're not that far off. If groups of young people can help farmers improve their productivity in Bolivia or dig wells in Cameroon, there's no reason why they can't travel next door on Saturdays to give poor American children an opportunity to express themselves in a safe and supportive environment. So yes, it's a similar idea. And I see I was right in thinking you'd understand."

"Is there money for this program?"

"That's a great question. One of your first jobs would be to organize some fundraising, to show that we've got the wherewithal to make this thing happen. If you're willing to take this on, Lucy, we can begin brainstorming and use the summer to work out all the details. Imagine—we've only got a month left before school's out."

"That's not much time."

"It sure isn't. Let's talk again sometime before next week's NHS meeting so we can start thinking about how to present this to the Society members, okay?"

"Sure..."

"In the meantime, you'll need to brush up on your brainstorming skills. They're going to come in handy over the summer as we plan this thing."

"I'll work on that, Mr. G."

21

ALBINA
Parkson, 1967—1968

Lucy

MR. GEDELMAN MAY HAVE ANTICIPATED more social unrest, but he couldn't have known how bad things would get, that other sparks were about to fly. By the end of August the riots that had burned through Detroit and Newark that summer had touched off in Portland too, leaving buildings damaged and a beleaguered neighborhood under even more strain after a community rally turned violent. But in some ways the communication lines were open, and Mr. G. worked his magic. Using his connections in the community and the city government, he managed to get permission to use an old Victorian house in the neighborhood that had enough space for dance, art, and music classes. A nearby schoolyard would provide space for organized sports activities.

Lucy and Mr. Gedelman worked together on a game plan and a budget, and she even filed paperwork to get the Board of Education to approve the use of school busses to transport students from Parkson to Albina and back on weekends. She organized the other members, and together they collected supplies and worked on curricula. Though he never brought up her family, Lucy sensed that Mr. Gedelman somehow understood her.

The school year began with bake sales and a push to raise funds to buy an old piano, which got moved in right after Christmas. The program opened the first week of January, but only two children showed up. Lucy quickly became a cheerleader, but not the kind she had once imagined, pushing her committee members to believe in their program, to hold onto their good spirits and inspiration, and to make no room for discouragement. The following week they had ten students, and by the third week eighteen.

By February forty students had enrolled, and each week a few more signed up. That was when Mr. Gedelman received a phone call from the Albina Arts Center, offering to open their doors to the program on Sundays. The next day Lucy and her team walked into an unassuming community arts building in an otherwise deteriorating downtown and were awestruck at the large rooms fit out with pianos, ballet bars, and floor-to-ceiling mirrors. Other rooms were set up as big, bright art studios. Despite the atmosphere of social disturbance and racial tension unfolding around them in the opening months of 1968, their commitment to the program had been recognized and welcomed by a community ready to embrace inspiration and hope wherever it was to be found. They moved in immediately without missing a single day's lessons.

That same community received a severe blow in April when news came of the assassination of Martin Luther King Jr., and a palpable sense of despair set in. When the Parkson students brought in the art supplies and began teaching jazz and dance to the children who were entrusted to their care, they could never have imagined that NE Union Avenue, less than ten blocks away, would years later be renamed after Dr. King; that in the same month, Robert Kennedy, then a presidential candidate, would open a community headquarters nearby in a building that has long since disappeared; or that the community arts building on NE Killingsworth that was their weekend home would one day become a non-profit feminist community center and bookstore.

People in Parkson—and Lucy in particular—remained removed from the broader impact of Dr. King's assassination and the efforts of Robert Kennedy to bring attention to social injustice in Northeast Portland that year. Thinking about it in later years, she imagined that Mr. Gedelman must have shared the burden of that death and the painful upheavals of the civil rights struggle in ways he never revealed to the students. Sheltered though Lucy was from the turmoil of the times and the fraught world around her, she embraced her role in the Albina Arts program with all the life she had in her. Her mentor, who shared her love of life and learning, lent meaning to her small part of the world and offered her a sense of purpose, despite the pain ripping apart her insides. Despite the uncertainties that swirled around them, the larger troubles that she hardly understood, and the depth of her parents' distress over her.

Spring still blossomed, and Parkson High School's Spring Reign festivities began. Lucy finally got to wear the one crown that she had dreamed of for four years. Her coronation as Spring Reign Queen and the weeklong celebration, including the traditional dance and a school-wide art show—her personal addition to the Spring Reign activities—were signs that not only had things come together, but she had broken the code. Her sister even showed up at the coronation, though she didn't tell her until she got home after the reception. Lucy had proven that with the right approach the social order could be changed. Her plan had succeeded. Amiability and hard work had won the day. But the coronation and fanfare hadn't brought her any closer to winning her parents' approval. She sat alone at the mother-daughter tea held in her honor as if she were attending a masquerade for an anonymous highborn celebrity.

One evening the phone rang while her family was eating around their small dinner table in their customary kitchen silence. Even though Christina was home from college, no one seemed to have anything to say. Lucy's interests and aspirations were certainly not up for discussion.

She jumped up to take the call. An operator read a telegram informing her that based upon her performance on the fashion board and the weekly reports she had submitted for *Seventeen Magazine* documenting her activities for the past year, a year in the life of a seventeen-year-old girl in America, she had won the journal's national competition and had been selected as their lead national representative. The message went on to inform her that in June, the day after graduation in fact, she and a chaperone would be flown to New York City for an all-expense-paid week of fashion shows and meetings with leading designers, top fashion models, and movie stars. They would stay at a five-star hotel and enjoy a taste of New York's food, glamor, and nightlife. Lucy dropped the phone and cried out, "I won! I won the *Seventeen* national contest, and I'm going to New York!"

Christina stood up, threw down her napkin onto the table, and screamed, "If you win one more thing, I'm gonna *kill* you!" She stormed into her bedroom crying, trailed by both parents, leaving Lucy alone in the kitchen with the dangling phone receiver emitting an angry reminder that it was off the hook. She hung up the phone, its silence giving way to murmurs from her sister's room, her heart twisting in a muddle of Christina's hurt and her own, the part Christina played in hers, and the part she played in Christina's.

Though her parents would never find a way to congratulate her, at school Lucy had accumulated a supply of social capital and was learning how to use it, learning to employ the talents she had, a little less prone to recklessly chasing after titles that she would never win. After many embarrassing campaigns, she would never manage to be elected to student office. But she competed in other ways, participating in a fabric design contest, one of many sponsored by *Seventeen Magazine* that year. Using a potato block stamp, she created a simple pattern—black ink on a white background—of pairs of people, one black and one white, standing with crossed arms, each pair set in a repeated pattern of identical rows across the fabric. "The Black and White of It" won and was purchased by a textile designer who printed the fabric and sold it to a manufacturing company where it was made into low-rise bell-bottom slacks typical of the time. The pants appeared in department stores, and though Lucy never thought to go out and buy a pair, Christina did, offering one more rare gesture of recognition that she might be inching toward accepting them as sisters.

The end-of-year celebration of the Albina Arts Program provided an opportunity for Lucy to grasp a handful of satisfaction by giving others a chance to shine as brightly as they could. On a sparkling day in late May, the families of the students who had participated in the program were bussed to Parkson High from Albina and welcomed as guests of honor. Parents and grandparents bearing neatly wrapped potluck dishes watched a pageant of dance and music recitals and walked through school halls displaying all the artwork that the kids had done, colorful, whimsical reflections of lives opened up to creating, spurred on by their Parkson mentors, whose families were also there—all except Lucy's. Every parent of every child in the program came. Every parent of every Parkson student mentor came. This was Lucy's show, Lucy's baby. The picnic was perfect. The day was perfect. Her team was perfect, if not a little taken aback by the magnitude of their success, the lives they had touched, the beauty of what the arts had given them all.

Mr. Gedelman's quiet way of showing his approval was all in his eyes as he watched the festivities, and it was in his voice when he sat across from Lucy at the picnic table and said, "Well, we did it. Rather, *you* did it." He looked her steady in the eye then, and continued, "I just hope you understand how important this work has been and how important you were in making it happen, Lucy. Not only did you bring light into these kids' worlds, you showed others how it's done. And by the way, you helped me fulfill a dream, sharing with me the belief that something like this could be accomplished with a handful of kids and a whole lot of heart. And just look around you at this dazzling display of creativity and good citizenship!"

"In the name of art," Lucy said, lifting her Dixie cup of lemonade the way she had seen people toast a special occasion on TV, holding a little finger up in the air.

"In the name of art." He lifted his cup, nodded, and took a sip. Then he reached across the table and gave her shoulder a nudge, leaning in toward her and squinting through the sun glancing his forehead.

"Remember that no matter how bad things may get, we can always find a way, if we look hard enough and care hard enough, to bring out the best in ourselves and in others. Promise me, Lucy, that if you ever feel like you're in danger of forgetting that, you'll think back on this day, and in that crystal clear mind's eye of yours you'll see the high spirits and the pride surrounding us right here, right now, and you'll remember that you made that happen."

"I promise, Mr. G."

22

SPOTLIGHTS

New York, 1968

Lucy

HER CHAPERONE'S NAME WAS TRACY. Lucy had never been on an airplane before. Tracy said she had been to Chicago to visit relatives and had traveled to New York several times and knew her way around, even on the subway. "But we won't be taking the subway," she said, "because they'll have a limo to take us everywhere we need to go."

They flew right over Chicago and Lake Michigan, which seemed almost like an ocean of its own. Lucy hadn't realized how tired she was, having stayed up most of the night packing, unable to let go of the excitement of graduation day, until they had flown across more than half the country and it all seemed to melt into the clouds. She fell asleep and dreamed she was drifting in her great-grandfather's rowboat on Puget Sound. The sun was in her eyes and grew brighter and brighter, reflecting off the water like molten flecks of stardust exploding into sparks and fire, blinding and disorienting her. When she woke up the sun was dropping toward a reddening horizon behind them and cut straight across the surface of the earth into her window as the plane leaned and began to descend into the largest city she had ever seen, the only major city she had ever seen like this—with its bejeweled bridges, concrete skyscrapers, and pulsing red-and-white rivers of traffic—sprawled out below an impossible vantage point, her looking glass, a small rounded window.

Once off the plane, they met the two men who were to be their escorts and the photographers from the magazine who were to accompany them everywhere they went. Their presence, at first incomprehensible, began to wind itself like a gilded frame around a picture of the girl, almost-glamorous Lucy, posing as a New York fashion designer-to-be, suspended on a golden thread. They stayed at the Drake Hotel on Park Avenue. Staying in a hotel—another first. Bellboys and polished marble. Ladies in summer stoles and evening gloves. There were editors and designers asking her what she thought about Bobbie Brooks and why she'd chosen the Brooks clothing line as her favorite. They introduced her to the head designers and the president of the company. Now was Lucy's time to practice how to be charming and polite and perfect and not pay attention to the fact that she was sick.

But it didn't take long for her to see how utterly foreign she was to this place, this alternate reality she found herself walking in. The 21 Club; fancy restaurants where food was served on silver—real silver—dishes; places at tables set with so many forks for which there was no hope of divining a purpose or system; and food she didn't understand, food that tore her insides apart: pâtés and mousses and hot buttered snails. Unnamed delicacies arrayed under glass domes and on enormous platters that were carried and expertly presented by waiters in white gloves. It was as if she'd been sent to her school's richest kids' homes, where she could only pretend to fit in, suspended there, bewildered, unable to run home afterward to curl up in the arms of her ragged but familiar world and let her guard down. Broadway, nightclubs, the ballet. At each venue she was taken backstage—hallowed ground—and introduced to the stars: the cast of *Hair*, Bolshoi prima ballerina Maya Plisetskaya, teenage actors Olivia Hussey and Leonard Whiting, the achingly beautiful Romeo and Juliet of Franco Zeffirelli's new hit movie. She met dazzling faces reflecting perfection back at her, Cheryl Tiegs and Colleen Corby, models she revered.

Lucy held on by her delicate gold thread, nearly crashing back to earth when Tracy caught her applying baby powder to her hair to absorb the oil, a trick she had learned while still following the coarse reflexive habits of personal hygiene she had grown up with. Tracy's look of disapproval bordering on disgust presented her with a brief and shameful glimpse of herself as an impostor in this world, though she still clung to the role she believed in, believed she had earned, somehow managing to hold onto a stubborn faith that she belonged here, despite an essential missing ingredient: trust.

June 6th, the morning of their last day in New York, the sounds of a gathering crowd began to travel up from the street just outside the hotel. A breaking news report came on over the TV as they prepared for the day. It echoed as they crossed the lobby on their way out, punctuated by the anxious clip-clopping of heels across the marble floor. Bobby Kennedy had just died after being shot in L.A. overnight. The street quickly became clogged with reporters and cameras surrounded by crowds of tense and distraught bystanders pressing against police barricades.

Members of the press jostled each other as they waited for an appearance from Bobby's brother's widow Jackie, who lived next door. Lucy and Tracy's escorts whisked them past a sweaty tangle of rumpled suits and poised flash bulbs, but an uneasy cluster remained when they returned at the end of the day. Like the milling crowd, the horror and immediacy of this fresh and incomprehensible tragedy were to linger, adding to the weariness Lucy already felt from this sojourn out in the world. She was heading home having already lost her tenuous hold on the public persona that she had so badly wanted to own.

They flew back to Portland amid the aftermath of the assassination, the long flight mercifully erased from Lucy's memory by a curtain of unconsciousness that enshrouded her in formless black space. They were met by another wall of press people, along with family members and Hi-Board members clamoring to greet them at the gate. Later on, Lucy's parents arrived with Christina to pick her up from the welcome home party, and she watched them shrink in discomfort as they were swept up among the publicity people. She knew then that she was not going to become a fashion designer. She was not going to move to New York or accept the full scholarship to Parsons School of Design that she had been offered. There was no golden thread, no braided picture frame. There was no vision of her going off to a private art school in New York or anywhere else.

She came home and collapsed, overcome by gastrointestinal distress of a new order of magnitude, convinced that her parents were morbidly gratified that she had returned with her tail between her legs to the safety of the world they believed she never should have left in the first place and never should have dreamed of leaving. Lucy had no idea what she was going to do and so began searching for a way to justify changing her dream.

23

MIND AND SPIRIT

2011

Kate

"BUT YOU MUST HAVE FINISHED high school at least feeling pretty good about yourself," I asked, anticipating at least a partial affirmative from Lucy on the other end of the Skype signal.

Her unequivocal "No" jolted any residual complacency right out of me.

"Because I did all of it for the approval of my family. I did all of it for the approval I didn't get from them. I just wanted my parents and my sister to acknowledge me."

"And they didn't."

"And they didn't. So no," Lucy said resolutely. "I never felt good about any of it because I didn't achieve what I set out to achieve. I didn't please my sister and instead just made her mad. And," she added, "my parents didn't recognize me.

"I confronted my mother about it when I was in my early twenties. We were pretty estranged by then. I was married to my first husband, Robbie Moore, the boy I'd had a crush on through high school, the boy my parents hated, the boy I lost my virginity to during my freshman year in college.

"While I was off in Eugene, my parents sold the house in Parkson and moved to a suburb of Los Angeles. I had become a buyer in retail, and I often traveled down to the L.A. clothing market but never even told them I was there.

Kate

I had just done this intense five days and it was the last day of the market. I was leaving a vendor's office and going out across the courtyard, and I fainted. I collapsed. I'm sure—I was always sick and just rose above it, but—the work-week had just been too intense this time, and I went down. Somebody called 9-1-1. I was revived. And I was quite shaken, so much so that I actually called my parents and asked if they would come and get me. And they did.

"On the ride back to their house Mom asked what I was doing there anyway. I told her it was part of my job, and she said, 'What's your job?' And I said, 'Well, I'm a buyer for Meier and Frank.' And she said, 'What's *that* mean?' And I said, 'It means I have a budget, and I go to market, and I buy things for a department.' She looked at me and said, 'Why would anyone have *you* do *that*?' You know, instead of 'Wow, way to go girl.' You know? I mean I was extraordinarily young to be doing this in the first place, and she couldn't even congratulate me for *that*!

"So we get to their place, and I'm still weak and shaken up, and I take a shower. And Mom is waiting for me in the bedroom when I get out of the shower. She's sitting on the bed, and I—finally—I don't even know what possessed me—maybe it was because I was in such a weakened state—I don't know why I would even address this with her—but there she was, and I just said, 'You know, there's something that's been bothering me my whole life and something I've always questioned within myself but never asked you, and I need to ask you now.'

"'I understand that parents can love one child more than another. I know that's natural and happens all the time. It was emphatically clear my whole childhood that you and Dad cared for Christina more than me. But what I don't understand is how you would allow yourselves to be so plain about it, to be so clear about it, to just blatantly show one child that you preferred the other. I mean, for one thing, Christina was in girls' chorus. You went to all of her events. I was in choir, which was a much higher achievement than girls' chorus, and you never came to a single one of my concerts. You went to everything Christina did but you didn't go to one thing I did, never supported me in anything that mattered to me.'

"After a very long silence Mom said, 'Your father and I watched your sister, and we watched you. She always struggled. You always succeeded. You always had friends. She only had friends in Tacoma. You always got by. You were a survivor. She needed help. You never needed help. We didn't think you needed us. We knew you were okay on your own.' And to her, that was the whole story." Then Lucy added, "You know, in context it gave me some peace."

Borrowing the voice of an adversary in order to fully grasp what I was hearing, I said, "'So therefore we don't need to be parents to you because...' is that what they were saying to you, that they didn't need to be parents to you because you seemed okay by yourself?"

"Just fine. Yeah. '... Because you're strong, and you're independent, and you don't need us.'"

"And did your conversation stop there?"

"It did. The next morning, I flew home. But the conversation helped me understand that at least it wasn't about favoritism, it was about my being strong. But I was strong because of neglect, because I had been rejected, because I had been taking care of myself since I was three years old. And there's just something very wrong about that."

"Absolutely, and terribly sad." I paused then, reaching for a hopeful segue. "As far as your strength goes, just to stay with your resiliency for a minute, given what you've told me, can you put your finger on something—aside from being neglected—that truly was life-giving for you and made you a stronger person, something that made you strong, not just in terms of survival skills. In other words, can you describe how you see your strength evolving?"

"Yes," Lucy said. "I think there's a new component that I'm starting to understand since coming to Alces. But I believe I was born with—this might sound weird to you—I was born with a whimsical, vital soul. It's the only way I can explain it. My sister had the same parents I did, and we've been nothing but completely alien to each other. And I think that my spirit is what sets me apart. Of course I've lived with a lot of depression and sadness, but I think I was born with a spirit that gave me room to suffer deeply for prolonged periods and still come out alive, ready to live. So I credit my soul with helping me survive.

"But I also think—and this is new, something I'm just coming to see over the last year or so—that I've had this kind of dogged persistence. I was not going to be held down. And I've been blessed to have that as a tool that allowed me to reason through things and seek an answer or a solution to a problem.

"So my life has been a series of problems that I've tried to solve in whatever way I could. It's as if my whole life has been a puzzle, a beautiful and sometimes painful puzzle. Maybe I would have gone crazy if I hadn't had all these problems to work out. I don't know. Does that make sense?"

"It does," I said, not completely satisfied. "I'm also wondering about something else, though. Yes, there's your ability to work though problems, and there's your vibrant soul. Your imagination. But it seems to me like there's also got to be a vision. It strikes me that in order to believe you can find a way through a problem, you have to be able to see a little beyond it, or at least to trust that there *is* something beyond it to strive for, don't you?"

"Yes, there's that."

"So if you'd say that's also part of it, I wonder how that factors into your experience."

"Yeah... that's perceptive and exactly right," Lucy said. "For many years life had no meaning for me unless I had an established goal, you know, something that was clear and defined and something I was working toward, like in high school. Like all those markers I went after from sixth grade on. And then after high school—of course college gives you different goals. And then I went into corporate life, and I was always striving. There was always the next step, and the next step for the next step. And I always had to have that vision. When I was a temporary sales clerk in retail, I envisioned being a buyer. And then I would reach the divisional level. So always I had my sights on what I was working toward. *Always*. You're absolutely right.

"And I also remember a time when I started to understand that a defined vision, a clear, closely held vision could work against me because I might miss something along the way. This might have been when I was preparing to leave my corporate life, when I was very uncomfortable in that world and coming to understand that the life I was living wasn't feeding my soul. At some point I remember not having a goal. I'm not sure exactly when that was, but I felt like I was coming apart, terrified because I had always built my life on this framework, and I realized I didn't have a purpose, and I got really depressed and even suicidal.

"And then, over time, I started exploring the idea of life without these goals, that there could be a different kind of life, that there could be a different kind of meaning and a different kind of goal."

"And maybe a different kind of structure?"

"Yes."

"It just seems like all that you've described is structure-oriented, that for a very long time you managed to create structure for yourself through the goals and the plans you followed, the framework, as you called it, and when it wasn't there, you felt lost."

"I did. And it's taken a lifetime to break free of that need and to live a life now where I often have to be in the not knowing, which can be uncomfortable for any human being; and for one who had a belief system that required me to have the next goal in sight at all times, it's been an interesting challenge. But I know that this is part of the plan, and I know that I was meant to break free of all that structure. And I do still have goals. You see them, but they're much more amorphous. And I'm willing to say that my goal is to live in the moment and to let my life unfold as long as I am humanly able to put one foot in front of the other. And my goal right now is to be able to continue to live an artful life. I don't need a more precise goal than that. And I understand that within the context of that there's a lot that goes on. But that's enough of a goal for me. Twenty years ago, it wouldn't have been."

"And it's remarkable that you have given yourself the freedom…"

"It's a process just to get here."

"Yes. But that in itself is a huge achievement, as much as reaching any one of those goals that you reached for yourself previously. In particular, just allowing yourself not to be driven by this self-imposed structure that you describe through your teenage years and beyond is quite a step in a different direction."

"Yeah."

"It seems like being strong enough to do that is hugely significant."

"I think that it's probably the biggest success of my life." Lucy paused to consider where this thought was going. "Because I think I truly did fear freedom, for all the reasons that you understand. And to break free of that fear and to live without self-imposed constraints allows me much more opportunity to grow as a human being. It's what allows me to live as—to be—an artist."

"And to live—and be—in the moment."

"Yes, I think it's the most profound achievement of my life."

PART THREE

24

RESCUE

2011

Kate

"So let me clarify something," I began, as soon as we had finished updating each other on the latest news from our respective home fronts. "Twelve months after you gave your notice, you left your corporate job. You've told me a little about what happened a little later on with Sam in Utah. But in between, my understanding is that you were still frail and unwell. You had made a huge choice—a leap—to open yourself up to a different kind of life, but you didn't yet have a sense of what was next. Is that correct?"

"Yes. Just making that decision and formally announcing it relieved some of the stress. I had established the amount of time that I would remain there. It wasn't forever, and I believed I could work my way through that, knowing there was an end date."

"What I want to explore is your process of coming back to painting, teaching yourself whatever you needed in order to relearn those skills while you were still healing, during this complicated time of leaving your long-established life and career behind. And then somewhere in there Sam walked into your life and changed it in ways you're still feeling, still processing. Of course I wonder if there were warning signs or red flags in the beginning, and we'll definitely get to that. But this period is what I'm interested in right now, your time of coming back to art, coming into a new life for yourself, and deciding, despite considerable resistance, to allow Sam into that process."

"Well, while I was still in my corporate job, I had begun working through Julia Cameron's *The Artist's Way*. I was doing her exercises every day, which involved quite a bit of introspection that ultimately led to me giving my notice. And then after I had formally announced my decision, I remained in a state of deep introspection. That period, it turns out, was much like the way I'm living now. It was the first time in my life I'd given myself space to be in my interior. And I needed to be there.

"This was a year of getting reconnected to my body. Up to then I had almost completely disconnected from my physical self. Even though in the previous years I had maintained some connection to spirit, head, and heart, I was entirely disconnected from my physical being. So that year was very much about trying to reconnect with myself physically and understand why and how I had disconnected. It was an awkward, gangly time because my body and I hadn't been integrated for decades. And all of a sudden we were trying to come together.

"In some ways it was like learning to walk for the first time. I felt everything, because I had dissociated so completely from my body to avoid pain. Now I recognized that there were messages my body sent when I was in danger, and I had to learn how to listen. I struggled to strike a balance between coming back to an awareness of physical sensation and not panicking at what were turning out to be the normal signals from my body because I didn't even know what normal body signals were. That became a big focus of my year right there. A fundamental learning process.

"I've always been a serious person, but I guess I got serious in a new way about living then, serious about beginning to form a relationship with self. That was when I actually started to envision what I wanted for my life. It's essentially when this life I'm living now began.

"During this time I lived in almost complete solitude outside of work. I mean work was intense. I had enormous advertising contracts with the Gap and Levi Strauss and high-powered meetings and projects to manage. But when I wasn't at work—and this was completely new—I became more conscious of my aloneness and of using it differently. I spent hour after hour after hour in solitude and silence. I didn't have the boon of this beautiful land that I have now, but I had my West Seattle neighborhood, with access to some magnificent coastal parks that were fairly wild. I could easily get in the car or walk through the neighborhood to get out into the dramatic natural landscapes of Seola, Arroyos, and Salmon Creek with their views of Puget Sound and their haunting madrona trees, and I was always only a ferry ride away from our place on Vashon Island. On Saturdays I often took the ferry out to my family's property on Manzanita Beach, the closest thing I'd ever had to a wild back yard. I was conscious that nature was there for me and an important part of this process of learning to listen to myself.

"But it was *The Artist's Way* that brought me to painting again. After I completed the entire book, I began to try to remember how to paint. At first the thought alone was threatening. And of course I had no supplies. It had been twenty-six years since I left college and my painting studies, so I had to buy materials. Just going into the art store was confusing and overwhelming to me. But I began to make trips to Daniel Smith as part of my 'artist dates' and gradually learned to let the experience be fun rather than stressful.

"I wouldn't go with the mandate that I had to buy something or add to my supplies. I would just wander. Take it all in. Sometimes I bought a tube of paint, sometimes a brush, and sometimes I wouldn't buy anything. Then one day I bought an easel. I just kept bringing these items home one at a time. That was all I could handle. I stowed them away in a closet and in various nooks around the house. I knew I was preparing to paint. I knew it was what I wanted to do. Though I didn't know exactly how I was going to get there, this was my process of taking small, gentle steps forward, just allowing it to be about gathering myself, my materials, and preparing to begin.

"And then one night there was a storm. It was a spectacular night in Seattle. The two houses I owned were in different parts of the city. I was partial to the one I had bought with my second husband, Terry. But later on, when a man I'd been dating for a while and I decided to live together, he refused to live in the house that I'd shared with my ex. So I kept that house and rented it out, and Drew and I bought a house together.

Kate

"I had never lived in a newly built house before and was a little surprised that I ended up loving that place. It was at the base of a green belt on the outskirts of town. So it felt like the house was in the country, though it was only twenty minutes from downtown. There were paths and trails instead of sidewalks leading down to the shore a half a block away, and we often saw foxes and eagles and deer in the neighborhood. It was a beautiful, beautiful place to live. It's also where I had my hemorrhage. But well before that, when Drew and I split up, I easily bought out his share and ended up owning it outright, and it became another refuge.

"The night of that intense storm I was in this kitchen looking out to the woods behind the house and the gushing rain and wind. We never got that much wind in Seattle, but this was one of those rare intense rainstorms that's cleansing and energizing. I felt inspired and decided to make my minestrone soup, a dish I loved to make because putting it together felt artful, each ingredient adding color. I put on an old Bonnie Raitt album and started preparing the soup, singing in that way that sometimes happens when you lose yourself in a creative act, when you seem to disappear—or part of you does. I felt suspended in time and space with the storm swirling around outside. And I found myself in a very soulful moment, just me, safe in the kitchen with the storm, with the soup making and the music. And all of a sudden I was ready to paint.

"I didn't let myself think about it. I held onto that suspended state with the music playing. I walked around to the various rooms and closets, still singing, and gathered all my materials. I set up my easel and put a canvas on it. I'd been preparing by taking photographs over a few months. I went through the 8 x 10 laser prints I'd made of possible images to paint and selected a photograph of my assistant Taylor. And then I started to paint. Just like that, I started to paint.

"I have no idea how long I was at it, but I nearly finished the canvas in one go. It had been twenty-six years, yet somehow my painting had advanced from where I had left off. I had become a better painter than I had been at twenty-one or two, when I left it all behind.

"And just as remarkable as that was, I loved what I was painting. The portrait that emerged was very free and loose and impressionistic. I had no intentions of showing it to anybody. It was just my own private gift to myself, but I ended up liking it so much that I decided to give it to Taylor.

"My second painting was a self-portrait that I painted from an old photograph that Terry had taken of me in the early, happy days of our marriage.

"Once I started to paint again, I made a commitment. I was still working long hours. But by then I was no longer working through the weekends. And though my boss still made a public display of disapproval when I came in late, he seemed to understand that I was still quite sick, and he allowed me to flex my hours if I was having a bad morning. I understood that he had to show production he wasn't playing favorites, so I didn't take his rebukes too seriously. We had enough trust that he could allow me to set my own schedule. I'm sure on some level he knew I would sooner die than arrive after 10:00 a.m. But that limited freedom bought me time on days that I was throwing up and couldn't get out of bed.

"I created a fairly strict rule system in which to begin my artwork. I didn't get to watch TV during the week. Friday night was my celebration night off. I became a great fan of the VHS at that time, recording my favorite dramas—*Law and Order* and *Hill Street Blues*—to watch on Fridays. I canceled my subscription to the newspaper because it ate up too much of my time. I came home from work every night, put dinner on, did my exercises in the gym I'd set up in the spare bedroom, ate my meal, and then painted, staying at it until bedtime. I painted all day on Saturday and Sunday, taking breaks only to walk Mackenzie. That was my contract with myself. That was how I was going to remember how to paint.

"I was dedicated to this process, in part because I was afraid of finishing a piece and not being able to start another one. So before finishing one painting I made sure I had the next one sketched out, never permitting myself to pause between canvases. It just wasn't allowed. This discipline arose out of fear.

"Even so, I believe that great art springs from joy and perseverance more than discipline. It springs from play. It springs from discovery. Of the many things that make art possible, perhaps one piece is discipline, especially when we're learning. For me the experience of coming back to painting was like being in school again, and I was my own painting teacher. I had my class schedule, and I demanded that I stick to it.

"Somewhere in the process during that year I had these little niggling awarenesses that this was exactly what I wanted to do with my life. I began writing at the time too and got a little piece published in *The Sun*—just one of those short 'readers write' things. As I was writing and painting, it would come up to my consciousness that this was how I wanted to live. But I would quickly chase such thoughts away. I didn't think such a life was possible. Even while my job was killing me and I knew I had committed myself to leaving it, I had no idea how I was going to earn a living once I left. I didn't believe being an artist was practical on any level. It didn't enter into my concept of what was possible. But the feeling kept coming back, refusing to submit, and returning with enough persistence that it eventually developed into a conscious idea that maybe what I'm supposed to do is paint and write.

"In my struggle to sort out where I was going, I talked to my friend Ivy, finally saying out loud that I thought this was what I really wanted to do. Ivy had demonstrated her love for me by saving my life after my hemorrhage, rescuing me from that unspeakably bad hospital and getting me safely to one that actually provided proper care. But in addition to that, I saw her as an eminently practical and committed mother of two who understood that my being alive at all was a miracle. I held her in high esteem for the way she cared about me, so her support of the idea of me becoming an artist carried a lot of weight. I even confessed my idea to my parents at one point, and they seemed open to me doing anything. After all, this time they really had almost lost me. Given the general amazement that I was still walking on the earth, how crazy could wanting to be an artist be?

"So the thought continued to develop and grow, becoming a part of my consciousness as I was painting. But I wasn't following a straight line to confidently pursuing this goal, and one day I became doubtful and despondent, thinking, 'Who the hell do you think you are! You're crazy! There's absolutely no way you can do this for a living.'"

"Sounds like the censor, Julia Cameron's censor, shouting you down."

"Exactly! I was berating myself, telling myself to get a grip. And right in the midst of that lecture—the most intense beating I'd given myself since the hemorrhage—the phone rang, and it was Paige Powell. She's a woman

I went to high school with, though we were never actually close friends back then. I mean, we knew each other, we said hello to each other, and she was one of the kids who participated in the Albina Art project with me. But I always considered Paige way too cool for me to touch. She inhabited a realm I couldn't even imagine entering. And what made her so cool was not only that she was beautiful and rich and had everything that all the popular kids had; Paige was also exceedingly creative, bright, compassionate, and politically aware. She had it all, everything that was important and good, along with the more superficial things that might draw people to her. At the end of senior year, she signed my annual along with Virginia Tanner—both of whom were in the same high echelon to me—writing how much they admired me and what I'd done with the Albina project. At the time I took their praise as the ultimate honor.

"Paige ended up becoming famous in Portland when she started doing PR work for the Portland Zoo back when they were raising baby elephants."

"Elephants?"

"It was noteworthy at the time when elephants were born and raised successfully in captivity. One of Paige's PR campaigns was ZooDoo, a program that helped put the Portland Zoo on the map by selling elephant manure for gardening. Fairly quickly she became an advocate for creating better environments for zoo animals. This, of course, raised her to a new and unprecedented level of admiration in my eyes. And then she left Portland.

"As it turned out, she moved to New York City. She was a big fan of Andy Warhol and his publication *Interview*. The way I understand the story is that she eventually ended up becoming an associate publisher there. I don't know the details of how her relationship with Andy developed or exactly what kind of relationship they had. But it's no secret that they were very important to each other. She was devastated by his death and ended up leaving New York City and returning to Portland.

"Paige's family had a place on the Oregon coast, which is where she and I had reconnected before that phone call. I hadn't kept in touch with her after high school, but my friend Janey, who had always been enamored of Paige, had followed what she was doing almost religiously.

Paige had become quite an animal rescuer and advocate, and one of her projects in New York City involved a TV program that facilitated the adoption of rescued animals. That program was responsible for saving many dogs and cats who would otherwise have languished in shelters or been put down.

"Paige had been staying at her family's vacation home on the Oregon coast when a big story broke. A woman—one of those people who hoard animals—had reportedly collected, and basically imprisoned, some horrific number of cats and dogs in a school bus. The woman was turned in, and all the animals were confiscated, many of them so ill that they had to be euthanized. As for the ones who survived, there was no local shelter big enough to take them all, so they were sent up and down the coast to shelters that had space. And no surprise, these victims became Paige's project. She traveled around the state making visits to the various shelters to walk the dogs and check up on the cats.

"A few months after my hemorrhage I had managed to take that vacation on the Oregon coast with my dog, and just before I left, Janey, true to form, mentioned an article she'd seen about Paige caring for all those rescued animals. That immediately inspired me to contact her. I thought what she was doing was important, and I understood what a huge job it was. So I told her I was coming down and wanted to help her walk the dogs. We made arrangements to meet at one shelter or another and walk the animals together. And that's how we got reconnected.

"While I was in the area, Paige and I had dinner one night. I was staying about an hour from her family's home. I mentioned to her that I had begun teaching myself to paint again, and I was surprised at how interested she became. She said, 'I really want to see what you're doing.' And I said, 'Well—I haven't shown it to people yet. It's nothing.' But she took my phone number, and sure enough she called me a day or two later, saying she wanted to see what I was working on.

"At the time I was busy on my third painting, a portrait of my tenant Cynthia. Some months earlier, in response to the economic downturn that had driven several of my clients into bankruptcy, I began to worry about the possibility of not being able to make my monthly mortgage payments and started to work on a back-up plan. I hired a handyman to turn the downstairs space into a daylight basement apartment. Cynthia became my tenant, as well as a good friend.

"I was working on the portrait of her lost in thought as she played with her cat. Paige found the image quite moving. She absolutely loved my work, all three pieces, my entire corpus. I had brought my two completed paintings with me as a reference and confidence builder. All this was still fairly new to me, and I didn't want to lose momentum or focus while I was on vacation. Though I felt that momentum strongly and knew it was important, I was thunderstruck by Paige's response because I thought my skills were still so rudimentary and that I had so much more to learn. Apparently she didn't see it that way at all.

"Still, in the weeks that followed, I found myself struggling. The vacation I had dreamt about for so long was over. I was back in Seattle with my contracts, my painful healing, my painting routine, and my doubts. I was running out the clock on my job without a compass for navigating my way forward once that clock ran out.

"Then, in the midst of my crisis of faith, the phone rang, and it was Paige. There I was, saying to myself, 'There's absolutely no way you can earn a living. Who do you think you are! You're an idiot for even thinking it could be possible.' I had found the thing I was most passionate about but couldn't envision a future in which I could actually support myself doing it. And then Paige called to commission a painting. On the many other occasions that were to come along after that, when I felt overcome by deep doubt, I reminded myself that the universe had Paige reach out to me in Seattle in that moment of despair, with the message that I was supposed to go forward, to keep painting.

"I took on her commission, which meant I had to make a trip down to Portland. She wanted a portrait of her dog, a rescue from the streets of New York City and a very fearful animal. Paige was worried that I might not be able to get a decent photograph. But I managed to get some expressive shots of the dog. I couldn't decide which of the two best photos to use, so I decided to paint two portraits, fairly large ones, and I was quite happy with them when they were finished.

"But then the time came to deliver the paintings. This was the part of doing commissioned portraits that would remain especially hard for me. I was always certain the people would hate the work I had done for them. Janey also lived in Portland, so I stayed with her when I went to shoot the photographs and when I returned with the paintings. She also came with me to deliver the finished pieces to Paige. I remember standing with both canvases turned around toward me and then turning them out to face Paige. Janey told me later that I was visibly shaking as I held the canvases on either side of me. I was terrified. But Paige was delighted with them and asked me to stand them both on the mantle, right next to an original painting by Andy Warhol.

"Then she showed me the other commissioned works she had displayed around the house. I was so grateful she hadn't shown them to me before I had completed the paintings. She had another painting of the same dog, but there were portraits of other animals done by famous painters, artists I had studied. They were spectacular. And there were my two works situated among them. Knowing that someone I respected so deeply, who lived in the world of the most elite artists I could imagine, thought so highly of my painting, kept me going.

"After I had painted a few more canvases, I got my first commission for a family portrait. I had been taking my paintings in to be photographed at the copy stand of the Seymor and Baird photolab and having transparencies made of everything I had painted. So in this process Loretta, one of my associates, had seen the completed pieces coming and going. One day I got to work and found a snapshot of a woman holding a baby, with a note from Loretta attached that read: 'I really admire your work. I was wondering if I could commission you to do a portrait of my sister and her daughter.' I told her I would love to paint them but that I didn't want her to pay me for it. She would have none of that and responded with something like, 'Lucy, you're never going to earn a living as an artist if you refuse to accept payment for your work. I insist on paying you.'

"So I accepted Loretta's offer along with a modest payment for the portrait. I believed this too was part of a larger message that I was moving in the right direction, though I still had no clear idea what that meant. And later, when another baby was born, Loretta's sister and her husband commissioned me to paint a second portrait of Proud Dad sitting with Baby Boy on his lap.

"The year went on like that, with great silences and some momentous strides, not all of which I recognized. I focused entirely on saving money to live on when I left my job, learning to paint again, and endeavoring to create a relationship with myself for the very first time. I had never had time, never made time, working so punishingly hard all those years. Perhaps, in the quiet I permitted myself to inhabit, I was learning to listen."

25

GOOD OLD DAYS
2014

Kate

MY GROWING DOUBTS ABOUT MY ability to build a coherent story from bits and pieces of Lucy's adult life finally drove me out of the house seeking a place to work where I might regain my focus and shake off a deadly sense of creative inertia. So much rested on my finding perspective, a fresh sense of direction. I packed up my notebooks and laptop and headed for a café in town, somewhere I hadn't tried to work before.

Nearly four years into the project, important threads were in place, and I had shaped the emotional substance of Lucy's formative years. But despite all the digging we had done together, I still hadn't managed to work out a reliable timeline for transformative events unfolding later in her life. This should have been the easy part. What was chasing darkness if not blindly feeling one's way along, perhaps coming up with a few fragments, and finding oneself standing there disoriented, squinting in the glare above ground?

I was coming to see that I had pushed Lucy as far I could. Watching her strength and mental acuity slip away through a series of debilitating and painful illnesses and continue to falter as her conditions became chronic, I had learned to hold back on requests, even small ones, when she seemed too frail or exhausted for even her most heroic effort to pay off. I was careful to avoid the slightest hint of a suggestion that would send her on an undeterrable mission of cooperation, refusing to acknowledge her diminished capacity, doggedly acquiescing to another interview, working through fatigue, worsening drug effects, and unrelenting pain to tackle a few more questions. Yet no amount of effort improved her diminishing access to the details I needed to close the gaps and move the story forward. I had seen it often enough to recognize the ways Lucy's historically spotty memory, which had become increasingly unreliable over the past two years, worked against her otherwise unchecked willingness to give everything she had to the process. I had also bumped up against something potentially unconscious, something that felt from my vantage point almost like resistance, though I wasn't prepared to call it that.

Not that I would be surprised to find pockets of shadow hugging the facts of Lucy's trauma. But I wasn't prepared for her, consciously or not, to leave it all in my hands or to feel so alone in prospecting for something precious and steadfast buried in her stubbornly thin recollections. How would I make Lucy's story whole if I failed to pin down its slipperier pieces, the parts—yes, I had to remember it was the parts and not the partner—that eluded me, eluded *us*. What if I simply couldn't make it happen? What if, in the end, I couldn't conjure the magic my friend trusted me to make? What if Lucy's health continued to decline and she didn't even live to see the resolution of her own story? Could I live with either of those endings?

The story I had set out to write went something like this: An artist struggles to overcome illness, adversity, and betrayal... finds redemption in examining relationship to family, to past choices, and to self as she sees it now... An over-reliance on will and some real courage allow a misguided search for approval to eventually lead to a creative path and the possibility of healing.

But the task that now presented itself was to fashion another narrative. Not only was I exploring the process of reconstructing self, I was witnessing it in real time, perhaps even influencing its direction.

The story I was trying to tell now wasn't going to materialize from a collection of facts pulled into a tidy narrative of what happened when. The negative space that had settled in, along with Lucy's deteriorating health and the flattening effects of the drugs that almost but never entirely controlled her pain, left me afraid of finding that space empty, or perhaps just failing to see what was in it. I was beginning to realize, in a tangled, anxious process, that *this* story would require me to work from a different system of navigation, one in which I would have to construct the waypoints rather than locate them on a conscientiously studied map. Only by entering my own unsettled space, where I could just as easily become lost or disappear, would I have any hope of understanding the part I played in this story.

Until now, feeling around in that space where Lucy couldn't accompany me, I had identified the convexities of things: the shell curves and cliff-edge corners of uncomfortable questions. How had Lucy allowed Sam into her life at the very moment she had started it over again, reaffirming long-suppressed creative dreams, reclaiming her art for no one but herself, holding on—if just barely—to a still incomplete recovery from her hemorrhage? How accidental was that first encounter in almost two decades, after two failed marriages, the hemorrhage, and the recovery she was still struggling through, when she'd said unequivocally that she was painting again and didn't have time for friendship? I was finally awakening to the fact that I was on my own in grappling with lingering questions that still had no satisfying answers. Whether or not they would ever be found, the search was mine to own and to carry as far as I could possibly take it. I would have to give the questions space and weight, life and breath, but not allow them to consume me.

In Lucy's telling of it, Sam had courted her, made her feel beautiful, adored, worthy of being courted in a way no one ever had before. But there was that incomplete story she told in which, early on—perhaps on their first dinner date at his place after reconnecting—out of nowhere, it seemed, he'd made a vicious insult about her body. The words themselves were lost, but Lucy recalled Sam immediately taking them back, gracefully enough, somehow, for her to dismiss them.

What had he said, exactly? Why had she let it pass? Lucy couldn't remember. Was it some kind of resilience test? And why did we seem to come up somewhere shy of substance when questions of the intimacy that developed after the inexplicable comment arose? I wondered about the overriding sense of connection that brought her to love again, to unconditionally love *this* man when she had vowed never again to fall into that kind of love with *any* man? I wondered why I was beginning to hear in those parts of her story a fixedness, as if the lines had been practiced somewhere in some nameless, formless, perhaps forgotten heartspace.

I claimed a small table in a dim hallway-like rear section of the café, placed my computer bag on a chair, laid out my papers, and walked over to the counter to order coffee. Returning, I opened my laptop, settled into my seat, and quietly thrummed my fingers on the cold keyboard. Ambient sounds of conversation faded in and out of my awareness as I oriented to the task. The precariousness of the project, the grand assumptions on both sides of Lucy handing it over to me in the first place, Lucy's faltering state of mind and body, the urgency of finding a compelling way through the holes. It all washed through me as did the jittery sensation of coffee-infused alertness and the warming of the keys under my fingers, their plastic smoothness receiving my nervous energy, about to turn it into something else, the morning sun flooding the far end of the café as people came and went to and from the street.

Sitting there 2,000 miles from Alces, I began to type a letter, as if driven by a plea for a hidden door to open, the words to break a spell. Lucy had only been able to recall the long-lost original in the sketchiest terms, clear only about two things: it was artfully written, and its effect profound. I realized, amid the chatter and clatter and the sound of frothing milk, that my friend had yet to see Sam's letter as the act of seduction it might have been. As I stepped out of my own way, I could imagine it clearly for the first time.

August 12. 1997

Dear Lucy.

I just want to tell you how much it meant to me. not just to see you last week. but to spend a little time with you. hearing you talk about how you're about to begin a new life. how you found the courage to walk away from everything you know and into an unfamiliar place where you'll be able to make use of your gifts as an artist. Lucy. I meant it when I said I don't believe in coincidences. I can feel that our meeting up again after all these years is already changing me. I know you said you're too busy for friendships now and are fully committed to focusing all your energy on your painting and getting your strength back while you finish up the last few months in your big-time job. I respect that more than you know. I don't want to distract you from that path or get in your way.

But seeing you again and seeing what a survivor you are brought me back to Parkson and a few good things I can remember about the place. you being one of them. My memories of high school are pretty mixed. and everybody knows about my somewhat 'spotted' past. but I want you to know that I still remember the kindness you always showed others. the risks you took for our buddy Robbie Moore. how you always covered for him. helped his family. and—I must say this now—how I was secretly devastated when you two got married. Yeah. maybe I was too 'cool' to admit my hopes of getting closer to Lucy Simkus. But when Steph came back after she and I broke up and told me she was pregnant. that was that. We love our son. but we never had what it takes to stay together for the long haul.

I never told you how much that letter you sent me in prison kept me from giving up on myself. giving in to the darkest thoughts. Your words reminded me I was in for just getting caught on such petty things like pot and stealing. and that gave me hope of getting through my time in one piece. At the same time. I wanted you and Robbie to be happy. I really did. He was a good kid. even though he took a few wrong turns. We all did. all except you. But most of Robbie's slipups were about trying to impress the hard guys like me. Even from a distance I could see how he strung you along. kept you thinking he might be interested while he went about his business. In some ways I don't blame him though. You were so innocent. It's okay— I'm a pushover too. Just don't tell anybody and ruin my image.

We both know old Rob was never the bad boy he wished he was. His little deviant escapades probably got him on your parents' bad side though. enough that they couldn't have been too pleased when the two of you tied the knot and settled down in Eugene. Must have been hard for your dad. you hanging out with all those hippie radicals. Your parents were always so stuck on appearances. weren't they? Lucky for me I'm tall and handsome. I remember my brother coming home with stories about him and Robbie sneaking around your mom. how she always held a grudge against the Moores. Still. you managed to use your powers of goodness to convince her to make those clothes for Marsha so she wouldn't have to keep wearing their dead mother's dresses to school. You saved that girl's skin so many times. and what did their drunk of a father do to thank you?

I wish I'd been there when they pulled Marsha out of Ben's mangled Chevy. Me and that kid brother of mine racked up endless hours rebuilding that engine to perfection. and then he went and totaled it and nearly killed Marsha while he was at it. He got such a bad rap for that and had plenty of scars nobody ever saw but me. But those Moores had the worst luck of anybody I know. except for them getting you. even if you did wind up leaving Robbie in the end. And way back when I bumped into you and Terry in the grocery store with your shiny new wedding rings and all. I wanted to see you happy. but I just couldn't quite imagine it. you and that pretty boy who acted like he thought he was better than you.

But back to the good old days. In case you didn't know. it didn't get past me that you were everyone's friend. a bright star in the neighborhood and in our little shit of a town. We all had our rough times. but nobody can say you didn't come out with a smile and a helping hand. Maybe your parents didn't deserve you back then. Neither did the Moores. I only hope they wised up over the years. And look at you now! Good old John and Ada must be proud of you for coming so far in the world. Knowing you. you would never make them feel like you'd left them in the dust. would you? Here I am pointing a finger at all the people who didn't deserve you. You must be wondering what makes me think I do. Yet I still can't help asking what I can do to get you to reconsider seeing me again. Will you just think about it. please?

Your old friend and admirer.
Sam

26

EUGENE

1968—1969

Lucy

"ALL I COULD THINK ABOUT when Robbie and I finished and I realized I had lost my virginity was a memory from years before: my mother's grip on my shoulders and being shaken as if my head would roll right off my neck. Her face was all blotched and puffy from crying. I had never seen that before, and it frightened me."

"Was this back in Tacoma?"

"Yes. I was nine or ten, maybe a little younger. It must have been around my birthday and the end of the school year, which, to my delight, always arrived within a week or two of each other. I'd just come home from school and walked into the kitchen, where Mom was sitting at the table dabbing her eyes with a hankie. I automatically ran up to her and asked what's wrong. She turned and grabbed my arm and said something like, 'Shelly Meyers is pregnant! I just can't believe it! Lucy, I don't know what I'd do if you were to disgrace us that way.' She was frantic and frightening, and I was just struggling to make sense of what this all meant. She said, almost as if she was pleading with me but in an angry kind of way, 'Promise me you'll *never* get pregnant out of wedlock like Shelly did, that little *slut*! Look what she's done to her family! And for what? She's barely seventeen years old! Your father and I would be devastated if you were even to *imagine* doing such a thing at that age! Believe me, it's not worth it. It never is.'

"Her distress scared me more than anything she said. I remember her musing aloud at one point, saying something like, 'I just don't understand why these girls are getting pregnant! It's not fun for the woman. It's not something you **want** to do. It's something you **have** to do once you're married, and that's all. I just don't understand it!'

"That's when she seemed to be overcome with fierceness and—I don't know if it was desperation or what. She stood up and grabbed both of my shoulders, and shook me hard, saying, 'Swear to God right now! Swear you'll never let that happen! *Swear it!*'

"Of course I said the words she wanted me to say, mainly so she'd stop shaking me. I was absolutely mystified, clueless as to the exact nature of the unforgivable sin Shelly Meyers had committed."

"Did you know the girl?"

"She lived in our neighborhood. There was enough of an age difference that it created what seemed like an enormous gulf between the teenagers and younger kids. I didn't have any direct contact with her. I remember, though, that even the younger kids in my circle noticed her. She was quite beautiful. That's how I remember her: that really pretty girl who was part of that crowd of older girls who were so much more grown up than we were, even more grown up than my big sister."

"So this memory of being confused and being shaken, literally and emotionally, by your mother and promising her something you didn't understand, this is what you were thinking right after you and Robbie slept together for the first time?"

"Yes. Even though I was eighteen going on nineteen by then and knew more than I did at nine or ten, I'm embarrassed to say I was still so innocent that I wasn't even certain we had completed the act.

"During high school Robbie and I tied ourselves in knots of intense necking. His family lived next door to us for a while after his mother died, but they would eventually end up in an even worse neighborhood. Most of the time he'd give me just enough attention to convince me that I was in love with him, just enough for me to believe he might one day commit to something more meaningful than those rounds of kissing and touching, which were all very tame by today's standards, and which, quite frankly, I

Lucy

loved. Throughout senior year I hung on the hope that he would one day realize he loved me too. I lived for the occasions—and these were never predictable—when he paid me notice. I was obsessed with him. But I'd given up hope of more from him when I left for Eugene that August."

"Leaving Parkson must have been an almost incomprehensibly courageous act of forward motion for you, given that disastrous trip to New York only a couple of months earlier."

"Well, if someone had suggested it to me at the time, I would never have accepted the idea that I was courageous about anything, but I think I felt like my spirit was in the process of lifting a little, maybe finding some shelter. I was starting fresh. At least in some ways it felt like I had a clean slate. And supported by my parents, no less, despite my choice of an utterly impractical—even frivolous—field such as fine art. I was pretty sure that my parents were allowing me to follow my passion and study what I wanted because the family doctor had led them to believe they'd nearly lost me that previous year.

"So I got to Eugene just as the fall '68 semester was about to begin and very soon discovered that I was falling in love in a new way. I loved Eugene. I loved school. I loved the cafeteria and the limitless supply of cold milk I was supposed to be drinking to coat my stomach and build back some body weight. I gained a few pounds and even started dating. I got asked out a couple of times and was eager to make a new life, new friends, blend in, and just be a student.

"My main objective was to live the art I had gone there to live. I was inseparable from my drawing tablet, but otherwise I was free. I imagined telling Mom and Dad I'd begun dating and wondered what they would say, knowing how much they hated Robbie. I think they accepted me pushing up against the boundaries of my station by going to college in the first place, as long as he wasn't part of it. I had argued with them when I first talked about wanting to get into a sorority for sophomore year, but I was determined to convince them that being surrounded by a buffer zone of girls who were serious about schoolwork shouldn't aggravate their concerns about me trying to climb out of my station. I needed to reassure them that I wasn't seeking to be anything but a regular college girl."

"Were you able to convince them?"

"I was. And it was true. But here's the thing: my parents believed—and had made this clear in one way or another to Christina and me—that the purpose of a college education was first and foremost to enhance a girl's marriage prospects. To them, this was the only acceptable way to raise one's social standing. Christina and I were the first people in our family to go to college, and they held up my sister's diploma, along with the teaching certificate she got around the same time, as examples of the proper steps that would get her a successful husband, a provider. And this was all confirmed by Christina's engagement, which couldn't have been more perfectly timed. She and Curtis got engaged right around the time she graduated, while I was still a senior in high school, and they ended up setting a wedding date for the following summer. So she had one year on her own between her graduation and her wedding. She was spoken for, preparing herself, and everybody was happy.

"By the time Christina's second child was on the way, Mom and Dad had bought and sold one and then another slightly nicer home in the Los Angeles area and found themselves flush with cash for the first time in their lives. Thanks to the housing boom, they were able to retire early, move closer to their grandchildren, and loan my sister and her husband $30,000, a critical first step in the process that eventually turned them into millionaires. That loan enabled Christina and Curtis to buy and clear cut a swath of pristine forested land along the Oregon coast and sell the timber for a sizeable profit at a time when making a million dollars was a much bigger deal than it is now. It certainly was to my parents."

"How did you respond to Robbie following you to Eugene after you had begun the process of moving on?"

"At first I was a little annoyed. I had started meeting people, and then Robbie showed up professing his love. He'd gotten his GED, if I remember correctly, and he was talking about pulling his records together and getting accepted into the university. He had applied for a job at a restaurant in town and was confident they'd hire him. When he first arrived he hadn't yet received his draft letter, but later on when the letter—or maybe it was a telegram—arrived with his draft number, he was already accepted. Deferment would apply as long as he was matriculated. He'd be the first in his family to go to college and I'd be the second in mine. He talked about being in this thing together, this adventure in Eugene where we fit in.

"It took me a little while to see this because I had left my hopes for a relationship with Robbie back in Parkson. I had gotten over him. I had spent two years totally infatuated with him and his bad-boy aspirations. I had stood by him and cared for him, even lied for him at my own expense, accepting the scraps of attention he offered me, always on his terms, always living for the next time he might seek me out. I had endured my parents' disparaging remarks, listened to them relentlessly belittle the Moores and criticize Robbie's manners. It's true, the Moores were a seriously troubled family, but I was astonished at the way my father diminished himself by mocking Robbie, imitating the slightly off-kilter way he walked. Though I was shocked on one level, this kind of shaming was fairly normal in our home, and although I was never comfortable with it, it was familiar.

"Over time I learned to avoid my parents' reproach by keeping my outrage to myself when they took shots at those less fortunate or those they saw as inferior. This is horrifying to think about now, but it wasn't until I was in my mid-thirties, after Dad retired and they came to visit me in Seattle after Terry left, that I stood up to them and told them that if they wanted to stay with me, they were not to express their racist and bigoted attitudes in my home.

"So Robbie followed me to Eugene, staying with some friends on campus, proposing that we go forward together as a couple. Even though the idea took me aback at first, ultimately I couldn't bring myself to turn him down, having lived for so long with those powerful longings. I had believed—and this turned out to be the way I thought about most of the men I've been seriously involved with—that he would eventually come around to seeing that I'd been right about us all along. I just needed to show him the way. And even though I had begun to explore and was enjoying that, there he was, so sincere, carrying less of a swagger, asking me to accept him, offering exactly the thing I had once so badly wanted.

"So I went along with it, and it wasn't that much of a stretch to imagine making this thing work. Robbie loved me. He was dedicated to me, to our making a go of it. In my mind the whole thing was about my art and his music. I valued his talent and revered his guitar playing. I was drawn to the idea of us being artists. I was also drawn to the student protests that were going on all over the campus, the energy, the anthems, the momentum all around me, pulling me into something bigger than I was. And so by spring break, when I took the bus back up to Parkson, I felt a new set of private hopes sneaking into consciousness, like little fuzzy roots grabbing into the soil."

"Guided by gravity."

"Right. But I hadn't realized—when I gave in to the excitement of being really alone with Robbie for the first time, with both of us aroused and me no longer surrounded by inquiring dormmates, and I let him lie me down without even undressing and wrestle around on top of me—that shame would so immediately and overwhelmingly bear down and crush me. That's when I heard my mother's sharp voice saying, 'Swear it to me!' I could see her hair—always so perfect no matter what, with a neat wave on either side of her forehead that she held in place with crossed bobby pins at night—and I could see her face powder not quite hiding the color that had risen to her cheeks."

"What was it like afterward? I mean, for you and Robbie."

"I can't remember what we did afterward, but I didn't stay. We didn't talk much, generally, and I don't think we talked much then. There had never been casual conversation in my home when I was growing up, and it was no different with Robbie. I remember feeling deep shame and overwhelming distress, being paralyzed by it."

"How did you end up with this alone time in the first place?"

"I was home on spring break that first year, and we had gone over to his sister Marsha's apartment in Portland. She was away, I'm not sure where. And I remember it being a particularly uninviting place, a drab apartment with dark tan walls, a horrible place. She had given us permission to stay there if we wanted while we were in town, and I told my parents I was staying with Janey that night. I ended up leaving fairly soon afterward and going to Janey's anyway. I don't think Robbie and I stayed there for more than a couple of hours altogether."

"But before you left, do you remember anything at all about how you spent that time?"

"I don't remember very much of it. I think he may have asked me if I was okay, if he had hurt me. I told him 'No,' though it did hurt. I said I was fine. I think I was thinking it wasn't what I expected, but I'm not exactly sure what I expected. It's possible I might have said that out loud. I did know that I had crossed a line, and as a result, I was and would remain a terrible person, a dirty person. I was sure of that. I was so filled with shame that I could barely breathe. It would be quite a long time before I was able to be intimate with him in that way again."

"Are you okay? I didn't hurt you, did I?" Robbie asked, reaching over and gently resting his fingertips along the rise of her collarbone.

"No," she lied. "I'm fine. I think maybe it just wasn't what I expected... but to be honest, I'm not exactly sure what I expected." A tingling in her lips and fingers reminded her to take a deep breath, which expressed itself as a sigh.

"Who is, anyway?" he replied, rolling onto his back and peeling away a damp swath of not-quite-shoulder-length hair that had wound its way around his neck and feathered across his face. He noticed a brown water spot on the ceiling. She noticed the thin sable line leading downward from his navel, which seemed as perfectly formed as a seashell, and the smooth field of his shirtless chest and belly. She felt a surge of remorse for having abandoned the principles she had always accepted and embraced, for having held onto them so firmly and then so unceremoniously giving in to this act that violated them. She sought calm in the familiar, allowed herself to feel comfort in the urge to sketch the contours of this form, its lovely blunt edges and soft-lined sinews that just caught the last of the new spring light receding from the day and lending false polish to the dingy room. She let the swell of that untarnished kind of yearning wash gently through her, as if to cleans away the other kind.

"Marsha's got to tell the landlord there's a leak in the apartment upstairs," Robbie announced, filling the empty space with something purposeful.

"Mmmm." Lucy muttered, acknowledging that something had been said and Marsha's name mentioned. "She's got to suspect what we're doing here though, doesn't she? I mean, when she suggested that we stay here tonight she must've assumed we'd be sleeping together."

"That's all right," he replied, shifting into defense. "I'm sure she assumed we were already doing it by now. But she wouldn't tell anyone. She's my sister, and she's your friend. She doesn't want us to get in trouble."

Panic trumped Robbie's sincerity. "But I'm sure I would never have given her that idea. God, I hope you didn't, Robbie... Did you?" Lucy pressed him, suddenly worried that their rudimentary plan—which had almost by default left space for a first night together—may have developed a life of its own, a life that she hadn't anticipated.

"I don't know, maybe we shouldn't stay, even if nobody knows we're here." Doubt and urgency held her body still, as if seams had suddenly welted up along invisible meridians that now threatened to split apart. What was she supposed to feel now? All the confused just-lived moments were already slipping away like an ebb tide which, having reached a brief slackwater, had begun to churn back on itself, carrying with it a rising fear that there would be no way to live those moments down.

Lucy stood up, picked up her shoulder bag, and walked over to a small mirror standing in a cheap picture frame propped on a dresser, the only furniture in the room aside from the bed. Leaning toward her reflection and mechanically responding without looking at the image before her, she straightened her blouse, combed her hair, and freshened her lip gloss. "I think I'm going to go over to Janey's. We have a lot of catching up to do."

"Well, I might give Ben Yaeger a call then and see if he wants to get some old Parkson boys together and jam for a while. Other than that, I'll be here if you change your mind." He sat up and began rebuttoning his shirt. "Don't worry, okay? Nobody's going to know, Lucy."

"The pill," Janey proposed in an exaggerated telephone whisper. "It's the only way to be completely safe."

"I'm not so sure. It doesn't feel right," Lucy objected. "It's not like we're— I wouldn't know where—"

"Listen," Janey asserted. "You did it once. You *know* you're going to do it again. That's the responsible thing to do."

"I guess so. I know we shouldn't take any chances. But—"

"Lucy, I think you've just got to do what the moment calls for. Nobody's going to know. And besides, he's here for you and you alone. He's your beau, not some frat-house creep out for a one-night stand. We both know that would be a different story."

Lucy pointed out that Robbie had already made friends at Sigma Nu and was bunking with them, confident he would pledge and get in by fall. She was pretty sure, though, that he wasn't going in for all that carousing, having done enough of that in high school. He was definitely growing up, more serious now, she thought.

"Well there you go. There's always plenty of reason to be ready for anything," Janey said, unruffled. "We both know he's not that kind of boy, though—and surely you're not that kind of girl."

"Still," Lucy reasoned, "I don't think he should know about this. I wouldn't want to give him the wrong idea."

"Of course not. You're just being safe."

Lucy could only yield, comfortless in the face of Janey's cheerful irony. "Oh, the bus is here. See you in a little while." She stepped out of the phone booth and into the settling dusk. The door of the bus opened with a rubbery squeal as she approached.

The next morning the two visited the local Planned Parenthood office, and by lunchtime Lucy had her first month's supply in hand. But the idea of taking the pills, organized in their pink circular package, sickened her, fixed her in her own mind as a fallen girl, unredeemable. She held out though and returned to Eugene for the late-spring term determined, wanting only to devote her energy to her classes and to remain steady on her feet with Robbie, committed but in control. He remained affable and patient for the most part, gently, hopefully, pressing for opportunities to try again.

Lucy moved smoothly through that first year, calling home every week and returning home often, as much to reassure her parents of her care and conscientiousness (notwithstanding her secret boyfriend) as to nurture in herself a sense of belonging. This feeling expressed itself initially as a mild homesickness, balanced to some degree by feeling more and more at home in Eugene, as if settling onto a path and, as it seemed she must, making space on that path for Robbie. Part of her believed unquestioningly what she had so often heard, that with her loss of virginity would go Robbie's respect. Not to mention what would happen if her parents were ever to find out. And doubtless, Christina was blazing ahead on the proper course, to be married in August, a comfortable future in hand. Lucy was happy for her, happy now that her family's attention was elsewhere.

She couldn't help but admire Robbie's musical talent, enough that she began singing along with the blues songs he was learning, that everyone seemed to be learning. She sang, and singing decided it: Lucy could believe in their creative partnership. Other parts of her saw honor in that—the belief in their art—and she found that she could, without too much effort, hold tightly to the truth she believed might come in seeking its meaning together. They could be carried along by the rhythms of the steamy far-away Mississippi Delta, the wailing voices of the deep South and the stark electrified Chicago streets, and from the sense of unity offered so freely in the everywhere calls for justice, peace, and human dignity. Lucy could envision, despite her one regrettable mistake, a kind of hopefulness in all this.

27

DEATH LETTER BLUES

Eugene, 1970

Lucy

By SPRING BREAK OF SOPHOMORE year Robbie was half-heartedly tending to his course work and doing a considerable amount of reveling. Lucy fairly quickly began to tire of sorority life, finding the music scene and concerts featuring a steady stream of newly celebrated blues artists much more compelling. Many of the greats—from Big Mama Thornton, Albert King, and B. B. King to Muddy Waters and Son House—came through Eugene on tour, and they saw them all. Robbie loved her. He was the center of her world, the only person she really cared about spending time with, but her parents had paid for her membership at Alpha Phi for the entire year, and she didn't see any alternative until she could explore her options for living off campus the following year.

Robbie and Lucy had privacy when he eventually got his own room at Sigma Nu, and she was beginning to grow more comfortable with the idea of their intimacy, aided by the sexual revolution that had begun two summers earlier and was still flowering freely around them. Still she hadn't gotten past her core of wariness and guilt about having had sex out of wedlock that one time—and maybe one other time since then. She returned home late one Friday night accompanied by a college friend, someone safe from the sorority who stayed in Christina's room and whose name she doesn't even recall.

Early Saturday morning Lucy was awakened by muffled voices. The house felt odd. As she came out of her room she could hear her father down below in his workshop. There was yelling, but it didn't sound like her parents having one of their typical fights. Something else was wrong, and whatever it was, it was very wrong. As she walked past the dining room table, she saw the round pink packet. Her mother had gone through her purse and found the pills.

Her father came storming out of his workshop, marching past her as if she weren't there and into her parents' bedroom. As soon as he closed the door he began wailing. Lucy heard the scraping sound of the drapes being sharply drawn. Her mother walked up to her, a powder blue kerchief tied hastily under her chin, her eyes glazed with anger, and asked who it was.

"Robbie," Lucy whispered.

Her mother shrieked, "I should have known! You *slut*!" and slapped her hard across the face. "You will never see him again, do you hear me?!"

Her mother turned and walked toward her parents' room to join her father. Before she slammed the door behind her, Lucy caught an excruciating glimpse of her father, a bulky mound filling their bed. They continued to wail and yell from inside about her being dead to them. She heard the word *whore*. She heard "if I ever see the Moore boy again..." and "she's not our daughter anymore." At one point she heard her father say something she couldn't make sense of, something that sounded like "she's probably been making pornography in the streets of Eugene."

Lucy's friend left and found her own way back to Eugene. That night Lucy packed up and left too, desperate to find Robbie and tell him her parents had disowned her.

When she got back to school, she moved out of Alpha Phi, knowing her parents would be further infuriated by the full-year's dues they'd paid for her to live there. She moved in with a complete stranger, the girlfriend of one of Robbie's friends who'd been looking for a short-term apartment mate for the spring quarter. By the time classes started again Lucy had a job waitressing in the restaurant where Robbie worked. As if waking up to her parents' wails anew every day, she searched for a way to come to terms with what it meant to be completely cut off from them.

Lucy

A week or so later, Lucy got a call from Christina. She was so starved for a sign of reassurance in her sister's voice that upon hearing it she immediately began to sob in relief, eager to let go of the pain of knowing she was dead to her parents, if just for a moment, eager for the comfort Christina would surely offer.

"How could you do this to Mom and Dad?" Christina barked. Lucy stood there in that still-unfamiliar kitchen, listening to her sister's punishing words.

"I can't believe I have a *slut* for a little *sister*! Of all the things you've done, Lucy, all the things you've done to hurt Mom and Dad, I never imagined you'd go as far as to make a *whore* of yourself, but apparently that's what you've done. You can be sure Mom and Dad will never forgive you, and believe me, *I'll* never forgive you for the mark you've put on our family name." She hung up.

Slumped on the floor of this stranger's dismal apartment as a local freeway droned past the open window, Lucy tried to grasp that she was dead to her family, the confirmation of the feelings she had tried for so long to resist—of being different, of being looked upon with disapproval. There was no question now that all her efforts to be good and deserving and worthy of love had failed.

But Robbie loved her. They had each other and they had their art. They had Eugene. They had bluegrass music on Sunday mornings, and they had meals with friends. They had the news of Robbie's idol, Eric Clapton, re-emerging from Blind Faith into a new band called Derek and the Dominoes.

They also had live blues. Newly appreciated artists were coming in from around the country giving showcase concerts on college campuses, part of a growing interest in traditional music and the previously undercelebrated lives of blues performers. Robbie and Lucy were regulars at these events. One song in particular that made her feel as if her soul was being ground to dust under the weight of a mountain and then reconstituted into something else. Like the bottom of the world could fall out and somehow there could still be something left to marvel at, to find beauty in.

Willie Mae "Big Mama" Thornton was slated to perform at one of the local concert halls they frequented, and Robbie made sure to get tickets as soon as they were available. Lucy had heard one or two of Thornton's recordings, but she had no idea what it would be like to see her perform in a live concert.

That night the band began quietly in a slow dirge, which grew—without it being clear just how—until the singer stepped out in all her elegance and took her place on the stage. She looked like a magnificently carved statue that swayed, her features perfectly chiseled and at the same time warm, radiant, alive, wrapped in the dull throb of the bass guitar that thickened and shaped the smoky atmosphere around her.

As Thornton began to sing, her voice rose so magically strong and clear that for a time it struck the audience dumb in wonder and awe, while before them she turned raw pain into something powerful and beautiful and triumphant. Her words and voice, despairing over the cruelty of one deeply and irrevocably loved, expressed pain so beautifully wrought that the audience seemed to fall into a state of religious rapture. The song's deepest longings may have been beyond Lucy's reach, though not beyond the inexpressible hurt living in her heart.

Yes, Lucy felt despair and bottomless loss that she didn't know how to live with or how to endure. Blood bonds only intensifying the pain. But she had seen, felt, and heard a transformative power and grace offered up as a gift rising out of someone else's despair, and it felt like golden glitter raining down on her.

Not long after that, she encountered that golden rain again. Another night in a similar venue, she watched as someone guided a frail Son House onto the stage, sat him down, and placed his National steel guitar on his lap. The old man began to pluck, slap, and slide on that guitar, making it yelp and cry, and as he started to sing, his voice rose out of the darkness like a ghost stirred to a restless fury after many lifetimes of torment. The song was a lament about receiving an old-time death letter, then rushing to his beloved's burial, and leaving the scene with a grieving so deep that the spirit was driven right out of him, rendering him unable to pray. He then returned home, overwhelmed by abject loneliness.

As Lucy listened, something deep inside wondered if perhaps he wasn't just singing about loss and a broken heart and having his guts wrenched out of him. Something inside her sensed that the total despair behind his broken spirit could be the very same force from which he drew the power to express the music in his soul, music that not only spoke for his loss but also offered comfort to a bereaved and broken heart like hers. She knew her heart could never be mended, but the ache was known. It had a face, a sound, and someone had turned it into poetry as he cried out for mercy on his soul and wailed his state of aloneness. Lucy wasn't sure what it would mean to say she had music in her soul, but she was able, at least in the moment, to connect with something deeply human—and in that way deeply beautiful—that was wrapped in this artist's voice and words and was too mournful and urgent to ignore.

28

RED GARD

Eugene. 1970—1972

Lucy

LUCY RECONCILED WITH HER PARENTS to some degree by getting engaged to Robbie. By that time, her dreams of living her art had already begun to slip away. She had begun to see herself trapped in a waitress's life, one that held nothing else for her. She had nothing to offer the world any more either, and as far as she could see it, she was doomed to this life she hated, the intense and exhausting drudgery of a job she was ill-suited to do. Her heart was so broken that by the end of her sophomore year she could no longer paint.

During the following academic year, Robbie and Lucy gradually drifted away from student life to embrace a social scene off campus. They concealed from her parents the fact that they were living together. While his world, and by extension hers, centered around new social spheres, they continued to be involved in music, which kept her spirits alive, despite feeling increasingly adrift and disconnected in every other way. As her twenty-first birthday, which was to be her wedding day, approached, she confessed to Robbie's sister that she didn't love him, that they were growing apart, and it felt like maybe she was making a mistake. Lucy anticipated some criticism, but she didn't expect the scolding she got from Marsha.

"What's your problem, Lucy! You've been pining for him for more than four years. He wants you, and now you don't want him? I can't believe what you're saying. How can you think marrying Robbie is a mistake? You can't back out now!"

Admonished by the would-be sister-in-law who turned her misgivings into something mean and shameful, Lucy went ahead with the wedding that summer but failed to rekindle her commitment to school. She dropped out before beginning senior year. Robbie, by now, was long past the idea of graduating and eased out of his college obligations without looking back.

A recession was steadily squeezing out job opportunities in and around Eugene. But some call to secure her own survival drew Lucy back to the world with which she had once been acquainted, and in a desperate move to escape from her hopeless slog waiting tables, she paid a visit to the new mall at Valley River Center, where she filled out an application for a sales clerk position at Meier and Frank, the department store that had chosen her to represent their Hi-Board back in Portland in her senior year of high school.

Although there were no openings for sales clerks, Lucy went back on a weekly basis to update her application. After several weeks of that she realized she needed a different strategy. So one day when she returned to the personnel office to update her paperwork, perhaps emboldened by her discouragement and by memories of past glory, she asked to speak to the personnel director. Lucy must have come across as unusually motivated because the woman at the desk scurried through a door and returned with the director, who invited her in for a brief interview. She told him she'd been coming in every week seeking a chance to demonstrate her abilities as a topnotch sales clerk. She was determined to show them what a dedicated employee she could be.

They hired her that day to work as a *red card*, which meant she had to get up every morning and be on call in case a salesperson called in sick or was otherwise indisposed. She had to be prepared to clerk in any department in the store, whether it was furniture, clothing, shoes, or housewares. If they didn't call her, she made sure to call them, just in case. She was careful neither to make a nuisance of herself nor to let them forget that she was ready to give them everything she had, that she'd be flawless in her dedication.

Lucy worked her way up and got to know people. After securing a permanent sales position she quickly rose to assistant manager. She and the department manager became good friends, and Lucy watched her colleague closely, studying everything she did and how she did it. She adored the work, making creative displays and making the department sparkle. Before she knew it, Sandra got promoted and Lucy became department manager in her place.

Eventually, Lucy was taken under the wing of a woman who initially noticed and appreciated her displays and then recognized her from her Hi-Board days. Barb had worked in the Portland store when Lucy represented them and had since become a kind of visiting display designer, setting up small eclectic boutiques around the store. When she recognized Lucy from the Portland Hi-Board, Barb put her on the spot with an announcement: "My God, people, do you know who this is? Do know who you have working for you? This young lady is a star! Lucy was honored in high school for her fashion sense, her artistic achievements, and her community service, and stood with flying colors on our very own Hi-Board! *Seventeen* even did a full feature on her, for God's sake! I'm saying it loud and clear, people: as long as I'm here she must be assigned to work with me."

So Barb, with her big personality, and Lucy, with her talent at turning clothing displays into mini-dramas, became something of a team. They hunted through the store, collecting furniture and even antiques from the furniture department to use as props in their boutiques. Lucy found herself doing a job that tapped into and rekindled her creative spirit and felt for the first time a glow of professional satisfaction and recognition. Seeing Barb float like a goddess through a department with her gossamer layers of clothes streaming around her as if she were a heraldic angel gave Lucy a sense of belonging. Following her keen artful eye, Barb affirmed Lucy's place in an artful world. But at the same time Robbie and Lucy were drifting more and more into separate spaces as the color and life gradually blanched from what remained of the one they still inhabited together.

Lucy was sent to management training and began commuting to Portland once a week as a step on the path toward upper-level management.

Corporate in Portland had noticed her, and after completing the four-month training program she was offered an assistant buying position. But the job was in Portland, and Lucy had no desire to leave Eugene. Hoping to keep her, the Eugene store offered her the job she had been dreaming about for a long time, one she had assumed would be years down the road: divisional vice president.

But Robbie insisted that they move to Portland. Lucy didn't know until they were further along in their breakup that this move was his effort to escape, to avoid the temptation of being drawn into a relationship with another woman he had begun to feel attracted to in Eugene. At the time, Lucy heard the message about a fresh start and wanted to believe that going to Portland would be good for their marriage, give it a boost. Later, when he filled in the details, she understood his regret over leaving someone he had begun to care for in an effort to make their doomed marriage work.

They moved to Portland, as he wished, and almost immediately the new job made her miserable. Lucy was assistant buyer in the menswear department during the era of the infamous leisure suit. At the time they were buying two-piece turquoise and plum colored polyester suits, and she was responsible for endless reams of paperwork. Where she had once been designing fabulous displays, she now processed all the returns to manufacturers. She never would have lasted if she hadn't struck up such a good relationship with her boss, a man who was convinced that men would never wear ties again and certainly never wear traditional suits again. Despite his flawed predictions, Mr. Ellis, the store's menswear buyer, was kind, and they worked exceptionally well together.

Lucy was drawn to the young men's department because she understood why it wasn't doing well. She identified with the customers the department was trying to reach and grasped their need for completely new products. Mr. Ellis encouraged her to pursue her passion. He gave her room to dream out loud, and in the process, to help him envision what a menswear department could be. In this way they began to shape a new image.

Mr. Ellis encouraged Lucy to write up her ideas into a detailed proposal. She put her heart into creating a vision for young men's apparel and

The next night Lucy's roommates went out to pick up men and never returned. She was left alone, numb and confused, wondering if there was anything left for Robbie and her to save. She returned home and left Robbie, without ceremony or apology, devastated only about leaving their two cats, an act which she regretted for years. But the pain of knowing she was abandoning Flo and Eddie didn't hold her back because she was done, empty. She had given up, with no idea how to fight the unremitting retreat of affection. She had completely dissociated.

In leaving Eugene, Robbie and Lucy had lost the spirit of song and community that she had relied upon to fill the space between them and to sustain the belief that they had a life together. Her parents had restored her bitterly lost seat at the family table, which even in the best of times came grudgingly; but she lost her last thread of respect for Robbie when he left his art entirely to work in a Portland guitar factory. She lost respect for herself, too, in leaving her own, until she happened upon a remnant of her creative spirit and reflexively clung to it like a ragged piece of driftwood carrying her down a roiling stream, presumably toward some quiet bank that she could not yet see, but where she might come to shore and rest.

PART FOUR

29

EARTH

Utah, 2015

Kate

THIS EARLY WINTER TRIP WAS partly about my hopes of stirring stubbornly elusive memories into Lucy's consciousness of a disastrous time in Utah over a decade earlier. It was partly about seeing firsthand the places Lucy had lived and worked, where her life with Sam had taken its most baffling and troubling twists and turns, and partly about the two of us venturing out on a brief but meaningful side journey together. Surely there was more to learn about lingering ghosts Lucy hadn't fully reckoned with, memories that had become less and less accessible, choices she had yet to fully reflect on.

I'd reserved a three-night stay at an inn just on the edge of Arena Roja Arts Village. We walked around admiring the design of the community— its dwellings and commercial plaza—all of which had been the brainchild of the developer who had created this place and who had once actively supported Lucy's ambitions as a teacher and local artist. We browsed the pottery, jewelry, sculpture, and paintings displayed in its small handful of shops and galleries, one of which had represented Lucy's paintings when she lived nearby. Another, it turned out, had been her teaching studio for several years. We drove by Lucy's old house in a now-crowded Fort Lyell development where she'd lived with Sam. We explored some ancient sites that she knew intimately and wandered through her most personal haunts, some of the nearby state park's least traveled paths. On this, our last full day in Utah, we had decided to hike up to one more ancient site that held a special connection to Lucy's past.

"You probably don't remember, but you mentioned finding a perfect spearhead when Will and I met you in your gallery that first day. You said you just reached down into a crevice or something and picked it up as if it were calling out for you to find it."

"I don't remember us talking about that, but yes, that is exactly what happened. It was a very spiritual moment for me, and it happened at the site we're going to right now, in fact. Did I also tell you that at the time I felt that the spearhead, which was completely transparent with a single green vein running lengthwise through the middle, was too special to leave the mesa, so I tucked it under a rock, thinking that one day I might come back to have another look at it?"

"No! Do you think you could find it again? Could it possibly still be there after—how many years? Fifteen?" I nearly forgot my task of steadying my injured friend. Despite Lucy's protests, I had been dutifully following directly behind, buttressed to her canvas daypack as we climbed a rocky trail that traversed the side of the small mesa Lucy had managed to locate from remnants of memory along an otherwise unremarkable road. Her seemingly perfect mental map belied her general difficulty recalling facts. This route, leading back toward Las Vegas, she said, was the one she and Sam had always preferred for the scenery.

We talked about heading back out on this old highway the next morning, through a wild promised land of Joshua trees, on our return to the airport. The idea of seeing a Joshua tree for the first time aroused my excitement, but the prospect of finding that piece of stone stirred both the young and the old parts of my soul to tingling as I minded my footing and tried to gauge Lucy's sense of balance from the rear flank.

On our way into Utah three days earlier, we had taken the main highway almost straight to Fort Lyell, leaving Vegas's tangle of neon just as dusk had begun to draw out the Strip's lurid brightness, and following the interstate as it cut northeast into moonless desert. Eventually I-15 channeled through canyons all but invisible in the blackness, but Lucy faithfully pointed each one out as if navigating a busy street for someone lacking the gift of sight. As I drove along the dark interstate, I struggled to reconcile this uncanny sense of spatial memory so incongruent with Lucy's relationship to the details of her past.

Having set out on this final trek, we poked carefully along the uneven path, navigating the gritty spaces between loose pieces of sandstone. Were Lucy's injured and unsteady knee to buckle, I, the smaller of us, would have been foolhardy even to pretend I could break the fall.

The incline picked up, and with some prodding Lucy reluctantly accepted one of the retractable ski poles I'd packed along. Over the previous two days I'd succeeded—by insisting that I'd brought the poles along for both of us—in coaxing Lucy to use one, but then only in the steeper spots. And now, intoxicated equally by the idea that we might find the magnificent stone treasure and by the chance to explore another unmarked and unexcavated site, I was determined not to let Lucy's torn meniscus stop us. I knew well enough my friend's capacity to ignore her body's warning signs, the most likely reason for the injury in the first place, I mused, and gently kept the watchful pressure on. We managed to reach the top with just one ungainly stumble and one wrenched ankle between us.

We had spent the past two days reverently toeing potsherds and glassy stone flecks at other remote sites, following sun glints for treasures in the hard-packed earth, stooping and shuffling along, lost to body and time, until eventually we wound our way back in each other's direction. Only when we paused did we feel the dry bite of mid-December wind, take stock, and renew our mutual astonishment at having made this pilgrimage to the waypoints Lucy had invested with such deep emotional and spiritual meaning. Places where her own history was bound up with the remnants of ancient people and their art. Places that might offer a meaningful glimpse of multiple paths intersecting, mine included.

One of the sites had fairly recently been protected as a cultural heritage site for its magnificent cliff-top petroglyphs and remnants of ancient pit houses that had been mostly left as they had been for centuries. Lucy encouraged me to stand in a pair of foot-shaped marks carved into a smooth stone platform overlooking the steep cliff across the valley below and the ragged black mouth of a gorge, and out over the rise of silver-ribboned mountains to the west. We studied each piece of rock art, our cameras playing with our own crisp shadows that fell across the strange semi-human stick figures, delicately formed animals, inscrutable geometric forms, and perfect spirals.

The other site Lucy found was a sandy wash at the base of a box canyon, small and intimate enough, I thought, to pass itself off as a private sanctuary in a red rock resort. Lucy identified several massive figures—her "Venus forms," she called them—cut by wind and water into the streaked and striated canyon walls. This had, in fact, been her sanctuary in years past. She had climbed into its clefts, wailed at the sky, meditated in its soft sandy bed, and learned a form of forgiveness here, company to the secrets of the people who had walked here and disappeared a thousand years ago. Having been stripped and flayed by life, she was partly reconstituted here.

That previous evening, we had watched those figures' languid outlines deepen and stretch, warping with the fiery last rays of sun that reached all the way to the back of the canyon and finally gilded the rim before the shadow of Mad Mountain grayed it all out. It was Lucy who urged us back down the dry wash and reluctantly out of our dusk-time reverie, as easterly clouds gathered, threatening a storm that rumbled softly but never arrived.

This final day, as we stood on the flat spread of the small, almost barren mesa, Lucy speculated that this site was probably inhabited by a less settled group than the cliff-top site we had explored the previous day. The larger and more established community had grown crops along the river valley below and had made use of a natural trap, a well-placed slot between massive stones narrow enough to be completely invisible from the level plain leading up to it but sheer and deep enough to be inescapable once an animal had been driven in. The image of a speared antelope, somehow more lovely than gruesome, marked the entry point of the stone pit, confirming its purpose and honoring its victims. In contrast, this last day's site broadcasted a quiet bleakness, a wind-burnt winter colorlessness. Lucy pointed out an area on the far side of the trail that she believed to be a burial ground. The tone was palpably different here. To me, the energy of this place came across as subdued but very much alive, dark, and terribly sad. It spoke of something beyond rage that I lacked the scope to gauge or fully grasp.

We crossed the top of the mesa to a cluster of petroglyphs carved into boulders tucked along its southern edge that were similar in style to the designs we had viewed the day before. Though no less dramatic, these appeared somewhat more sheltered among the rocks and conveyed a slightly more muted character, almost as if their purpose, whatever it was, involved a smaller audience or more intimate ceremonies.

Lucy suggested that this smaller site might have served as some kind of specially dedicated tool-making area. We found plenty of evidence across the surface of the mesa: stone benches surrounded by flakes and tool fragments, a number of anvil-like rocks, as well as oblong mallet-like stones. I walked around with what I believed to be a beautifully weighted hammer stone resting comfortably in my hand until I finally lost track of where I'd lain it down among all the gray-tone remnants of ancient handiwork at my feet. We came across small collections along the tops of flat stones, loose mosaics of weathered potsherds and pieces of axe heads arranged by contemporary hands, as if to say, "We found these treasures and respectfully leave them for future visitors to marvel at." Somewhere along the way, Lucy picked up a delicately shaped spear point, a fragment of an exquisitely long tapered tool knapped from translucent yellow stone. But it too disappeared somewhere along the trail, refusing to be carried off, slipping back into the protective camouflage of the earth.

We eventually worked our way to the north end of the mesa, which broke into a wide, sharply sloping field of rocks and boulders that eventually coalesced into a steep escarpment overlooking the trail that had brought us to the top. Somewhere around there, Lucy gestured with a ski pole leveled across the rock field, was where she'd hidden the spearhead.

"I placed it as far back as I could in the hollow space underneath a rock that stuck out horizontally."

"Do you remember how large or small that particular rock was or any marks or landmarks that might have distinguished it from the others?" I asked, quieting any doubt that might threaten to creep in as I waited for direction or even the faintest gleam of my own intuition about where the artifact might be. Rather than dwell on the size of the rock field or its utter lack of distinguishing features, I headed in, navigating around tangles of partially exposed sage roots and faded shrubs twisted by the weather on the battered northern edge of the plateau. Already a little fatigued and beginning to chill, I knew we still had to work our way back down that bedeviling trail, which was already slipping into shadow.

Our three days of trekking and our rough final climb had brought into focus how unreliable Lucy's judgment about her own stability could be. Still, the rock field posed a formidable enough obstacle to dispel her ambitions of joining me in the hunt for the spearhead. She hung back as I poked my way along, stopping every few steps to dig around in the soil, heavy and damp from holding onto the icy dregs of a recent snowfall. Nose to the ground, I could see that dirt had been washing and shifting around over years of sudden rains, deep freezes, intermittent snows, and constant wind, filling one swale here and creating another there. Gravity had conspired against me too, drawing anything without roots toward lower ground.

I wondered what the chances were of a rattlesnake venturing out to warm itself in the rocks on a wintertime afternoon and how much dirt might migrate over fifteen years' worth of desert frosts and thaws. I called back up the slope for direction and opted for digging with a stick rather than poking my hands into the dark spaces under whichever boulders seemed to protrude in the way Lucy had suggested. I loosened and scraped first and then reached in with my hand, hoping to divine something hard and crystalline and sacred. All around me the rocks and crevasses looked and felt the same. Still, I approached each one with a small burst of new hope.

Then I recognized the scrapings around rocks I'd already worked on. No harm in trying again, I thought, fighting a sense of futility that had begun to creep in. Retreating into my own past, I recalled a particularly inviting early summer morning when I'd led my five-year-old brother into the woods behind our house, intending to retrace my steps to an old abandoned chicken coop I'd discovered during one of my previous wilderness forays. I'd stumbled upon it as I wandered along chewing on wild onions and collecting sticky sprigs of pink laced mountain laurel. Going on seven, I was old enough to understand that the relic structure that had stopped me in my tracks had a story to tell. What was an old chicken coop doing in the middle of the woods? I had no way of knowing these woods had once been fields, barnyards, and cow pastures whose stones had been laid by farmers in low walls following the rise and fall of the land, now crisscrossing even the deepest parts of this second growth forest and emerging somewhere on the other side, most likely in someone else's back yard.

We entered the woods at the edge of the old apple orchard that bordered the rented property we lived on. The realization that we were lost came when I discovered that we'd been wandering in circles for some time. After an hour or two of calling for help, our small, frightened voices were finally heard by a distant neighbor, a man I'd never ventured far enough from home to know about before. But I recognized him as the father of one of my classmates. Though I didn't know the boy well and don't even remember his name, I immediately recognized his face in the man's features. The man, by some mysterious grown up powers, recognized our name and knew where we lived.

As I tried to reorient myself among the mesa rocks, I remembered the feeling of awkward relief in being found, the kindness in the striking aqua blue eyes of the man who consoled us, gently collected us, and drove us home. I remembered sitting in his car watching the woods go by, astonished at how suddenly Kenny and I had returned to the world I knew and that it was just a few steps from the one I didn't.

I continued working my way down the rock field, listening hard and scraping earnestly with my stick, but no messages or inklings from within, from Lucy, or from the stones came to guide me in one direction or another. My thoughts shifted to Kenny's suicide the previous year. I saw his own seven-year-old son's face, so startlingly like his own at that age, staring back at me as if part of a hall of mirrors trick. I pushed the image down and dug harder, refusing to yield to a creeping sense of futility and loss.

"You're never going to find it!" Lucy called down from the plateau, her lameness visible in her tripod stance, the weak knee over-extended, backpack askew, tendrils worked free from her silvering braid alive in the wind.

Kate

I dismissed her jarring shift of allegiances. "I'll just try over here," I called back, returning to my task, tending the hope that the prize was near, that there was still a chance my stick would pop it free from the earth and I would drop it like a diamond into Lucy's hand.

"It's impossible! You're not going to find it down there!" Lucy called.

I wanted to shout *I can't believe you're giving up! Open up your spirit channels and help me, for God's sake!* but instead just continued down a few more steps toward the ledge. "Do you remember how far down you might have gone or how far in along the edge? I'm kind of in the dark here."

"Just come back up. It's gone. We're not going to find it."

I stood up and looked out over the expanse of mute gray shoulders, along the bleak escarpment and back up to where I'd started. All those grim backs turned stubbornly toward me. The earth was silent, hopelessly silent, dark in every direction. The sun was gone. I had to get Lucy down the trail and back to the car.

30

WILDERNESS

Utah, 1998

Lucy

WINDWORN RED ROCKS, CATHEDRALS OF Navajo sandstone weathered into roundness, crumbling black lava flows, bleached white canyons, one-time oceans of blowing sand turned to elephant skin hills. Lucy had less than a week to get her bearings in a space that felt endless and empty at first. So much sky to reckon with. Darkness deeper than she had ever known in the Northwest. In barely two days she would be entirely alone in this new bleakness, in the absolute silence that made the Seattle green belt seem like the interstate—except for the soft murmurings and padded landings of cats or the geriatric scamper-dance of Mackenzie across the polished wood floor.

Eight days on and six days off. Sam would be gone for week-long stretches, regular ones, completely offline in a different wilderness, perhaps greener, three hours north, in his new job at one of the therapeutic wilderness programs for at-risk youth that were popping up around the state. Sam and Lucy had talked it through. It made perfect sense that he wanted to give something back after his own troubled son Kevin had been turned around in his brief time at a therapeutic boarding school.

Lucy could communicate with her Seattle gallery long distance and would paint straight through her alone days. That way they could spend his off days together. She'd use part of that time taking care of bills and book-keeping while he worked with near-religious devotion on his four-wheeled baby out in the garage, which served as a kind of office that he had even fit out with a desk.

Sam's cars, as well as his troubled son, could have easily broken them apart in the first year they were together. Despite Lucy's absolute commitment to her painting life and her certainty about never marrying again after Robbie, and then Terry, that year had become their engagement period. But she'd been steadfast and supportive and, when necessary, jumped in and set conditions on which going ahead with the marriage would stand. She knew Sam's early indiscretions had only arisen from his passion for the Mustang, the allure of rebuilding and fine tuning that machine to perfection, restoring the power behind a supremely elegant body. That was the irresistible part for him, to the extent that sometimes he seemed to prefer time in the garage to intimacy with her.

They had begun talking about his low testosterone by their second year together and had even seen a doctor who suggested injections that Sam found impossible to endure. Lucy quietly grieved their diminishing sex life, finding it especially painful to watch movies where couples found their way to love. Those exquisite revelatory kisses just made her cry for the sting of going without one for so long now. But she convinced herself that they had plenty else to keep their relationship alive and fulfilling. They were best friends.

For Lucy, though, the early days of their engagement had been unsettling in their own way. She loathed the act of pressing Sam—or anyone for that matter—more than she loathed the necessity of pressing, but she felt there was no choice but to put him on the spot after bill collectors began leaving messages for him on the answering machine and she caught him ignoring their calls. Once confronted, he admitted that he'd concealed a considerable amount of debt from her. She was confident that they could put that behind them well enough, approaching the situation with sober reasoning and something that felt like tough love. Still, the engagement would be off until and unless he dealt with his debt.

Without hesitation Sam sold his house, freeing up about $65,000 to put toward the amount he owed and displacing an ex-girlfriend who'd been living in his basement for a year or more. Lucy accepted his apologies for failing to tell her about the debt, and she would have even if he had delivered them with far less tenderness. And she managed to neutralize in her own mind any concern she may have harbored about her husband-to-be's lingering attachment—if that's what it was—to his old girlfriend Patrice. He was terribly generous and something of a pushover, she thought, and she loved that about him. She couldn't find a way to criticize someone who accepted some discomfort or inconvenience in the process of helping someone else.

Lucy paid off the remaining ten grand, and they agreed that Sam would move in with her. She found ways, aided by his disarming entreaties, to shore up her trust. Any doubts she may have had about his fiscal lapses were relieved in their clean-enough resolution, which they both welcomed, and in the excitement around carrying on with their engagement plans, Lucy and this man who had so assiduously gone about courting her, accepting her, adoring her, and making her laugh and feel supported in ways no one else had ever tried. She quickly came to feel that she had never trusted anyone as completely as she had come to trust Sam.

She listened with compassion and a few pricks of jealousy to the story he told about living with Patrice and her nine-year-old daughter, how devoted he'd been to the two of them, so grateful to be part of such a perfect little family, how he thought the world of Lydia Suzanne, loving her as his own, easing effortlessly into a fatherly role, and happily watching Lydie Sue and six-year-old Kevin take to each other like brother and sister. It was easy enough for Lucy to love vicariously the memories of Sam regaining his own footing while helping to stabilize a young family and to wonder at the glimpses of Kevin as the agreeable little boy he'd been before morphing into a destructive teen charging through the first two years of their lives together and railing ferociously at the world. These memories helped shape the picture that emerged in the day-to-day trials Lucy and Sam had borne together of a man committed to being a loving and supportive father, even under the most trying circumstances.

The impulse buying—most of all Sam's secrecy about it—was a tougher problem to manage, but certainly a challenge Lucy could rise to. She had become quite a good business woman, after all. Now, as they began planning ahead with two moves—the first to her rented house and then, hopefully, two years on, to somewhere in the country—Sam shared with Lucy his dream of owning a vintage Mustang.

"Wouldn't it make sense to sell your Mercedes first?" Lucy suggested. "It feels like at this moment, while we're trying to sell my house and consolidate, the practical thing would be to sell your working car before buying another, don't you think?"

"You're right, Luce, but I'm thinking that if we started shopping for that dream car while we're moving along with the sale of the Seola house, it would give me something to chew on, you know? I'd like to have a new project in place by the time we settle into the new neighborhood, so I can start off there with an engine waiting for me to fix it up, something to structure my weekends and help me settle in after all that time I spend in motion driving the rig. Course, I know you'll be there for me to come home to, but you know me," he said, putting his arm around her waist and squeezing firmly, "can't sit still, always looking for a new conquest of one sort or another."

As he talked, Sam's confidence in this vision of things grew: "We could make it a team project. With your talent for finding the right deal and mine for talking my way to an even better one, I'm sure we could find that perfect muscle car and line things up to your satisfaction so we—or more likely *you*—could choose which deal to wrap up when."

"I wouldn't mind shopping around with you," Lucy added, imagining the joy it would give him and the hopefulness of having something new to share with him that would occupy his downtime, tap into his passion, satisfy his creativity, and counter his restlessness. They were looking ahead to so many changes, so many unknowns. This would ground him as they moved into new territory together.

Lucy had time to ease into the idea of leaving Seattle. Leaving Kevin, who looked like he might—if he stayed on track—actually graduate from high school on time, after two years of upheaval that finally—almost puzzlingly—seemed to be subsiding. They were both counting on him finally figuring out how to live in his own skin, and he seemed, at the moment, to be doing just that.

Over the coming months Sam and Lucy went back to the same therapeutic program catalog that their family therapist had recommended as the ultimate sourcebook when they were looking for a program for Kevin. He had spent the better part of a year in a therapeutic boarding school and had since gotten into an alternative high school where he seemed to be thriving. Sam said he was intrigued by the idea of working at one of those intensive wilderness programs for at-risk youth, helping troubled kids get to the heart of their issues without the comforts or the dysfunctions of home, without the distractions and interference that family and friends presented. The more he read, the more he thought he could make a difference to some of those kids if he could work with them in that kind of *pure* environment. After all, he'd been a swim coach and loved working kids through the paces in order to build strength and character, to discover and develop their abilities, to work as a team.

But during this time Sam's income had steadily dwindled. A decade before, he'd been able to take advantage of a long standoff between the local trucking and rail workers unions, a dispute that played a role in preventing a rail extension from being built to the Seattle piers. The ongoing battle meant that he could work fairly lucratively as an independent contractor driving containers between the piers and the rail yard. He owned his own truck, had a license for hazardous materials, and could carry just about anything. But eventually a new spur went up, bringing in a wave of other trucks, and the competition had steadily brought the rates down so low that Sam had to work longer and longer hours to bring in any kind of sustainable income. In addition, his rig was badly in need of repair. Lucy knew what it would cost to fix his truck or to buy a new one. She came upon him one evening, sitting in the living room studying several trucking magazines, which lay open around him on the couch.

"You know, hon, the income's getting so low, and you're exhausted all the time," she began. "And it's going to cost us a fortune to replace that truck. You've been saying that you'd love to work at a program like the one that got Kevin back on track. Maybe it's time to just let the truck go and try to reach for this dream you've had."

Sam looked up, cheered by her suggestion, and ran with it: "Maybe we should plan a completely new start somewhere, now that Kevin's coming around."

Lucy

He went ahead and applied to a few programs over the summer and got invited to spend a week at two of them, both of which happened to be in Utah. They visited and investigated a brand new housing development in the shadow of Mad Mountain, with only two other completed homes on it. Soon Sam had two job offers and chose the Hawk Ridge Wilderness Program in central Utah, a three-hour drive away. Though they had yet to buy a house, they prepared to put the Dakota Street house on the market.

Lucy began to embrace the idea of leaving the Northwest for the first time in her life, leaving familiar streets and people and sounds and her freshly leased life for a sparsely populated and fairly wild place. At the same time, she would be giving up ready access to the one relatively wild place she had known and loved, despite her inability to spend even a single night there alone. Regular Saturday getaways at the Vashon cabin would be gone for the foreseeable future, the mossy evergreen hills and boggy marshes of Puget Sound giving way to an almost inscrutable earthscape that for eons had scarcely known a green thing. She would embrace that land, adapt to it, learn to understand it, trading the ghosts that had unfailingly hounded her off the island on the last Saturday night ferry for ancient totems etched onto patinated rock faces and the primeval spirits of petrified trees cast in chunks of marbled stone that occasionally broke the surface of a long-quieted red-sand sea.

Kate

"Just do your best to recall whatever you can of those experiences, early on—anything that comes to mind—when you were in the process of learning more about who Sam was, even unwelcome things, red flags, questions from which you may or may not have drawn any conclusions at the time."

Lucy was visibly tired. She'd developed a bad case of shingles and had been disabled by months of chronic neuropathic pain. I'd watched helplessly from afar as the virus had outstripped her already compromised immune system, exerting its capacity to live with her indefinitely in a semi-active state, stealing her drive to create, and consigning her to a life-altering reliance on opioids in order to function at all.

Seeing Lucy so drawn, I was tempted to retreat, to follow the urge to shrink from the added pain that difficult recollections would cause. At the same time, I also saw her dig in, almost obstinately, to respond to my opening with a rally of confidence. I met the brave face of her effort with guarded hope, given her condition and my rolling struggle to point her back toward the details of her life with Sam. Despite my determination, those particulars seemed to resist our shared attention and scrutiny, as they tended to dodge hers.

I had, over time, learned to treat Lucy's certainties with some skepticism, disheartened when the packaging didn't always ensure intact contents. Nonetheless, we had to work with memories in whatever form they presented themselves. If they came with a warning label, it might have read something like this: *A certain amount of settling in the aftermath of life's nastiest ordeals may cause variations in size, shape, and quality*. I was also learning to file thoughts like that in a safe place, get out of Lucy's way, and just listen. She gathered herself around the prompt and took us back, once again, fifteen or so years.

Kate

"From the earliest days of our relationship, Sam spent Saturday mornings playing pick-up basketball with a group of friends. These guys had been playing on Saturdays for something like twenty years in the court of a local YMCA and had become friends around the weekend routine. Sam loved that.

"We were in the process of selling what I'd come to call my Seola house. Our plan was to sell the house we'd been living in down by the bay and move into the other house I owned, the one on Dakota Street, which I'd rented out for the past ten years. We would live in the Dakota house for two years to avoid capital gains taxes and then sell it and move out of Seattle altogether. We were just becoming confident enough by then to imagine Kevin graduating from high school and not needing Sam as much as he had over the couple of years we'd been together. We were beginning to imagine ourselves, two years on, venturing out of the comfort zone of Seattle and exploring the idea of a quieter life in a quieter place, though at the time we had no idea where that would be. It all seemed pretty remote, but our hopes were real, and we'd begun to allow them to grow.

"That particular Saturday morning, while Sam was at the gym, I realized that some paperwork I was preparing, a document related to the closing on the house, required both of our signatures. It was something relatively urgent that I had to bring to the bank before it closed at noon. So I got in the car, drove down to the gym, and walked into the court looking for Sam. The guys were familiar enough with me to know who I was there for. It hadn't registered with me yet that I hadn't seen Sam's car in the parking lot.

"I said hello and asked for him. After an uncomfortable moment of hesitation, one of his friends volunteered the truth. 'He's not here. Hasn't been here for months.'

"I have no memory of whether or not I responded or asked if they knew where he was or just turned and walked out. But I remember groping my way back to the car, blind with confusion and panic, my sense of trust shaken from its footing. I was sobbing uncontrollably but managed by some miracle to maneuver the car in the direction of home and get there safely.

"Several hours later, Sam arrived, walked in casually, and stopped short when he saw me.

"'Hon? …What's wrong?'

"'Where've you been?' I asked, frightened by the unfamiliar flatness of my own voice and his initial breeziness.

"Without bothering to find out what I did or didn't know, he said, 'I was afraid you would find out. …Luce, I— I bought a car.'

"So it wasn't a woman. It was a car. A '60s vintage Mustang. He'd been keeping it hidden in a storage unit and going there every Saturday to work on it. It wasn't a woman! Part of me was so relieved the rest almost didn't matter. My fear of being abandoned for someone else had been completely unfounded.

"But Sam's betrayal was deeper than just buying a car and hiding it from me. A couple of months earlier, when he'd begun talking about the idea of buying and restoring a classic Mustang, we'd discussed the timing and acknowledged the fact that we were in the midst of the stressful process of selling my home and moving. We agreed—and I think I was the one who said it—that the best thing would be to find a buyer for his old Mercedes before taking on a big expensive restoration. A buyer turned up not too long afterward, and we began looking at Mustangs in earnest. We made it a regular activity, a project, going out a few nights a week to pursue offers and check out the cars that looked promising. We found a beauty and bought it.

"But what came to light that Saturday was that Sam had *already* bought his dream car—before we'd found that buyer, and apparently even before the conversation when he first mentioned his initial desire and we agreed to go car shopping. He'd bought a car, hidden it, and then proceeded with the plan we had agreed to.

"And now, astonishingly, we had *two* Mustangs. I was shocked and bewildered, completely blindsided. Of course Sam apologized, saying he was sorry and 'I know I should have told you. I know it was wrong.'

"I insisted that he sell one of the cars; he would have to choose one to get rid of. We couldn't afford to own both of them. I said, 'Look, I don't want to be your mother. I can't be the mom to your bad boy.' I didn't want to be a controlling bitch, but I was as scared as I was confused. I couldn't stand by while he continued spending money we didn't have. Someone had to tell him to stop, and it had to be me, though I felt absolutely hateful doing it.

"Our family therapist Sara, who had helped us with Kevin during our ordeal with him, said it directly: 'Apparently Sam has serious man issues that for whatever reason he hasn't shared with either of us.' She recommended a men's group run by someone she knew and trusted, but Sam never attended.

"He did sell one of the cars, but he continued pouring money into the other, buying accessories and special parts, and I continued to come at him with what was starting to feel like nagging. 'Sam, we have a limited budget. We can't do this right now. It would be fine to set money aside for particular things you want to buy, but we don't have the money to buy all these things out of hand. We've already been through this, and you promised to be more responsible. We're supposed to be talking to each other.' As horrifying as it was to realize it, I saw and heard myself becoming my mother. Meanwhile, Sam simply got a credit card and continued to put charges on it.

"I must have been in an especially weak moment when I called Mom and told her about the predicament. I should have known better than to reach out to her when I needed support, but I didn't know what to do. Her response caught me off guard.

"'Years ago,' she said, 'I took $200 out of our savings account to help one of my sisters when she was in a terrible bind. I knew it was wrong, but I didn't tell your father, and he was furious when he found out. I apologized, and sure enough the whole thing blew over and all was forgiven. I hope you can find it in your heart to forgive Sam.'

"Shaped by our uncomfortable history, my expectations were limited. All I wanted was for her to tell me it would all be okay. I didn't need her to point out that if not for my behavior, perhaps he wouldn't have been driven into secrecy in the first place. As it was, I had more than enough scorn for myself. And I realized that urging me to get over Sam's indiscretion was the best Mom could do."

31

SHADOWS

Utah. 2002

Lucy

THE LIGHTS OF THE OTHER houses in the development-to-be were visible in the distance, steady, alive with a sense more than a sound of the thin buzz of current, reminding Lucy of the presence of the two other families who had moved in just before she and Sam arrived in Fort Lyell. It took a while, but eventually she associated the small shapes of house light with the two little girls who lived in one of the newly built homes, with quiet sounds, pulled from memory, of dishes being stowed after dinner or children getting ready for bed.

The darkness of unbroken empty space—except for those small lights and for stars layered and folded in vast fields and reefs deeper than the limits of her imagination—made her more self-conscious than streetfuls of city lights ever had. The desert didn't frighten her, but it was still foreign—or, more precisely, she was, after several months, not yet part of it. Its emptiness—what felt like emptiness anyway—still unsettled her at night. All that unfilled space pressed her to close the curtains, to shut even those familiar beacons out, pull the bedcovers up extra tight, and sink down into them. That first summer a string of wildfires had spread up the back side of Mad Mountain. For two nights she watched, mesmerized, across the perfect blackness and up high, jarringly far above where anything earthbound should have been, to the ridge of flames blooming in the hot night wind and raking at the heavens.

Staying busy. Keeping up a schedule. Lucy had initially set up her painting days following the five-day workweek that had structured her time before leaving her corporate life, and from the beginning of her return to painting she applied the same framework to her artist's life. Back in Seattle she had established strict rules for herself in her relearning phase: painting all day with breaks for lunch, dinner, and a workout on her gym equipment while dinner simmered or baked. No television until Friday nights, when she treated herself to a back-to-back screening of the shows she had recorded during the week.

In Utah the rhythm of the household was driven by Sam's schedule, so Lucy adopted an entirely new structure, painting straight through the eight days he was away and saving all her off days for when he was home so they could hike, explore, and relax together. She organized that time carefully, reserving just enough space on his six home days for business-related tasks and bills, which she did while he busied himself in the garage.

Though their habits seemed to settle into place fairly easily, Mackenzie's did not. Within the first two months after their move, the shepherd's behavior took a strange and erratic turn. Something seemed to be unnerving her, driving her into wild-eyed and inconsolable outbursts of barking and frantic scratching at the door, panicked behavior she had never exhibited in Seattle or even on Vashon Island. Mackenzie had moved with Lucy three times over the past few years and had adjusted surprisingly well. She had bravely crisscrossed Puget Sound on the Vashon Island ferry as well as ferries to several of the more northerly San Juan Islands, and she seemed oblivious to the ghost-fears that prevented Lucy from spending the night in the cabin alone. Lucy could have understood if Mac was spooked by the yips and whines of coyotes at night, but the bouts of anxiety came during the day too.

At first Lucy assumed the dog's distress arose from missing Sam. But as the pattern developed, it got even worse when he was there, despite the long walks the three of them took across the dry flatlands skirting the monstrous boulders that weather and gravity had brought down around the base of the red cliffs, walks Lucy and Mackenzie frequently repeated together when Sam was up north. The vet prescribed medication, but it had little effect.

The fact was, Lucy had been feeling an odd but persistent discomfort as the months of that first fall to spring crept along to the far side of summer. The heat had been relentless, so intense that on one afternoon that reached 127 degrees, Lucy found the core of her car's steering wheel melted into putty. She failed to identify a specific source, something she could point to as evidence that Sam was acting strangely, not himself. She tried to dismiss a nagging sense that he seemed to radiate a different energy, definitely, inexplicably sexual, but somehow not meant for her.

She fought them off, but thoughts of the possibility of an affair began to intrude and became so persistent that she finally came out and asked him directly if he was seeing someone up in Barnes, making sure in the process of admitting her suspicions to remind him how completely she trusted him. They had already dredged and come to terms over those old lapses and his bizarre efforts to conceal them. At least Sam always owned up, asked for forgiveness, reassured her. Even though new secrets might come to light, Lucy accepted his promises to do better, held onto faith that he would. And she believed him when he insisted he wasn't having an affair. Still, she couldn't shake the feeling that he was wearing some kind of invisible second skin, something not quite palpable and not quite him. Something strange and odorless and toxic that trailed in with him on his returns from Barnes.

Preparing to launch into a new painting, Lucy had ordered a set of new paintbrushes that had arrived several days earlier. They weren't the quality she had expected. In fact, she decided immediately that they were flat-out unusable. She'd have to return them, but like all transactions labeled business, this one would wait until Sam got home. One more day. She could keep her momentum going with her worn-out brushes until then. But something called her loudly to the brushes, not an inner voice exactly, but a persistent, almost urgent feeling that she absolutely must take care of them. Now.

Deal with the brushes.

That's business. He'll be home tomorrow.

Deal with the brushes.

But it's a painting day.

Deal with the brushes!

Where had she left the catalogue from the art supply store? They kept the last two- or three-months' worth of paper and glass in the garage, intending to take it out to the recycling center on the edge of town. It was a chore that they'd put off with the searing heat, not wanting to waste an entire morning loading up the car and dragging all the way out there, just to render themselves useless and prostrate for the rest of the day. There was plenty of space in the garage, and the storage containers didn't get in Sam's way while he worked, so they could ignore it until the weather grew a little more bearable.

Lucy walked through the kitchen, out to the garage, and over to the far side of Sam's desk. She took a handful of magazines off the top of a stack piled in a blue plastic bin and began thumbing through them. This didn't make sense: a *Victoria's Secret* catalogue? *Victoria's Secret* wasn't Lucy's style. The catalog was addressed to Sam A. Yaeger at a post office box in Barnes. The order form had been torn out. He'd placed an order.

But why was he hiding this? They had talked about this sort of thing a couple of times before, back in Seattle, when once or twice other lingerie magazines had turned up. At the time, Lucy had been very clear: we all have our private issues, and even spouses should have their privacy, she maintained. She assured him she was comfortable with that and understood that he may have needs he had to satisfy by himself. The main point was if he had to go there, she didn't want him to feel he needed to hide it. It was okay with her. Topic dismissed. So what was this about?

She sat down, picked up Sam's desk phone, and dialed the 800 number, feeling like a snoop, knowing and hating that digging into personals like this was an extreme departure from the person she believed she was. As she dialed, she had the odd sensation of being led along a path, as if receiving instructions about what to do rather than guiding herself forward, as if a switch had turned off her own volition, her natural ability to consult her own internal reasoning system.

A customer service representative, who seemed young and perhaps fairly new to the job, readily provided information about the order status and history for Sam A. Yaeger. More than twenty orders came up under that name. Mostly panties and bras.

"That's what I see in the current file," he offered cheerfully, "But I can go into the older files if you want to check anything there."

"No—no, thank you. That's fine." Lucy said. "You've been very helpful."

As she hung up the phone, her first impulse, which seemed to be a bona fide message from within, was to call the friend who had saved her life once before.

Ivy was baffled but sounded almost matter of fact to Lucy's wildly racing mind.

"That doesn't sound like Sam, having an affair," she puzzled. "Maybe he has a crossdressing thing, something he just can't admit to you?" She paused. "But he's in the field another night, and you're going to suffer until then—you know you will—worrying yourself sick about whether he's involved with someone up there or not. The fact is you've got to look through the house and find the underwear. So you'll know."

Lucy sat mute, losing feeling in her fingertips. Ivy continued. "I know it sounds creepy, but you've got to go through every room, every drawer, and just find it. If you do—and I'm pretty sure you will—at least you'll know. You'll know it's not for someone else."

"I guess so," Lucy muttered. "I'm going to be worried sick no matter what. I couldn't bear it if those things don't turn up—I mean, I don't think I can live with what that would mean..."

"Look, Lucy, I feel like I know you guys pretty well, and I just can't see it. I can't see what you're imagining. Sam's not like that. You've always been great friends."

"That's how I feel. At least that's what I thought. But this... My brain just can't make sense out of it any other way than he's messing around with someone. You know how charming he is. He could easily have charmed another woman, someone... gorgeous." Lucy struggled to hold onto what she thought she knew, what she trusted with her soul, and to consider Ivy's explanation. She agreed to search the house, but she found nothing.

Then the guiding message that spoke without speaking returned: *the garage*. She followed, almost mechanically, walking back through the kitchen and once again out to the garage. She passed by but didn't even notice the art supply catalog, which sat in plain view on the counter where it must have been for the past week since she'd ordered the brushes. Flipping on the garage light again, she entered the illuminated room, this time taking in Sam's personal space, the smell of motor oil and the faint taste of metal and dust. She listened. *The desk.* A loose pile of papers, clearly automotive in nature. No.

Lucy

She sat down and pulled out a drawer. Photographs of families: bathing suits, beach scenes, splashes and smiles. More catalogs. No underwear. *The car. Look under the seats*. A robot with a thrumming heart, Lucy opened the front door, leaned in, reached under the bucket seat, and felt a box. She pulled it out.

More photographs. Young women and girls, naked, in bathing suits, in shorts and halter tops, in gymnastics leotards. Some didn't make visual sense until Lucy studied them more closely. Children's faces had been meticulously pasted onto fully blossoming female bodies. The work had been so carefully done, matching the perspective and lighting perfectly enough to be easily overlooked. A stab in the gut stole her breath.

She came upon an older photo, oddly familiar. A young teen in short cut-offs stood with her back to the camera as she hosed down a car. The girl's face was turned away, but Lucy recognized the scene. She was thirteen, proudly washing her big sister's new car. Sam wouldn't have even known it was her. Suspended in time as her world tunneled and began to collapse, a vague memory presented itself: a collection of photos that Sam's mother had left behind when she died, family photos from the old Parkson neighborhood where both families had lived for a time when Lucy's first moved in. They couldn't have been there long when that photo had been taken. Could it have been her father who snapped it? Flotsam images bobbed about and bumped against each other in her mind: summer... going into eighth grade... Christina, enviably grown up, with enough money saved from various after-school jobs to actually buy this old but marvelously perfect car.

She rocked slightly back and forth, struggling to make sense of the pieces laid out before her. The forty-year-old Parkson photo, the unsettling composites, Dayna, the eight-year-old from the other end of the development playing with not-quite-big-enough fingers on Sam's guitar. Her older sister Deirdre, mid-cartwheel in the sage field, legs forming a splayed blur above her. A scrum of girls on the swim team that Sam coached, one peering back at the camera with water-slapped hair and a look in her eye that Lucy recognized. The look, directed at the person behind the camera, projected a plain, unselfconscious "No." The child's gesture, half lost amid the freeze-form exuberance of her teammates, pushing through her innocence, mirrored for Lucy the unwanted gaze from which she, the girl, was shrinking.

32

PHOTO FETISH

Utah, 2002

Lucy

LUCY GOT UP FROM THE garage floor. At first she couldn't feel her legs, but the numbness didn't matter. That made more sense than everything else: the photographs, the lingerie orders.

I've got to call Sara, she thought. But her body didn't want to move in the direction she intended. *The kitchen...* She willed it forward, needles of blood returning to her legs as she dragged their dead weight up the short steps and through the door. Her mind, equally resistant, required its own instructions. *My address book... Sara... What day is it?... Yes, she should still be in her office.*

Lucy found the number and her mind flashed to Sam's face, smiling, cheerful, energized as he turned to leave, there in the kitchen, seven days earlier. She punched the keypad on the phone, the singsong of tones, then Sara's voicemail.

"Hello, Sara? This is Lucy calling from Utah." She winced at the thin, faraway sound of her own voice. "It's urgent. I need you to call me back as soon as possible. Something terrible—I mean—I've found something—I'm frightened. I don't know what to do. Please call me back."

She hung up and waited, choked by her own heartbeat, Mad Mountain standing silent out the kitchen window, infinite blue behind it. She picked up in the middle of the first ring.

"Lucy? What's happened?"

"Sara, I've found something. It's Sam. I mean, he's not here, but there was a box in his car filled with photographs. Of children—little girls—kids I know. Our neighbors from Fort Lyell, little girls he coached back in Seattle. I found one from Parkson, where we grew up." A circumspect silence tugged on the line like surface tension hammocking a leaf on the water, enabling the wind to catch it.

Lucy continued. "They're wearing bathing suits. Some are naked. And this is the scariest thing: some of the photographs have been doctored."

"Okay, Lucy, just take a breath and tell me exactly what you're looking at."

"There are photos of bodies—mature, but maybe not adults—with children's faces spliced in very carefully. I mean, the lighting, the perspective, it's all there. The work is so nearly perfect that you might not even notice it if you weren't really looking for it. But at the same time, it's completely jarring when you do. The images are sickening—just... sickening. Sara, this doesn't make sense..."

"Lucy. I am so... so... sorry." The weight in Sara's tone caused something soft and not fully formed to collapse inside her.

"But you must understand... Sara, I love him. We *love* each *other*... He's the love of my life! We've been through so much together. You know that. You were there with us through that whole awful time, helping us get through those years when Kevin was totally out of control, when we weren't sure he'd ever come out in one piece. You saw Sam. You *saw* us! You saw how incredibly strong and good—how magnificent—he was through all that. You saw us at our best in the worst circumstances! Well, at least what seemed the worst at the time. You *know* us as well as anyone." Her throat tightened and grabbed at the words, "I just don't get this, whatever *this* is!"

"Lucy, where is Sam right now?"

"He's in the field, at his job in the wilderness program up in Barnes."

"Right. With a group of kids?"

"Yes, he's been in the field all week. He's supposed to come out tomorrow and get home tomorrow night, I'm not sure what time."

"Okay, Lucy, listen. I must speak with him. Is there an emergency number? Some way you can reach him up there and have him call me?"

"The only way I can reach him is if I call the main number at Hawk Ridge and tell them it's a matter of life and death. Family members are under strict orders not to contact staff members for any reason unless it's that serious. No exceptions. Only life and death."

"I'm afraid it's that serious, Lucy. You're going to have to make that call. Do you think you can do that?"

"I'm—I'm just not sure what I'd say. Sara, I'm so confused. I'm not thinking straight."

"Lucy, I'm going to help you with this, okay? You're not alone. But this is really important, and I need you to hear me. As soon as we hang up, you're going to call Hawk Ridge. Tell them there's a dire family emergency and Sam's got to come out immediately. That's all you have to say. Can you do that?"

"Uh huh. I think so."

They were on their way back to Seattle. Just like that, they packed up the car with a bewildered dog, three peeved cats, and a couple of suitcases. Lucy's parents knew only that there was a serious crisis that they couldn't talk about and they'd need to stay in the Vashon cabin for a while. A testament to Sam's ability to help Lucy reclaim her relationship with them, they gave their daughter and son-in-law permission to stay there without pressing a single question. Their affinity for him aside, they were, as always, true to their own absence of curiosity.

Lucy and Sam were both so frayed, so frightened and shaken, that the otherwise overwhelming prospect of living for what they were told would be four months in the tiny shoebox her father had built out of scrap lumber seemed almost reasonable. The cabin stood on its perch, a narrow shelf John Simkus had leveled straight back into the slope of a steep hill rising behind Manzanita Beach. The parcel was high enough for the cabin's narrow face to peek out from behind a row of larger, more inviting bungalows along the shoreline.

Lucy

By the time Lucy was in her late twenties, her parents had all but abandoned it, until she and Terry dug it out of a heavily armored blackberry thicket one idealistic summer. They spent that season of their marriage restoring it with their own hands, intent on making a life there as writers, before his affair with his young secretary began and their marriage abruptly ended. Even with the window frames they salvaged from derelict structures in the woods, which brought in a little more light and a better view of the bay, the space was austere and claustrophobic. But the idea of Lucy and Sam living there in that one-and-a-half-room cubicle with their animals and a dark bewildering hole ripped through their lives seemed an easier challenge to face than the betrayal itself and all that lay behind it.

The cabin was a place Lucy knew, a place of past comfort. She clung to its small ring of familiarity, as if it could shelter her from the depths of her own anger and from Sam's shame, his black rage at being exposed, the part of him that he'd protected so well, probably for most of his life. The part that now had no pretext to remain hidden. The part that, it turned out, disdained her and wanted to see her hurt. The part that would, in the coming months and years, relentlessly test her resolve, her will to fight for them. The darker, more potent part that had been and would always remain locked in a bitter struggle with the tender and loving Sam who had been Lucy's best friend and soulmate for five years.

The question of whether or not they could survive there on the island while he underwent months of intensive daily therapy seemed a small concern, an inconvenience, compared to facing the raw truth about who he was, what he had done, and how they would find a way forward into whatever lay ahead of them. At the time, Lucy saw only that they were deep in crisis and needed to mobilize. She knew how to do that, but she was naïve, even willful to the point of blindness, unable, for now, to see that this very process would alienate the part of him that was so sick, so powerful, and now so desperate. Instead, Lucy turned the crisis, the illness she had inadvertently driven from its refuge, into another project, another problem to manage.

They left Utah in early September, ten months after they'd arrived. The land shone with parched reds and golds, washed out sage, blonde grasses. The sky, the day they left, was that same iridescent sapphire that had received them the previous fall, an unbroken blue Lucy had never seen before, white horsetails sweeping across without casting a single shadow.

She left her painting behind as if to hold a place for her in their empty and uneasy house until they returned. How strange to think that it would be winter then. This was their time to work on healing. Though there was no choice but to embrace—or at least tolerate—painful uncertainties, it never occurred to Lucy that she and Sam would ever come apart, that they would ever not be together. They were going to fix this. As a couple. The therapists Sara had found for them—a whole team of them in fact, who specialized in handling cases like Sam's—were going to help. Lucy would support him, he would get better, and they would go back to their lives, even if those lives weren't quite what they had understood them to be before Sam's secrets emerged. These were Lucy's truths, and they were unassailable. But so was the other Sam, bristling, injured, no longer beholden to his better self.

33

MONSTERS

Utah, 2003

Lucy

THEY SAID SAM WOULD NEVER be free of the part of him that lived in the shadows, thrived on secrets, followed the forbidden. Lucy would remember this prognosis, but she's not sure she ever fully understood its implications. Survival requires hope, and hope requires a merciless focus on what can be hoped for, shutting out what cannot. Fairness and wisdom notwithstanding, some truths must simply be denied space in a sharply narrowed universe of the possible.

Sam would always be driven by impulse and dishonesty, chased from within by the abused child he'd been, though he held no memories of that boy. With a long-term commitment to therapy, the therapists maintained, he had a chance to change the balance of power within him, to strengthen the healthy part so that it might maintain more control over the part that had all along played a dominant role in his behavior and personality, despite—if not as a direct result of—how well he'd concealed it. He would have to own the fact that he was a pedophile by admitting it openly.

He was instructed to tell everyone he cared about who he was in his own words. Though this was not meant as a punishment, Lucy was convinced it had to feel like one to Sam. From her uneasy vantage point, Lucy felt like a participant in the punishment, but she clung to the instructions as their only lifeline. If she could just keep the directives straight and make sure she and Sam followed them correctly. Still, in some deep place just out of reach, beyond the clarity of reason, a question gnawed at the roots of her consciousness. It wasn't more than a gut sense of doubt that she couldn't express or even acknowledge, a vague feeling of foreboding that somehow the remedy could also feed and strengthen the punished Sam's grievances. While her sympathies were capable of aligning with those grievances, they failed to recognize the active and still-tender part of her that had learned a long-ago unmotherly lesson that applied to her and her alone: when in doubt, consider punishment deserved. Had that lesson wielded the power to preempt more basic reasonings, the power to silence questions about the deservingness of sympathy as well as the merit of punishment? Even in the absence of such a malign philosophy, the heart's allegiances might find themselves tested.

Based on the story Sam told, the therapists concluded that he had never actually violated a child. Lucy had no reason to doubt the truth of this assessment and every reason to invest her trust in the Sam that had managed to hold himself back from his darkest and most destructive impulses. Strength can always be found in believing, and believing in the resilience and salvageability of Sam's goodness prevailed through the relentless stripping away that took place during his intensive therapy, as it played out on the blind path they crept along together. That faith held, but just barely, even when Sam was instructed to confess things that anyone would question, abhorrent things she couldn't wish away or ignore but had no idea how to respond to, how to live with. She couldn't turn away from the obscene belly of the monster that presented itself, nor could she escape the ugly rage that came home with them on the ferry back to Vashon each day after the sessions. The humiliation of Sam's deepest secret self—outed, examined, and probed—found its way into Lucy's bones as he was forced to acknowledge the shame he'd kept safely buried along with the true nature of who he was, the source and signature of that shame.

That self taunted Lucy with traps he set and watched her stumble into. She wanted to deny him the satisfaction of seeing her distress at finding a revealing photo of a child planted under the washing machine lid, or a pornographic video in the VCR, queued up to a particularly disturbing scene so she would catch a glimpse before realizing what it was and fumble to eject the cassette. She wanted to see clearer signs of a battle with himself to sabotage or save their relationship, though if there were signs of sabotage, would she have been able to see them? She could believe he was fighting the other battle when he begged for forgiveness and promised away the lies he could no longer hide, when he went through the motions in treatment to appease the therapists and to keep her believing he was trying to beat his monster back. Lucy watched, she saw, she believed the promises he made, and she forgave him. She believed he was doing the work he was being instructed to do and that she was helping him.

But she too harbored a poisonous subterranean rage. It flew about in the dark corridors of her anger and hardened her into a severe creature able to peel away from its own soul to grasp at remedy, which seemed accessible only through exerting control. A hard lesson's learning is sometimes only stored as muscle memory, having lost its own story's thread but remaining poised as reflex. For a time, an old familiar monster dressed itself in her own skin.

Lucy and Sam flailed their way through a fogbound fall in their tin-der-packed burrow with their uneasy animals, barely able to speak to each other without exploding, afraid even to imagine how they would possibly reclaim their lives. Yet her eyes saw only one path forward, the one that required her to hold on with life-and-death grip to the conviction that they would figure it out, that she wouldn't lose him. That she still had one hand on the truth.

PART FIVE

34

LIVING PAIN(T)

2016

Kate

IT HAD TO BE ABOUT the paintings. There was no other way to get past the questions that I'd finally come to accept would never be answered. I'd fumbled with scraps in my basket of remnants too brittle to stitch together, and found myself turning to the works themselves in order to probe them, seeking their help to resolve Lucy's story in ways memory refused or simply failed. Perhaps the transcendent elements that lived in what Lucy had made over the years held the power to speak to me, if I were to enter their space and lose myself a little inside them. If I listened with the soul's ear, looked deeply enough with the spirit's eye, might they reveal a hidden path to the place where our journey would end? Like shards of an ancient clay bowl for which only a few pieces, properly arranged, could suggest the complete form, those remaining fragments, along with pieces of art Lucy had produced across the extraordinarily painful arc of her journey, would have to stand and speak for a shape, while marking the edges between what she'd lost and what I had managed to reconstruct. I hoped—hard clay edge to invisible edge—they would tell a story, sketch an outline, and create a sense of almost wholeness.

Three folders of digital images appeared one day in a shared folder that Lucy and I used for photos we'd taken on our trip to Utah seven months earlier. The dates attached to the digital files—fifty or so paintings—seemed to indicate timestamps that provided a record of when images had been uploaded, but they offered no clear record of when the original pieces had been created. While some bore dates that might have corresponded to a true date of completion, whole groups shared a single date, presumably the day they'd been saved or moved, and so assumed an arbitrariness that buried interpretable elements of their past. They didn't appear to be arranged within the folders in any particular order that I could discern. Still, the puzzle gave me a new sense of narrative purpose.

I noticed that nearly all of the images marked 2002 or 2003 had been supplied with a secondary frame. The paintings in the photographs had been propped against reddish earth-plaster walls, which created a peculiar visual and contextual dissonance around the edges of each otherwise unframed canvas, a duality that resonated most strongly against the city street scenes that were saturated with the blue light of the Northwest. Even those whose palette more closely matched the red walls seemed to give undue attention to the space in which they were placed, its demarcations, its suggestion of some other vanishing point. With those dubious markers, I set about finding attributes that might guide me in organizing the works into a series of waypoints along Lucy's artistic path.

Hurried notes heading the three folders might offer some help: "Paintings when I first arrived; Paintings when the gallery told me to paint Fort Lyell; Paintings when I learned about Sam." One, titled *Morning Coffee in Arena Roja,* bore the caption, "This was smashed in house," a reference I recognized. While we were sitting in Arena Roja's only café the previous winter, Lucy mentioned that one of her paintings had been bought by a woman who lived directly under Mad Mountain, a massive slab of which had fallen one day while she was out and crushed her adobe home, destroying everything in it including her art collection.

After the folders appeared, I learned that in the process of expanding her Alces studio space, Lucy had recently emptied a storage closet and thrown away the rolodex that held the records of when each of her paintings had been completed, its original title, its fate: whether it had hung in a gallery, been sold, gifted, or simply painted over. In addition to two paintings that had returned to Lucy in the three months since her mother's death, her walls were covered with the paintings she'd kept over the years. Her most recent work hung in Randolph Markey's gallery waiting to be sold, waiting for the economy to recover enough to make it possible to survive as an artist again, waiting for Lucy's health to return. Other than two portfolios containing 8 x 11 reproductions of some of Lucy's older paintings separated by quite a few inexplicably empty sleeves, whatever else that had been reproduced now lived in bytes on her hard drive, a layer of thumbnails on her desktop, a skein of wings bending across a fading sky.

Lucy developed her genre paintings while she and Sam were still living in West Seattle. They had moved into the house on Dakota Street after selling the bay shore house she'd lived in for ten years. From the beginning, her parents had been strongly opposed to her keeping the Dakota house. The idea of a single woman owning property she didn't even live in was abhorrent to them. Unflinchingly oblivious to their daughter's resourcefulness, they remained skeptical about her making the payments. But the house was part of her, an important part that she wasn't willing to give up. It had seen her through a second marriage and the overwhelming loss that came when Terry—once his infidelity was discovered—left. Lucy had sat at the window overlooking Puget Sound and the Olympic mountains in a director's chair, the only thing he'd left behind, and reimagined herself.

She'd resisted the pressure, refusing to give in to her parents' doubts and we-told-you-sos and for the first time claimed what she wanted, what was hers. One of the first things she did after Terry left was fix up the basement and rent it out, collecting a steady income from her tenant. After she began painting in earnest, she focused her painting life on taking commissions for portraits. Even when a man she was later involved with insisted that he couldn't live in the house she'd shared with her previous husband, Lucy kept the Dakota house as a rental property.

Years later, when she moved back to Dakota with Sam as part of their long-term plan to leave Seattle, Lucy managed to finally fix up the house and the garden the way she'd imagined they could be when she lived there with Terry. She had the kitchen completely redone and the entire yard artfully landscaped into a magnificent thriving garden. The two men she hired to design and build it became trusted friends and continued to nurture and shape the living space around her house throughout the two years she and Sam lived there, adding lavender, among many other things, which brought the comforting hum of bees, and butterfly bushes, which invited glorious painted wings into the graded rockery in front. One of the landscape designers commissioned Lucy to do a portrait of him and his son. She also painted her tenant Cynthia, with her broken-tailed cat sitting by a wall of railroad ties in the side yard.

The portraits of people and pets kept Lucy going and helped her gain confidence, though she struggled with the pressure and at times with the constraints of a somewhat static style. She gradually came to realize it was time to try something else. She wasn't yet familiar with the term *genre painting*, but she had the idea that she wanted to paint her time, to paint examples of how we live now, to create snapshots of life as we're living it, with the Styrofoam and paper cups and straws and street signage and cars and license plates and baby strollers and shopping bags, scenes vividly depicting the things we value and the things we devalue. She wanted to paint a portrait of how we live in the contemporary world that would stand up to time. And place was an essential part of that.

Lucy began by painting a bright, active scene outside Seattle's Pike Place Market, filled with people walking along the brick tiled street, a dog straining against its leash, people carrying shoulder and shopping bags, wearing T-shirts, tank tops, wind breakers, a woman with a hoodie tied around her waist, and a line of parked cars, awnings, and parts of buildings framing the market entryway. She'd been teaching herself how to blend acrylics based on what she saw rather than on any notion that they were particularly well suited to blending, let alone to matching the textures of the world she sought to closely represent. She now took on the challenge of figuring out how to paint buildings convincingly and to adjust the degree of focus to match the visual patterns she recognized from photography. It was particularly important to find the right balance between representing the world accurately and truthfully, and allowing the medium to speak through the composition.

After she had a second painting finished and a third fairly well under way, she took a leap one day in a moment of wild inspiration and responded to a call for applications from a local gallery. She included a slide of the first painting in her application. When the director called, the conversation went something like this:

"This is Monica Grimes from the BayWest Art Center calling. We received your application, and after looking at the sample piece you included, I'm interested in knowing a little more about the work you'd like us to show. First of all, where are you currently represented?"

"Actually, nowhere."

"No gallery is representing you?"

"No."

"Why did you only send one example of your work?"

"It's the only one I have—well, that's not entirely true... I have one and a half more done."

After a pause, she asked if she could meet Lucy in her studio.

"Sure. When would you like to meet?"

"Would you... be available... now?"

Monica came directly to the Dakota studio, where Lucy showed her the other pieces. She admired Lucy's third painting of a vivid street scene featuring a woman walking by in a loud red skirt and was impressed enough to regard Lucy's meager inventory as a gallery owner's dream. Here was an undiscovered artist who appeared to have come into the world fully formed. "You're there," she insisted, "with work that is easily gallery quality." She told Lucy she liked what she saw and was planning to hang a two-person show. But as she stood in the living room admiring another piece, she smiled and reconsidered. "I think we're going to make it a one-woman show." When **Red Skirt** remained unspoken for at the end of that show, Monica quietly purchased it herself.

Lucy's work appeared at Monica's gallery that spring, and several large canvases sold, two to a wealthy collector. The gallery also sold a somber portrait that Lucy loved of her nephew sitting, lost in thought, at the family's vintage chrome and Formica kitchen table in the cabin at Vashon Island, a painting that drew the attention of several potential buyers at the show.

By the time Lucy's second show was in progress at a different gallery, Sam was traveling to Utah for interviews at the two wilderness programs that sought to hire him. Lucy was committed to supporting him and his desire to give back to a program like the one that had helped Kevin come out whole when he was in crisis and lashing out wildly and self destructively at the world. She had happily invested $150,000 of her savings into his various therapy programs and tuition. She wanted their lives to be made easier with the income Sam would bring in from this new job, after his trucking livelihood had continued to dwindle, and she accepted that she couldn't afford to keep the Dakota house and buy another. They put it up for sale during her second show.

While the house was on the market Lucy battled a severe bout of the flu that turned into a deep upper respiratory infection that lingered for a month or more. During the same time her Crohn's disease flared up badly. She couldn't stop coughing, couldn't stop throwing up. The house sold in September, just after the 9/11 attacks. The world seemed lost in turmoil, and so did they. When Sam accepted the position at Hawk Ridge and went out to Barnes for his first extended training session, Lucy was left to pack, grieving for the Northwest and facing a move to a place she had seen only once and never yearned to go. She had never held any fascination for the desert. Ever.

They made one house-hunting trip over a single weekend, under intense pressure to find a home in Fort Lyell. Following an ad for a house that appealed to her, they walked in and Lucy surprised herself by imagining it working for them. Despite all the unknowns, the house suited her, and she felt reassured and excited by her positive response to it, but Sam caught her off guard. He was set against it, adamant that it was too close to other houses and didn't have enough yard space for Mackenzie. So they looked at another house, which she ended up buying in a nearly empty but fully planned development.

The Tuesday before Thanksgiving the movers came, loaded up the truck, and left. The rest of that day Lucy held herself together, knowing they would see the truck again in Fort Lyell first thing on Friday, but she was too sick to spend the evening with a good friend of theirs who'd invited them over for a farewell dinner on their last night in Seattle. The morning of their departure, Lucy walked into the living room at sunrise and looked out the window at the mist shrouding the bay, overwhelmed with sorrow. She began to shudder and sob. She saw her childhood, the little girl riding her bike all the way out to Tacoma's Point Defiance Park to look across at Vashon Island, the little girl who grew up gathering stones there and learning to swim in the deep green water of Puget Sound.

She told Sam she didn't know how she was going to leave that house and all it stood for in her life. But for some reason he reflected no empathy back at her and seemed not to respond at all to her distress. He walked her out of the house and to the car, where she remained slumped in the passenger seat hacking an ugly, raw cough, grateful she was no longer throwing up, and otherwise feeling completely alone. Lucy knew Sam was concerned about leaving Kevin and was taking a huge leap of faith in their decision to leave the Northwest, measuring in her mind enough of an understanding to support her belief that they were in this together. In the handful of years with Sam, she had managed to grow closer to her parents, who adored him, and they were now leaving them too. She hated that she'd been so hopelessly sick and unable to help during the final days of packing. She hated the strange lack of empathy from Sam, this new feeling of separateness.

They arrived at their new house at 1:30 in the morning on Thanksgiving Day, did their best to settle the cats and Mackenzie in their beds after spending almost nineteen hours in the car, and slid into sleeping bags on the cold floor. It wasn't until the brilliant Southwest sun rose and poured itself into the room that Lucy was able to see or feel anything but a cold blackness and despair. As she walked around the house watching the animals cautiously explore it, she felt their curiosity and the golden sunshine lift her spirits. No, the house hadn't been her first choice, but it could be a fine home for them, despite the overwhelming foreignness of it all. Later on, they basked in the thoughtfulness behind the take-out turkey dinner that the real estate agent had left for them in the refrigerator.

The movers arrived on schedule the next day, piled in the boxes, and assembled the furniture. Less than twenty-four hours later, Saturday morning arrived and Sam drove off to Barnes, leaving Lucy to unpack

and explore this new life and the new landscape that came with it. Though at first she feared every insect she came upon, expecting it to be a scorpion, she fairly quickly learned to appreciate the desert's strangely beautiful creatures, its striking scarcity of water, its nights of total darkness and boundless silence. At the same time, she set about painting the world she had left behind, the world she had always known, like the **J-M** street scene *(SEE PAGE 278)*, using photos she had brought with her and carrying forward the style and palette that had been so well received there.

ZION WAS THE LAST PAINTING Lucy completed before she found out about Sam and they hurried back to Seattle, stunned and shaken. It was also her first attempt at painting a Utah setting, Utah people *(SEE PAGE 279)*. Though Lucy and Sam hadn't begun to reach out socially, in the nine months they'd lived in Fort Lyell she'd begun to experience herself in the world beyond the Northwest, to extend her sense of place and her frame of reference beyond the colors, shapes, textures, and energy of her old home. It would be months before she would attempt to paint again, having lost all inspiration and the inner light from which her creative powers arose.

She had been forced to see the underbelly, was beginning, maybe, to understand Sam's illness, but Lucy still believed in the man she thought she knew, the humanity of the person whom she believed to be her best friend, who adored her and whom she cherished. Sam would heal, she would heal, and they would figure out how to heal their relationship. He'd gone through four months of intensive therapy and knew what he had to do to restore and nur-

ture the healthy part of himself, the part that was kind, loving, charming, funny, and so very bright. The part who loved her and cared about them.

They'd been told that the success rate for people with an illness like his was dishearteningly low. There is no cure, but with years of work—for reasons long forgotten the therapists stressed seven—and continued therapy, borderline personality disorder can be managed. The words Lucy heard the loudest were *can be managed*, and that was what she held onto most strongly. What she knew how to do. It didn't matter that questions remained about how far the shift could go or how much stability could be achieved. Lucy had no doubt that Sam would do the hard work and that with her support he would get through this, that together they would find a way through. If Sam's illness could be managed, she would make sure they did just that. If after careful evaluation this team of experts considered him an anomaly because—whatever he had done or might have wanted to do—he hadn't allowed himself to physically hurt a child, this was where her hope and comfort would rest.

Once they decided to return to Utah and were preparing to leave Seattle, they were given a set of instructions. When they got home, Sam was to retrieve all of his hidden fetish boxes and all of the journals he'd kept over the years. He was to show them to Lucy, and they were to destroy them, one by one. Fairly early in the process he'd been instructed to tell Kevin and Lucy's parents the truth. Over the phone he explained to her father and then to her mother that he was a pedophile. That he loved them dearly as his family, and that he loved Lucy. That he had never hurt a child. That he took pictures. That Lucy had chosen to stand by him and he hoped with all his heart they would be able to make it through this together.

Staying in Seattle was not an option. Lucy and Sam contemplated living in the cabin, but that was untenable for the long term. The cost of living in the Northwest had risen out of their reach, especially now that Sam would be out of work until he got a new job lined up, and most of Lucy's savings had gone to the tuition for Kevin's therapeutic boarding school. They were confident that they would find a good therapist for Sam, like the ones who had ushered them through so far. So they departed, armed with a few referrals for mental health providers in Las Vegas, the closest major city where there were qualified specialists who could help Sam move forward and stay ahead of his illness.

Sam also had to go back to Hawk Ridge to retrieve his gear and formally terminate his employment. He was gone for several days. During that time Lucy struggled with a strong and troubling sense that he had unfinished business there. That sense, however it managed to insinuate itself in her mind, came across as a relationship of some kind that went beyond his professional responsibilities. Perhaps it was a colleague. She agonized about whether or not to tell the program about him and nearly did on several occasions. But his therapists were unequivocal on this point: her emergency call had interrupted Sam's process of grooming a particularly vulnerable fourteen-year-old who had been in his sights. He had come out of the field the day before he was set to act on his plan. Informing the program of his illness would cause hysteria and bring on a legal and emotional firestorm which would be long lasting and difficult to contain, leading to a wave of destructive consequences from which little good would likely emerge. People would be hurt. Conflicted as she was, Lucy felt she had to trust their expertise. And somehow trust Sam.

The betrayals—the ones she was aware of, at least—were painful enough, but reading his journals seared her to the point of overwhelming rage. Sam had dated mothers of children he coached. Lived with the mother of a couple of girls he knew from his bartending days, befriending them while they waited after school in the front part of the establishment where he worked. Every day they sat in the pizza parlor, where their mother would pick them up as soon as she got off from work, while Sam tended bar in a back room. Sam's journal described him coming in one night when one of the girls slept alongside her mother. He joined them, insisting that the child never woke up, and masturbated near her. Eventually he hired the same girl to babysit for Kevin. So many unbearable what-ifs.

For years he had followed a good friend's daughter around with a camera and encouraged her friendship with Kevin as they were growing up. When she was twelve or thirteen he took a pair of her panties from a clothes hamper when he was visiting their home for some big family celebration. Lucy read the words, slapped him, screamed at him, and pounded her fists into his chest.

"This! How could you do this? You held her as a baby! You watched her grow up! You're like family to her—to her parents! How could this be possible!"

She shamed and humiliated him with her own words as they uncovered the gruesome story of who he was and how he'd operated under everyone's radar, including hers, over the years. He taunted her and threw barbs that were meant to cut and cut deeply, always timing his snipes to catch her with her guard down. The deeper their wounds, it seemed, the more desperate their clashes.

Sometimes Sam fought back fiercely, screaming with a powerful booming voice that terrified Lucy and sometimes succeeded in shutting her down. But most often he went through the motions of submitting to the miserable process of sharing and destroying his materials. Only later would he submit to the malignant part of his personality and set his traps, seeming to delight in the shock and hurt they caused, turning Lucy's guileless nature back on her, knowing she would rise to the provocation when she discovered a lurid journal entry left open for her to read, a photograph left out for her to find as she did her chores, wise to the way she would recoil at a jab about her appearance or her work, inflicted at a moment of exposure or vulnerability. That part of him was masterful, playing cruel games with her mind, artful enough in the delivery that she was often left wondering whether she might have imagined the offense altogether.

And still it never occurred to Lucy that they wouldn't work it out. She clung to every resolution of every bitter fight, convinced of an underlying strength and resilience in the way they eventually remembered who they were and managed to find respect and love between them. Every time Sam returned to her that way, she was able to believe that as long as they recovered their bearings together and returned to a place of understanding, they would keep their wounds from festering and gradually figure out how to stop tearing them open again. Lucy maintained an unwavering certainty that part of Sam believed this too, the part that always tried to bring things back to that hopeful place. And that part always seemed to find its way back into their relationship, one way or another.

35

....

PEOPLING THE DESERT

Utah, 2003

Lucy

> In cultivating compassion we draw from the wholeness of our experience—our
> suffering, our empathy, as well as our cruelty and terror... Compassion is not a
> relationship between the healer and the wounded. It's a relationship between
> equals. Only when we know our own darkness well can we be present with the
> darkness of others.
>
> — Pema Chödrön, *The Places That Scare You*

A NEW GALLERY WAS OPENING in Arena Roja. This felt like Lucy's time,
her opportunity to establish herself as a local artist worthy of being represented there. The manager of the one existing gallery in the arts village
told her very matter-of-factly that her work would not sell there, insisting
that scenes of Seattle street life would be of no interest to art patrons in
Utah. Their visitors were seeking landscapes of the Southwest. In the dark
weeks following their return to Fort Lyell, Lucy thought she might never
paint again, but eventually she gathered her scraps of energy and turned to
painting what Utah presented to her. She was never happy with the resulting landscapes, but they were her attempt to follow the advice of the one

expert she had met so far. It turned out that expert wasn't satisfied with those paintings either.

"Surely," the manager said, "our desert doesn't look like that! You don't really understand what our desert floor looks like!"

She may have been right because even though Horsetail Gallery agreed to show Lucy's work when they eventually opened, those first landscape paintings never sold.

It had been a nearly hopeless and painfully unproductive time. For months while Sam searched for a new line of work, Lucy had no desire to paint, couldn't open her heart to it. She had no vision, creative or otherwise, and felt dead inside, and her first efforts at painting, based on the dictum she'd received, reflected this. But eventually Lucy got a commission from a fellow student working with a Buddhist teacher whom she and Sam had found when they were in Seattle for his intensive therapy. Juliana had agreed to work with them long distance in the immediate aftermath of the crisis, and over several years that followed she became an important source of support and insight for Lucy. She even brought a group of students out to Utah for a working retreat, a pilgrimage to the petroglyphs at the ancient sites Lucy had spoken of so rapturously. With that group's encouragement she began painting again in earnest and putting people back in her paintings in what felt like a step toward remembering who she was.

Lucy took many small steps and stumbled often. Though Juliana didn't admit it directly, Lucy understood that she had encouraged the commissioned piece as an incentive for her, fearing, as Lucy herself did, that if she didn't reconnect with her art and her spirit she might never paint again. Despite the weariness and grief in her heart and an overwhelming sense of being completely lost, her trust in Juliana as a guide reawakened the motivation and courage she needed. She painted Juliana standing with two of her students and an old cowboy engaged in a conversation along the edge of the ancient site Lucy had taken them to explore, with the canyon dropping off behind them. The cowboy was old Charley Dunn, a Fort Lyell native who had recently hired Lucy to take small groups on horseback up the trail to the ancient canyon site. This painting, which felt like her first success after finding out about Sam, helped her reclaim some sense of artistic energy, to see a flicker of light returning, if only tentatively.

But she was still drawn to Mad Mountain and couldn't shake herself free from its presence, its gravitational pull. So in another painting that she'd originally done as a landscape, Lucy went back and added a group on horseback, viewed from behind. She integrated the figures from a photo she'd taken while working for Charley, in order to create a more dynamic foreground with a small band of people just setting out, moving off into that familiar landscape she couldn't let go of. Lucy was searching for something there that she needed to get right.

Sam's search for work led him back to driving a truck. He found steady work delivering loads of compressed hay cubes to Los Angeles. It was supposed to be a day job requiring him to go back and forth two or three times a week, but occasionally he'd call to say he was too tired to complete the trip and needed to stop overnight in Las Vegas to get some sleep. He was spending time there each week anyway in a therapy group. Except for Sam, the group was made up of convicted sex offenders who'd previously been in jail. The sessions provided an opportunity for the men to sit in a circle and talk about their problems. Lucy understood Sam's complaints and agreed this wasn't a good fit for him, but they'd met with two other therapists in the area who seemed to have even less to offer him. There appeared to be no other options, so they went with this one and hoped, rather desperately, that the work he did there would be helpful.

Lucy began to seek out ways to live more in the moment and to examine herself, but Juliana's constant emphasis on fixing Lucy rather than fixing Sam continued to puzzle and annoy her. Lucy was raw, at times nearly as angry with Juliana as she was with Sam. She struggled and mostly failed to comprehend why the focus of therapy always came back to Lucy and what always seemed like her faults and shortcomings in responding to Sam, rather than Sam's deceit or his hurtful and destructive behavior. Juliana talked about self-love and about unconditional forgiveness and compassion, which

Lucy wanted to believe she could achieve, but mainly as a way of freeing herself from the searing pain that she was desperate to escape.

For a long time, she resisted seeing Sam as her teacher rather than her partner, that living with him, broken as he was, could provide opportunities for her own growth. In their very first session, Juliana couched their marriage in purely conditional terms, "if you should make it through this together, it will require great strength." What did she mean, *if*? Did she think there was a chance they wouldn't come through this? Lucy did love him, even though that love had come as a kind of surrender after she'd promised herself she would never fall that way, lose herself like that to another man. And still she'd fallen in love with him.

Yet she believed she could learn how to set blame aside and replace it with acceptance of who he was and who she was. Lucy had nothing and everything to lose. She hungered for the wisdom underlying Juliana's approach, though she often found herself bristling at elements of Juliana's message. In the end, perhaps time has proven the most effective intervener, helping by altogether different means to advance the idea that she may have thought she understood more of that message than she actually did.

Lucy

Once again, Lucy's path to living rested upon journeying back to—and forward with—her art. And that path brought her back to portraiture, though she rediscovered it with eyes that were just beginning to open, eyes that would, over the next two years, allow her to begin to see herself and others differently and help her establish a salient theme for her work. That theme would eventually crystalize into what had begun to draw Lucy in most powerfully: strong women *(SEE PAGE 280)*.

Seeking strength and connectedness, she ventured out under a pale winter sky into Arena Roja, which itself was just coming into being but hadn't quite found its footing yet as an arts community. She came, finally, to see this emerging place she'd heard about, which was at that time just a small cluster of newly constructed red mud-style buildings including a coffee shop, a pottery studio, and a small art gallery around a plaza built to reflect and integrate with the flat terrain of the desert scrubland at the foot of Mad Mountain. How had she and Sam not been shown Arena Roja when they'd come out house hunting? Low-slung but light and airy spaces seemed ready to become shops, galleries, or studios of some kind. High-end homes were being custom built in the surrounding chaparral. There was even a small open-air theater space. As far as Lucy had heard, Arena Roja was being developed with the specific intention of attracting people into a new community built entirely around the arts. Once she walked around the small but comfortable village, she easily imagined being part of it.

Red Jasper Gallery was open, and the woman keeping shop seemed keenly interested in the fact that Lucy was not just a new face but a working artist living in a neighboring town. They talked for a long time, both passionate about art and its place in life and community. Leslie was eager to hear everything Lucy was willing to share with her about her painting, about her views on art in general. Lucy was drawn on that cold day to the warmth of the brightly colored pieces on display, mostly pottery, glass, and jewelry, but also some modest paintings filling the space, feeling soothed by someone reaching out to her, acknowledging that she had something valuable to offer. Even though she didn't share the aesthetic of all the work represented there, her conversation with Leslie in that gallery felt almost like a welcome home in this strange and isolating place where she'd spent the past year unmoored and lost.

Lucy went home and began working on her portfolio, doing little else for three months. When she returned in the spring to present her work, she discovered that she'd become the subject of a story that had found its way around the village about a serious painter who was new to the area, a painter who possessed a "real" and "true" sense of art, who walked in one day and then just disappeared. Andi, the gallery manager, looked through Lucy's work, asked her about her relationship to the Northwest, and asserted that she needed to self-assuredly embrace Utah with her polished skills and distinctive style if she wanted to make a living there.

So Lucy went back home and again began painting Utah. Her style and her confidence had grown out of painting people in their world, a world that was a universe away. Here, a land, a vast space, an even vaster sky, and a palette she was still learning to read and interpret presented challenges nearly as great as starting over again. Leslie's support proved invaluable when, as the opening of Horsetail Gallery approached, she pushed for Lucy's work to be represented there.

Following her initial attempts at landscape painting and newly inspired by the hope of having a new artistic home, Lucy began to study the arts village from a more familiar angle, drawing from the sensibility she'd developed in the streets and vibrant marketplaces of Seattle. Though this new center of activity was just a tiny, artful, pedestrian plaza, hardly a busy thoroughfare, she began taking photographs of people going about their business: visitors browsing ceramic planters at the pottery studio, an artist warming her hands on a mug of coffee as the bright morning sun begins to take the chill out of the early spring air. The scenes of life in Arena Roja came with a built-in backdrop of red rock and smooth orange-brown earth walls contrasted with mat green cacti, decorative grasses, and other desert plants that she was coming to love.

She painted steadily as spring progressed, opening herself to glimpses of life being lived, to scenes that were more suited to her aesthetic and her interests, finding color and texture as she once again worked to paint place. Fairly quickly, though, Lucy began to run out of material and found that she had to extend her supply of photo scrap to include images of the wider Southwest region. There was something important that she needed to draw from, something she had touched upon in the experience coming out of that earlier painting she'd done from her snapshot of the two women walking as if their lives depended on getting inside the visitor's lodge at Zion National Park. But finding similarly dynamic content would continue to be a problem going forward in a sparsely populated area where the intensity of the climate often kept people indoors.

While working on new material and hoping for an invitation to participate in gallery opening, Lucy began to dwell once again—at least on the canvas—in a peopled world. She contacted her old high school friend Paige with the germ of an idea, and they talked about getting together so Lucy could photograph her and possibly include her in a series of paintings.

Desperate to give themselves a break from the distress they had been battling for months, Lucy and Sam took a trip to the Oregon coast for a few days, where he could do a little surfing, an old favorite pastime of his, and she could recover a long-lost sense of comfort and catch up with Paige. Lucy was painfully uneasy about being in a public setting with him, particularly at a beach filled with families and especially young girls in beach attire. But it was hard to turn down an invitation to stay at Paige's sister's exquisite summer home, which happened to be empty at the time. And during one of their long walks along the familiar shore that had always given her comfort, Lucy photographed Paige and her dog in the grassy dunes near Seaside, with Tillamook Head, so dear to her, in the background. In painting that portrait many months later, she would remove the distinctly Oregonian landmark and unashamedly replace it with the red sand hills of the desert Southwest.

36

SCAPESTONES

Utah. 2004

Lucy

LUCY HAD BEEN COLLECTING ROCKS since she was a little girl in Tacoma. She couldn't play in an alleyway in their neighborhood or on the beach at Vashon without scanning for stones and finding some treasure worth saving. In her walks through the deserts of southern Utah, she came across mountainsides of red, green, white, and yellow jasper, filling bowls with banded chunks of agate, blonde and blue topaz, slabs of selenite, pale green fluorite pebbles, lumps of oxblood colored hematite, and assorted fossils. Her counters, tabletops, and shelves became a display case of minerals and gems of all sizes and colors. She loved them all as both part of herself and part of the earth.

In the face of their efforts to live day to day as a couple, Lucy refused to give up her belief that she and Sam could survive, and she agonized her way along, trying but never quite managing to learn how to believe in herself. Somehow, she thought believing in them automatically meant believing in her. Having given over so much of what she thought their relationship was about to him, it was only now that she was beginning to see that she'd made it all about him, his needs, the story he wanted her to believe. Under the weight of their distress, she recoiled and sunk into a numb resignation at every thought of what fetish he might be following or feeding when he was on the road. And she bristled at Juliana every time she suggested that as long as Lucy continued to see and understand who she was purely in relation to him, she diminished her own potential, relinquished space for her own needs, desires, and creative dreams.

Witnessing Sam's battle with himself made it seem as if they were both caught between the dark, cruel, capricious personality that now had license to test its limits as well as hers, and the charming, funny, caring one whom she still loved and who managed to show himself when she had to be pulled back from abject despair. The one who hurt when she hurt. The one who seemed more and more in retreat from the one capable of throwing out a lacerating comment like, "All your paintings look the same, Lucy. I don't know why you bother."

One night he took her to the emergency room after her Crohn's-related internal bleeding had started up again. Once Lucy was safely in the hands of the hospital staff, Sam disappeared and didn't return for hours. Every wound, whether inflicted upon her directly or enflamed vicariously through Sam's old and unexplored injuries, the taproot of his pathology, the traumas of his buried childhood: all this ripped the scabs from her own childhood wounds that had never healed over. She was beginning to understand, though only on the most rudimentary level, that she hadn't really begun to do any kind of deep healing and that she might look to the desert, in all its intensity of heat and harshness and silence, to draw some of the poison out.

Emotionally ragged, Lucy sought to sort out her feelings in some way. In an effort to explore her capacity to love this person who was herself and to release energy around all the hurt, she began writing words in a note-book, naming the feelings that consumed her. Eventually, the idea came to her that she could give them physical weight by attaching them to stones. She chose the heaviest rocks from her collection to represent the biggest, most difficult emotions, and using her acrylics she painted the names of those feelings onto the stones, turning the naming and assignment of weights to her feelings into a project. Finally, she tore the notes out of her notebook, and tied them to the stones with pieces of twine.

Lucy continued this process until one afternoon she decided to hold a ceremony of release. She collected all of her named rocks and put them in the back of her jeep, along with a small hibachi. Fire would be required to match the strength of the feelings she wished to discharge. She drove her cargo up the long hill to the nearest and most heavily decorated of the ancient sites and carried several loads to a large flat slab that stuck out over the edge of the canyon. She had often stretched out on her back there and watched the sky, crying out to it, hoping she might absorb some healing energy from the massive platform that had been worn smooth from all the contact others before her had—for whatever their spiritual or mundane reasons—brought to that spot. She sat for a long time with the rocks, their names, her rawness, and the energy of the place from which she had drawn remnants of strength before, a place she hoped was infused with a kind of sacred wisdom that might, if she was open enough, help her learn how to be in this world without so much suffering and strife.

Standing on what seemed like the edge of the world—her world, at least—Lucy slowly and reverently untied the notes one at a time, separated each from its keeper stone, unfolded the note, struck a match, and brought fire to the torn paper in the bottom of her little crucible of a grill. She watched each one as the flares rose and quickly reduced the paper and the words written on it to ash. After each note had completely burned away, she held its stone in both hands, visualized what it represented, took it into herself to try to reach that deep place where that feeling lived, then hurled the stone as far as she could over the side of the canyon, imagining it taking a portion of emotional weight from her heart as it dropped to the bottom. She didn't expect to feel liberated; she simply hoped to ease the burden. She thought if she could release the pain, she would be able to heal herself and make peace with the sorrow that had consumed her relationship with Sam. Even so, it was still about keeping him.

After she'd thrown her last rock down, she sat facing across the canyon to the west and watched the sun turn a streak of clouds into blazing violet, red, orange, and pink. Then she bundled up her gear and drove home.

Lucy

Labor Day weekend was coming up, and the Tuesday immediately following would be her first day of class. Leslie was her first official painting student, though Lucy had been working privately with Arthur, a local physician. After seeing a few of her paintings at Horsetail Gallery, he had asked Lucy if she would teach him how to paint. She refused.

He loved her color. It was clear and beautiful, he said, and he wanted to learn what she knew about making color like that. He'd taken lessons before and failed. She told him she had nothing to teach. Lucy had never taught, didn't know how, and though she had studied painting in college and had taken a master class, she was basically self-taught. He was earnest and said he just wanted to learn how to mix color like she did, and that's all. She thanked him and said no.

Three months later Arthur's wife called. She said she wanted Lucy to know that Arthur hadn't gotten her color out of his mind. She was insistent. He was absolutely sure that Lucy had something to offer him, and he wanted to hire her for private lessons. Lucy admired his commitment and liked that he'd followed up so many months after she'd turned him down, so she agreed, and he began taking lessons three days a week in her home studio.

Through his persistence and his passion, Arthur taught Lucy that she did have something to teach after all. She saw him come alive on the canvas. She saw him become spiritual and open-hearted in his painting. He shared his excitement with Leslie, who talked—the way people in a small village talk—with Arena Roja's developer and community manager and asked if he could find or create space for painting classes. Their combined enthusiasm initiated the decision to offer Lucy temporary space in the arts village community center, and that is where, on September 2nd, 2003, she was to teach her first official class.

The Friday before the holiday weekend Sam had a therapy session in Las Vegas. He'd left that morning and never returned. There was no call to say he was delayed, exhausted, afraid to disturb Lucy by calling late. He'd taken to disappearing on weekends, usually ending up in California for two or three days, surfing. At least that was what Lucy believed. She wouldn't have said she was accustomed to this, but it had happened several times before. She suspected he might go straight to work on Tuesday. So she waited until 5:00 a.m., his usual time of arrival, to call him there. His boss stumbled a little and said Sam wasn't there. Lucy asked when he expected him, and he said, "I don't. He called this morning and said he's not coming in and he isn't sure if he's coming back at all."

The boss's wife, who was also the receptionist and secretary for their small trucking business, took note of the number he was calling from on their caller ID and recognized that it wasn't a Utah area code. It turned out the call had come from a motel in Florida. Sam was sound asleep when they rang his room. It was a little after 7:00 a.m. there. Lucy knew immediately from his voice, groggy and disoriented as he was, that she was speaking to the Sam of the black heart. She had learned to recognize the coal dark curtain that came over his eyes and the chill that flattened his voice when that Sam held sway.

"I don't understand," she said.

The monster replied, "Okay, so let me explain. You're a bitch, and I want nothing to do with you. I want to be very clear, so you don't turn this into something it's not. I've left you, and I'm not coming back."

"But... why?"

"I hate my life. I hate everything about it."

The only words that she could pull up were broken, pathetic, her voice, too, sounding like someone else's. "—But you've left all your stuff here."

"I don't care about my stuff. Do whatever you want with it. Just sell it, or better yet, burn it. That would be a good exercise for you." Sam's bitterness was so potent that despite all that releasing Lucy had done, she could feel herself—her heart—snapping shut again.

At that point the only thing she had to hold onto was the work she'd been doing with Juliana, coming out of a relentless focus on helping Lucy understand the role she played in their relationship. She had flailed her way through that struggle, intent on recovering a marriage she couldn't let go of, still just barely inches into the process of learning what was in her control and what was not. Though she didn't know how far she had to go, part of her sensed she was a long way from understanding the lessons she might learn—or as Juliana would say, was *meant* to learn—from this ordeal. Now, blind in her grief, despite all the time she'd spent alone, she still had no idea how to forge a meaningful relationship with herself.

As soon as Lucy began developing Leslie's portrait from a snapshot she'd taken that first day they met for class, through the distress she bore in learning that Sam had fled, she knew she was beginning something important. *(SEE PAGE 281)* Just surviving that day, leaving the house immediately after learning where he was, allowing the hurt in, and going to do something completely new and undeniably scary was a test of her will. In the weeks that followed, she felt herself being drawn inward and at the same time following her inner eye to a place she'd never gone, as if looking inward and outward through the same window. Perhaps she was getting closer to that elusive something she'd been searching for in the landscapes and the arts village scenes.

Sam was gone. The way he disappeared tore away at her heart. It caught her in a spiral of shock and disbelief, unable to shake off her sense of re-

sponsibility for his unhappiness, struggling to accept him for who he was rather than to see him as an adversary, and terrified by the gaping space she had no idea how to fill because the partner she had relied on so completely for a sense of purpose was gone. She set about navigating this new world in which her role, suddenly, was to guide people to find their art. Alone, but with this new and mostly unsought responsibility, Lucy began looking in earnest for her own courage.

She advertised the class, and people steadily signed up. It wasn't long before she had about ten students. But the group's lively and expanding presence in the community center began to encroach upon ongoing activities in that space, so Alan, the village developer, proposed that they move across the plaza into a model house he'd built. It would be theirs as long as it remained vacant. September shimmered, brightly marking the summer's passing, and the real estate market would likely remain quiet through the winter months.

Meanwhile, Sam and Lucy resumed communication. He called to say he was surprised by her caring tone and he'd like to think about them trying to make their marriage work, if that's what she wanted, but he needed a separation for a while. Over the next week or two he floated the idea of coming back to Fort Lyell for a short visit to celebrate his birthday and Kevin's, which fell on the same day in late October. They talked about making it a family event. Of course, Lucy seized upon this idea, desperate to get back to working on **them**, wanting only for him to stay. She'd missed him terribly, refusing to—unable to—imagine life without him. All she needed was to hear that old friend in his voice, and she was powerless to question it or to doubt the integrity of this arrangement.

The plan was that Sam would book a flight back from Florida, Kevin would fly in from Seattle, and the three of them would spend a couple of days together. But within hours of Sam's arrival, a call came in from Lucy's mother saying her father had gone into congestive heart failure and she had to get out there immediately. He was dying. Lucy cried, guilt ridden because her sorrow in that moment was not for her father at all. She cried because Sam had just arrived, she had longed so badly for this reunion, and now she had to leave. Sam was in the shower when the call came in, and

Lucy

Kevin sat with her, trying to comfort her, as she allowed him to assume the obvious about the cause of her distress. Sam would stay behind to get Kevin on his pre-arranged flight back to Seattle the next day and then drive to Oregon to join Lucy and say goodbye.

Once she was on the plane, she did cry for her father, and bitterly. She ached under the urgency to be there with him and prayed he'd still be alive when she arrived. When she got to the hospital, she did her best to attenuate her unruly emotions, align herself to the bend of awkward tension that her presence so often seemed to inspire in her family, this time compounded by the strain of her father's grave condition and her mother's out-of-control nervous energy. But when Sam arrived, he cut through all that with an ease that calmed everyone's nerves, magically neutralizing the electric charge Lucy carried and stepping comfortably into the position of the grieving son. Sam walked straight to the hospital bed, put his hand on the side of his father-in-law's head and said, "So good to see you, Dad!" bringing a smile to John Simkus's face, something Lucy hadn't seen in a very long time.

Her parents and sister loved Sam from the very start. He returned their love, which always came across as genuine. He enjoyed an unchallenged place in their hearts that gave Lucy a slipstream to ride in on. When they embraced Sam, they embraced her in a way they never had before and never would again.

During that visit, Lucy and Sam assumed their expected roles as loving partners because that was what the situation required. And then her father perked up, surprising everyone, including the doctors. He seemed recovered enough to be sent home, so Sam and Lucy left, having completely foregone any hope of a happy reunion.

They set out for the fifteen-hour drive back to Fort Lyell in one of Sam's muscle cars, and as soon as they were alone together all restraint and decorum vanished. They fought fiercely, with screaming and renewed ugliness, lashing out at each other with all the anger each of them had carried inside for months. Lucy's fury about his disappearance, his serial betrayals; his rage at her for outing him, for ruining his life, bringing on a world of shame. It all came out with hurt piled upon hurt.

They drove through the night, alternately flaring at each other and falling into a loaded silence, until sometime before dawn on a Nevada freeway, Sam began nodding off at the wheel. Lucy shook him a couple of times and told him to pull over. But he shoved her hand away and began to speed up, closing his eyes in mad, suicidal rage, holding them tightly closed and locking his arms out straight. She screamed at him to stop, but the accelerator went to the floor and the car roared up and topped 100 miles per hour. She begged helplessly, knowing she'd be unable to take over driving his souped-up car with its powerful engine and standard transmission, even if he'd have allowed it. He growled through his teeth that he'd stop at the next rest stop and sped on without easing up on the gas pedal. Mercifully, a rest stop did appear, and he pulled off, dropping immediately into a snoring rejoinder with his hands still on the wheel.

Within a day or two after Sam returned to Florida, Lucy got another call, this time from Christina, informing her that their father's brief upturn had reversed. He'd been rehospitalized and immediately put in hospice care, and Lucy had to fly back to Oregon. This time he did die, but she had enough time to tell him how much she appreciated the art he'd given her, that the creative spirit he'd never gotten to enjoy in his life was very much alive in her. Lucy told him she wanted to honor his gift to her, that from then on she would make art for the both of them, and she would take his name. Going forward, the name she'd sign at the bottom and along the sides of her canvas frames or include in any promotion of her work would read *Lucy John Yaeger*.

37

THE PATHOLOGY OF TRUTH
Utah. 2005

Lucy

> Life is a process of becoming, a combination of states we have to go through. Where people fail is that they wish to elect a state and remain in it. This is a kind of death.
>
> — Anaïs Nin. *D. H. Lawrence: An Unprofessional Study*

SAM WAS COMING HOME FOR Christmas. To stay this time. Once again, he and Lucy were going to try to make it work, and she was fully on board, ready. After all, she'd begged him to stay in October. But he hadn't, and she'd begun to grow into a rhythm, busying herself with getting to know her students, painting steadily, even painting her students and other women in Juliana's Buddhist training group. New joy presented itself in expressing what she saw in each personality, the beauty she found in each woman who had in some way touched her life and added to her evolving sense of what a strong woman could be, independent of what society dictates about the shape and style of beauty.

Though it was officially a temporary arrangement, the painting class had found something of a home in Alan's model house. He had built it on the edge of the plaza, but its magnificent view over a broad, empty expanse

of desert and the mountains far out to the west gave the impression it was the only human structure for miles *(SEE PAGE 282)*. As the weather grew colder, the fireplace kept them warm and the surroundings kept them inspired. A couple of students complained that the space was too cramped or the acoustics inadequate, but to Lucy, working there was a gift that she could never have imagined. Interest in the class was high enough that she began planning an *Artist's Way* class, following Julia Cameron's book, as well as a youth painting class which ultimately gave her a chance to understand mentoring in a whole new way.

Though it should have been obvious that Sam's return would be difficult for both of them and at best unlikely to succeed, at the time Lucy was entirely caught up in hope, in the belief that what they shared was love. Compared to what she'd known as a child, his demonstration of friendship, the affection that he showed early on, the way he courted her—before his "testosterone problem" developed and their intimacy ended—felt deep and real, a bond to be cherished at any cost. Perhaps it had always been about seeking protection, or about unlearning how to live without the idea of someone to love, the idea of being loved.

Lucy

She failed to make sense of Juliana's argument that Sam was holding her back from her own life, her own power and potential. Lucy thought something was wrong with her teacher-therapist, that perhaps she was simply opposed, in principle, to marriage. When she thought about it, she couldn't name a single one of Juliana's students who was still married.

Lucy also dismissed the horrified urgings of an energy worker—someone she trusted—who, after one private session with Sam, was so distraught by whatever it was he presented to her that she began Lucy's next session by urging her to get away from him as soon as possible. Lucy knew Jen's alarm was real, real enough to leave her frightened and sobbing on the table, but afterward she closed herself to Jen's appeal. She heard the words, "You must get away from that man. He's a monster. You can't imagine what he's doing. Lucy, I'm asking you in the strongest terms I possibly can to leave him." But all she could do was shut the words out.

Part of her understood Jen's genuine fear for her. And yet she couldn't find the courage to ask exactly what she'd "seen" in him, heard him say, or felt in his energy that had caused alarm extreme enough to bring her that far outside the scope of normal protocol. Lucy submitted to the part of herself that couldn't bear to know, which might have been the same part that had never developed a reflex to protect herself. Either way, she never went back.

But as she continued to catch Sam in lie after lie about where he was and what he was doing, she began to have moments of clarity. They didn't last, slipping away almost as soon as they came, these moments when she glimpsed herself being played or when she fleetingly understood that living as if she had the power to control another person was a delusion. She would briefly sense the futility of trying to be reasonable with a person who operated under a system in which neither reason nor honesty applied and begin to acknowledge the possibility that they might not come through this. During one of these moments, after she'd caught him lying again, this time about going to therapy in Las Vegas, Lucy took off her wedding ring, placed it on the counter, and said, "I'm done. We can't do this anymore. I can't believe you, and I can't withstand any more lies. I just can't survive this anymore. It's over."

As if a switch had gone off, he threw up the screen of the tender Sam and cried, begged, and promised her that he would be a better partner, make more of an effort to work with her, and be more transparent about his comings and goings. He apologized for being so careless and unforgivable in hiding things from her and promised that he'd make it up to her because he cared about them so much, more than anything, more than all his stupid, foolish mistakes that he kept making because he was such a scared little shit who didn't appreciate her, and how sorry he was that he'd hurt her yet again, and wouldn't she please not break both their hearts by giving up on them. Lucy was unable to hold onto that scrap of knowing, scared to let go of her resolve, scared to leave him. So she put her wedding ring back on and they continued.

Then something that felt like an answer presented itself. That previous winter Lucy had gone to one of Juliana's ten-day silent retreats. She and Sam had talked about how profound the experience had been. Returning to that conversation, he said he thought that sitting in silence with himself might give him a chance to listen to what he honestly felt and find the strength to share it with her. She suggested that if he could just find a way to be completely honest with her so she knew what she was dealing with, so she knew where she stood, she'd be able to make an informed decision.

So Sam spent ten days in silent meditation, and it had been powerful, he said. But they fell immediately back into their normal dynamic and landed in an argument the night he returned. As the fight began to escalate, he suddenly stopped and looked at Lucy. "I can't do this anymore," he said, his eyes filling up.

"I know this is a horrible thing to say, but I don't want to stay in this marriage. I see it now, and I'm so, so sorry. I see what I'm doing to you. I see that you're going to hold on and stand by me no matter what, and I can't let you do that anymore. I have to leave because I see now that you won't leave me. There's no other way to stop all this."

"Wait—what are you saying?"

"I'm saying that I'm a pathological liar, Lucy. Nothing I've ever said to you is true. Nothing. In all these years we've been together I've never told you the truth. It's all lies."

Lucy

In the weeks following Sam's moment of truth, he tried several times to retract the things he'd said, insisting he'd overstated the lying part, that, yes, he'd lied to her, but it wasn't as bleak as he'd said it was; and he didn't really want them to break up, that he thought they could make it work. His strategy of hiding in plain sight had, for all intents and purposes, proven successful enough. But this time Lucy saw and heard a uniquely unadulterated truth. She recognized it, even in this unfamiliar form, as genuinely and believably Sam.

Lucy had finally seen who he was, and with that fleeting moment of transparency, she was able to begin the agonizing work of letting him go. Whenever she felt she was wavering—and she was constantly in danger of that—she repeated his words to herself, the words she could now hold onto because she recognized them as the heart's remnant of a true Sam, a brief flicker of unprecedented clarity. A vestige of empathy, a gift of knowing there was one small true place that had managed to survive and to break through. Once again there'd be no way to unbelieve. There'd be no unseeing this pathology of untruth now that it had reduced everything she'd thought their relationship was to a lie.

Lucy would once again dwell in a dense airless space between devastation and healing. Sam found an apartment in Fort Lyell. He signed a nine-month lease and they made arrangements for him to take the cats on the weekends, for which Lucy paid the extra fee. He borrowed one of his boss's company trucks for the move and got help from him with the larger pieces to be moved. It was a hot summer Saturday, and Don's two children tagged along with their dad. The girls wore typically short shorts and skimpy little string tops, inviting Sam to slip right into a game of surreptitiously antagonizing Lucy. He got her attention whenever he could, exaggerating his friendliness with the girls, positioning himself so that Lucy would catch him turning his face toward the nine-year-old's crotch while lifting something into the truck, lingering there just long enough to shoot Lucy a wild grin. As the morning work continued, he began using a pet name for one of the girls, effusively calling her Bon-Bon and then Bun-Bun instead of Bonnie, ingratiating himself with childlike silliness, each time provoking a wave of giggles.

Summer progressed, and Lucy noticed that even the cats' behavior changed. They began to shy away from Sam when he came to pick them up for the weekend, and Silver, who'd been especially close to him, one of the two he originally brought to the marriage, began to hide from him. Silver was so devoted to Sam that Lucy had moved the cat's bed near the door because during those long stretches when he was off at Hawk Ridge she spent most of her time sitting there waiting for him, refusing the comfort of her softer spot in the bedroom. Silver had been thrown from a moving car as a kitten and had suffered severe neurological damage. While they were still together, she would curl up against Sam at night and twitch as she slept. It took months for Silver to accept that kind of comfort from Lucy who, in hindsight, eventually came to understand that when Silver finally did lean against her, her birdlike body shuddering into sleep, she too must have been letting Sam go.

They continued to remain connected in certain aspects of their lives, usually around efforts to save money, now that they were keeping two households going. One of these arrangements developed around recycling and trash. They'd paid for a yearly permit to use the town facilities and decided not to purchase a second sticker. So Sam brought his paper and trash to the house each week, usually on Friday, and he would pick up the two cats so they could spend the weekend with him.

One morning after he'd dropped off a container of paper to be recycled, Lucy noticed a long receipt sticking out of the top. Thinking it was an airline ticket, she pulled it out and found it was a bus ticket dated from the previous weekend, the destination, somewhere south of Los Angeles. She asked Sam about it, and he admitted that he'd been taking weekend trips to California by bus, afraid of putting more wear and tear on his car or having a breakdown. In order to hide his travel activity, he continued to take the cats on the weekends, leaving them alone in his apartment from Friday night to Sunday night with the air conditioning turned off. They'd been suffering in the triple-digit Utah heat for weeks. He would never under any circumstances take the cats again. Lucy didn't hesitate when it came to protecting the animals. But whatever defenses she had constructed to hold herself together also prevented her from wondering what else he was capable of.

Lucy

A month or so later, Henry, one of the cats they'd rescued together, got sick. He needed regular infusions of fluids given through a needle under the skin, not a painful process for him, but a challenging one for Lucy. After several days of thunderstorms that sent him into hiding, she couldn't manage to get him out from under the bed for his treatment. So she called Sam, as he was only a few minutes away, and asked him if he could come over just to help her get Henry out.

"There's something I have to explain," he said. "I'm coming over to help, but I'm not five minutes away. It'll take me a half hour to get there. I'm heading over right now."

He did come, and they took care of Henry. Then they sat down at the kitchen table and Lucy asked what was going on. It turned out that Sam had left the apartment, after changing the term of the lease from nine months to six, and was living in a trailer in the parking lot of Don and Pamela's business. Lucy sat there stunned, just trying to grasp the entirety of what that meant, when he added that he was moving to California. Following that announcement, he launched into an unsettling litany of regrets and reversals: he'd made a mistake, he shouldn't be moving away, he shouldn't be leaving her.

"I can change this," he said. "I'm gonna stay."

And then he was gone, as if the tender Sam had tried to rise up to the surface again, only to get shoved back down. In the aftermath, Lucy received a flurry of tearful phone calls from Pamela, who was openly and shamelessly distraught about Sam leaving. Lucy didn't ask questions. She didn't allow herself to dwell on the nature of Sam's relationship with that family, his motives for working his way closer to Pamela, or what might have precipitated his decision to leave Utah permanently. She had no choice now but to figure out how to manage on her own.

Before Sam left Utah, Mackenzie died, and a month later Henry followed. Lucy's high-strung Aussie shepherd, who never fully recovered from her original abusive household but had learned from Lucy to receive comfort, had struggled for years to regulate her body temperature. Mac's condition had steadily deteriorated into frequent bouts of heat stroke, even though Lucy kept the house climate controlled at 65 degrees for her around the clock, year round.

Both Sam and the vet responded as if they thought Lucy was imagining the frequency of the dog's strokes, but she managed to convince Sam that they needed to take her in. As they were standing there and Lucy explained what she had observed, Mac stroked and went into a seizure right on the table. The vet put her down on the spot. Not long afterward, Henry had to be hospitalized in Las Vegas. He'd developed fairly severe neurological problems that progressed into seizures, which continued as Lucy and Sam made their way to the animal hospital from Fort Lyell. When they arrived, the vet explained that the seizures were painful and traumatic, and that it would be inhumane to allow the cat to continue to suffer with them. A staff person brought him out to see them, IV tubes taped in place. He purred heartily, and then they said goodbye. Within a week Sam left Utah for good too.

38

RE-PRESENTATION

Utah, 2005

Lucy

Oh to be free— and purely artist. To care only about art.

—*Incest: From 'A Journal of Love:*
The Unexpurgated Diary of Anaïs Nin

THE MODEL HOUSE SOLD TO a photographer, and once again Lucy had to find space for her classes. The rest of the winter they met in the Fort Lyell Fire House. For a while she could do nothing but hide her grief from her students, determined not to impose her sorrow upon them. Winter transitioned into an unusually bad fire season that quickly became serious enough to force them out in order to make room for additional emergency responders coming into Fort Lyell. They bounced from there to a temporary and untenable arrangement in a students' home, with diminishing hope of finding opportunities in the village. Then Lucy got a call from Alan's secretary. A bookseller had decided to leave a large, well-lit space in the heart of the arts village, creating an opening for a new teaching studio. The space was perfect, but Lucy was concerned about the cost. Her insecurity around holding onto teaching space and her increasing worries about paying high

Lucy

rent in Arena Roja prompted her to begin dreaming about starting a cooperative painting studio, the only way that seemed feasible for her to occupy
a central location and sustain the $700-a-month rent.

The original class had grown into a group of engaged, serious-minded
students who were deeply committed, not only to painting but to selling
their art. They had thrived and were doing extraordinary work. To Lucy's
dismay, though, a few of them had come to define success in terms of selling paintings. Her emphasis had always been on the guiding principle that
successful painting should be about process, about finding and following
one's inner eye and painting from the heart, without attachment to a set of
rules or a price tag. But they'd become attached to the idea that making art
was all about selling, that a painting could be considered successful only if
someone bought it. While Lucy was pleased by their level of commitment
to their art and the distance they'd come since they'd begun painting, she
was uncomfortable, as they were about to mount their first show, with the
motivation expressed by some of the most strident members of the group.

A strong-willed few relentlessly pressured her to tell them what their
work was worth and immediately dismissed her reluctant suggestions, of-
fended that they were too low. She argued that this was a personal decision
made by an artist, and it wasn't her place to set prices on others' works.
One student, insulted and determined to prove her wrong, set her paintings at top price and actually did sell a small piece that Lucy had considered
overpriced. She knew she had neither the strength nor the will to fight that
sort of battle.

During their first meeting to explore the co-op idea, the most assertive
students insisted upon setting up rules about who would be allowed to
join, pushing to control everything from forming a standards-driven board
who would select members based on portfolios to banning the practice of
playing music while people were working. They met twice, and both times
Lucy left in tears, feeling besieged, unable to imagine anyone painting in an
environment like that, unable to accept the group's elitist approach, which
stood in opposition to her vision of a working studio shared by a community of artists and students with varying levels of experience, sharing
space and inspiration, supporting each other, giving one another room to

follow their creative calling in whatever direction it might take them. She wanted anyone with the desire to learn and the passion to paint to be free to explore their art and to grow, just as those fifteen had done when their classes—and their journeys as painters—began.

Perhaps Lucy had given them a little too much confidence in themselves in the ways she'd encouraged and cajoled them into making that next brush stroke and finding their way through to a completed work. She praised their efforts and their finished pieces and let them know when their paintings approached gallery quality. And much of their work was that good.

Many of them had arrived wounded and shut down by unkind instructors in the past. Now they seemed poised to become arbiters of others' success in ways not unlike the rule-bound and dismissive treatment that had once been hurtful to them. Lucy had seen and been part of the process through which they had found and developed their capacity, and she had seen their art soar. Perhaps they just possessed strong personalities and hefty egos. Perhaps she'd fed and shored up those egos more than she should have. But two things were clear: the adversarial dynamic of this group, talented as they were, threatened to undermine her vision of an open studio, and taking the cooperative route would mean any control she might hope to maintain over the direction, tone, and approach to making art in that space would be lost to a few obstinate voices.

So Lucy decided to risk everything and rent the studio on her own. The only way she could manage the overhead was to subdivide the space into twenty-foot floor sections attached to lofty wall space that individuals could rent from her. Many of her students had no space in which to paint at home, so this seemed like a need that such an arrangement would fill.

She would hold classes there on a widely published three-day-a-week schedule, and studio time would flow around that. Renters would have their own keys and have access to the studio whenever they wanted. She would give private lessons, and she would continue to take her own painting forward into the new territory she was exploring, having become increasingly drawn to the abstract work that a handful of students had done under her guidance. The wonderfully high ceilings would allow any and all studio members to display their work. They would hold open studio events and otherwise be surrounded by vibrant examples of all the styles representing their individual creative processes. That floor-to-ceiling display of diverse styles—none of which was imitative of Lucy or anyone else—would embody her vision of success. And with that vision Lazuli Studio was born.

When she made the decision to rent the studio, Lucy knew that Leslie and Arthur were on board, but she signed the lease entirely uncertain about whether or not any of the others would follow. They all did.

That first year in Lazuli had been one of profound grieving, a painful struggle to realize that she could live her life without Sam in it, and a process of finding strength in holding onto the principles upon which she wanted her studio to stand. And thrive. Perhaps she didn't realize how much oxygen he'd taken from her, how much energy and life-space she'd traded for a love so dark and doubtful.

Early that year Lucy received a state teaching fellowship based on a presentation she gave demonstrating the remarkable journey of her students as they transformed from beginners into the skilled painters they had become. She was also invited by a local university to paint a themed show that eventually came to include two other female artists, one a painter and the other working in three-dimensional media. The three of them shared an interest in probing questions of how we see strength and beauty in women as subjects, and their show drew from that concept.

Lucy had already begun painting a show for the Horsetail Gallery, but when the invitation came to paint for a larger venue with a much wider audience, Alan and his staff encouraged her without hesitation to go ahead. Though she initially struggled with the decision to accept the new project after having already committed to the Horsetail show, the Arena Roja Arts Village management graciously assured her that the university show, to be held in a corporate-funded museum gallery with strong academic affiliations, was much too important an opportunity for her to turn down. Alan had wholeheartedly supported her in her teaching, enthusiastic about the energy and engagement her classes had brought to the village. His faith in her commitment to keeping the vitality of the village alive and his appreciation of the role she played in its growth comforted her and gave her a sense of belonging she hadn't known there before, if ever.

It had been four years—and what seemed like a long and improbable journey of her own—since her work had been the focus of a major gallery show. Still, in a fairly short time Lucy had become a far different painter from the artist she'd been in Seattle *(SEE PAGE 283)*. She saw and felt her steady growth over the two years she'd worked on that show; in painting the women's portraits that signaled her movement toward abstraction, she hadn't considered—nor could she have anticipated at that time—how much more she might grow, or what circumstances, like extremes in weather that narrow or widen the rings of a tree, might mark the history of her inner eye and her creative spirit.

39

LIGHT AND SHADOW

LUCY AND I CAME INTO our friendship while she was still in the glow of a renewed sense of connection, what she described as a "deeper communion with the land, with place, and with self." She had left Utah less than two years earlier, in what seemed, paradoxically, both an abrupt and painfully long-overdue departure. I think, perhaps, it was only then that she'd begun to truly navigate her way through the depths of grief and the shifting terrain of selfhood, exploring an internal landscape that might have become just a little more knowable because she'd come to live in a wildly beautiful and beautifully wild place that felt, for all its mystery and power, like home. And this altogether different desertscape is where she came to more fully realize her transformation into an abstractionist.

In such a place, safety can be less a state than a sub-audible sound pattern, a resonant frequency perceived by the spirit that can act as an invitation to peer more deeply into the unexplored parts of who we are or to envision who we might become. Although she probably experienced it quite differently, when Lucy and I first met, I sensed that she wore a layer of protection around her as she traveled within one bounded phase of her journey. She also seemed to carry with her a sense of having arrived, shaking off the habits and the trappings of past explorations, past wreckages.

She already knew what it was to live skinless, as she called it, but there were undreamed of degrees of rawness and fire she had yet to pass through. New dimensions of illness she could never have anticipated. She wasn't lost, but her path had led her beyond the perimeter of the worn out map she'd carried on her way out of her previous life. I'm not sure how aware of this she was, but some part of her must have known she was in the midst of a brave gamble. Reflecting on that momentous invitation she made to me, I see now that it was her own leap of faith that enabled me to set out on the journey I so badly needed to take. Without coming into that arc, I wonder if I would I have mustered the belief necessary to sustain an inspired encounter with the unknown or to take the risks required to give a buried imagination another chance.

It's been ten years since Lucy asked me to give voice to her story. At that time, she needed to unburden herself by sharing it, perhaps not realizing how complicated a story it was or how difficult it would be to tell. But she believed it had the power to help others seeking or struggling to live an artist's life.

Her impulse to guide others toward their art took a consequential turn when we met that day in the gallery on the edge of a small village on the edge of the world. The conversation that began there under her painting *Child of Darkness* (SEE PAGE 273), as I stood transfixed by that enigmatic piece, goes on. I like to think that on some level Alces had spoken to each of us, primed us for the journey upon which we were about to embark, whether we knew it or not. No doubt it's still speaking to us.

Even more than the experience of that particular place is where and how each of us chose to meet it within ourselves, how it called us forward, allowed us to break free of the constraints under which we had lived until then, constraints that had kept us from thriving. Our mutual transformations could not have happened without that "communion" with land, place, and self. For some, the relationship with the landscape drives the spirit, steadies the inner compass. Perhaps it's that sense of connectedness that gives us the courage to step into the unknown without a map and the openness to embrace the wild idea that living a creative life is possible, if not within reach.

Lucy once described her first step after moving to New Mexico as letting go of everything she had held as true about herself. However, even before her arrival, the first phase of her dramatic shift from representation to abstraction was under way. That process is reflected in the six paintings that are referenced in the previous chapters, where they mark important stages in Lucy's path through loss, grief, and despair. The complete transformation that this body of work initiated would only be fully realized when, knowing she was on her own in ways she had never been before, Lucy began to internalize a new reality. She would eventually own that reality when she was able to say, "No one was coming to live my life for me." If she had previously lived her life almost entirely for others—and Utah made that all too painfully clear—New Mexico freed her to live for no one but herself.

In those two years when Lucy was learning to leave Utah behind and to accept its hard lessons, I'd been working my way deeper into denial. Looking back now, knowing Lucy's particular sensitivities, I wonder if I came across to her as radioactively so. I was acutely aware that I'd been living too much for others, allowing their demands to define my purpose. That mode was all I knew. I'd spent two years grasping at anything that would allow me to believe I could keep moving along through circumstances as they were. Beyond the glimmer of awareness that I needed to make space for creative work in my life and that I had no breathing room to do so, I initially dismissed Lucy's suggestions about rethinking my professional choices, my life as a teacher. Her ready willingness to state such a thing directly unsettled me. Yet six months after meeting her, I found myself sitting in a window seat on a flight to New Mexico, desperate to find a way to make that space to write but not comprehending what it really meant. There I sat, the great expanse of the Plains rolled out in winter mist below, writing notes in a tiny notebook, knowing—and fearing—that Lucy would probe me about how I was going to make writing a part of my life.

I wrote the words that sounded right, formed a neat schedule, a plan in which I'd commit to setting aside small bits of time each week for that purpose. As I wrote the tiny words on tiny lines, I tried to dismiss the fact that I was barely keeping up with the workload as it was, already grading papers and other assignments until midnight every night of the week and all day on the weekends, getting up extra early on weekdays to plan my classes. But I formed the words, made lists on the tiny pages outlining my big plan to make time for me. People did this. Right? Come summer I'd be able to do so much more. I even mapped out the summer weeks. Time would be very tight, considering the new courses I'd already committed to developing for the fall. But I'd find a way. Until then I'd get started in small steps each week and keep feeding the dream. It had to be possible to keep a small fire burning and not let it die.

On that flight I convinced myself that I could make adjustments, clear enough space, even if it was just an hour or two a week. I had absorbed just enough of what Lucy had been saying in our email exchanges to believe in this tentative arrangement. I didn't own the words yet, but I intended to. Still, Lucy's messages seemed to suggest that she saw the idea of making space in the life I was living as a compromise. I recoiled every time she urged me to seriously reconsider my priorities. They weren't priorities; they were just what had to be in order for me to do my job. But here I was, impulsively taking the better part of a week out of the precious three I had, knowing I needed every last minute to recover from the fall semester and prepare for the spring. Disregarding all that, I was on my way to visit a woman I'd spent at most an hour with the previous summer. One of her paintings hung on our wall. We'd exchanged emails for six months. This one time I might just have to begin a semester less than fully prepared and catch up as I went along.

I'm not even sure whose idea it was for me to return to Alces during winter break, but I don't think it was Lucy's. The pretext was that she would interview me as part of a blog series about people finding their art. I wasn't comfortable being showcased for something that was still only aspirational, but dubious as my survival scheme was, the aspirations had a hold on me. In the intervening months of our correspondence, Lucy had kicked into life-coach mode, and I'd reluctantly given myself permission to go along with that. Something had begun to shift inside me, pulling me more powerfully than any rational reasoning against it in a direction I hadn't fully embraced and didn't understand. For what it was worth, I was willing to imagine, a little afraid to want more, and certainly not expecting it.

Surely Lucy understood this state all too well, but I wouldn't begin to comprehend how deeply she identified with my circumstances until many months later, when I had become the interviewer and we had dug down into the existential crises she had survived in her own life. In learning about her journey, I found myself drawn to her difficulty walking away from unhealthy relationships and situations long before I recognized my own struggle to break free of mine. I went ahead and planned the trip that I didn't have time for. She had already tapped into my need to locate and support the part of myself I'd allowed to slip away for longer than I was willing to admit. She watched me cling to the image of myself as the dutiful college professor inching my way toward tenure, my availability spigot locked in open position. She was persistent, and so was I.

We had been reading each other from the start. I sensed Lucy's desire to influence my direction in ways I wasn't prepared to be moved, and initially I was a little put off by it. While I welcomed her personal interest and admired her altruistic nature, the suggestion that I think about giving it all up made me bristle. She didn't seem to appreciate my hard-earned and relatively late-starting academic career, our dependence on my salary, my long-standing commitment to teaching. The satisfaction I derived from the craft to which I'd attached all of my professional energy. I knew it was possible for some people to teach full time and write productively. Why did such an arrangement seem like an impossibly long reach for me? Why did she seem to dismiss that as a viable option?

I wondered what my colleagues knew that I didn't, what they had figured out about how to survive the daily onslaught, how they must have hardened themselves to all the deep reservoirs of need and the endless demands in ways I couldn't or wouldn't. What was the mystery behind others learning to protect those essential parts of their personal lives that I'd constantly left exposed or untended in order to tend to the needs of students who seemed to be growing needier and more distressed—and sometimes more belligerent—every semester? These were not concerns I could share with Lucy.

Not until I came home so sick from that stolen handful of days in Alces and was still sick three months later did I begin to consider the choice that Lucy kept reminding me I had, the choice that in its wholesale form I had rejected, believing I would eventually figure out how to make it work both ways. Not until I had completely lost my ability to speak, facing the potential of never regaining my voice, did I begin to understand how dire my circumstances were. Not until years later would I see how badly mismatched that particular college and I turned out to be. Only now am I able to see myself as having once been a beleaguered soul fighting for survival in a beleaguered institution, to see myself as something other than a failure for giving up that fight.

By spring, whether or not to continue teaching was no longer a choice. My body had made it for me. And Lucy, having come out the other side of a major catastrophe or two, had already primed me for that eventuality. It would be a long, uncertain recovery running parallel to a long, uncertain initiation into the process of reading and writing someone's life. It has taken the years since to understand that I didn't lose everything I was when I turned away from my teaching life to gather myself up and begin living an artful one.

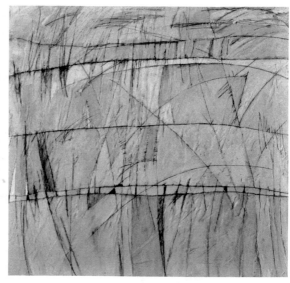

As I worked my way slowly toward completion of the manuscript, Lucy began painting again following a three-and-a-half year illness-driven hiatus. She returned to her easel with a subtle palette and a new celebratory take on the land around her, a new appreciation for simply standing and facing a canvas, brushes in hand, spirit flying. That process began with a lightness, a dynamic sketchiness exemplified in *Storm Over the Jemez (SEE PAGE 274)*. Painting the earth as it spoke to her, now that she could hear and see it once again through still-raw pain, she turned this into yet another recovery, an awakening from another dark time. Once again, painting gave Lucy the inspiration to embrace light and color in the world again.

Gradually, she worked her way to a louder palette enlivened by an exploration of line and depth. The next phases of her work show the artist playing with dimensionality, paint surface, and white space, as she lightly invokes familiar earth tones and geometrics.

In the works from this period, I see another shift—albeit a gentle but unmistakable one—along the spectrum of abstraction to a softer, brighter, perhaps simpler space, dominated by stripped-down but no less recognizable hills and arroyos, fences and trees, fields and horizons. *Red Willow (SEE PAGE 275)* displays a lyrical sense of movement, reflecting the

energy of another interseason, when signs of growth appear once again on a still snowbound land. Bold patches of color awaken two-dimensional space like small, clear voices piercing a vast silence, a bright message emanating from an irrepressible spirit declaring itself—despite all improbability—still here. These forward-calling voices illuminate us from within, even as they speak to a beautiful creative mystery: how we keep them alive.

Along with the signature fracture lines that have distinguished Lucy's work for much of the past decade, I now see the emergence of a different kind of negative space, which somehow feels more lived in, even where white canvas dominates. *Llano Vista* (SEE PAGE 276) accentuates the ambiguity between the architecture of nature and the work of human hands that have incorporated simple found materials into the marking of boundaries or the building of enclosures. All seems in some way of the earth, evoking a starkly understated landscape of small canyons and fields, perhaps a village or a series of rough hills, a comfortably uncertain horizon.

Lucy's later works announce an openness to possibility and the interplay of depth and flat space. They represent a return to life, to the joy of walking the land, taking in its rises and falls, its seasons and stories, its unfinished business. The unfinished business of living. They mark the artist once again reveling in beauty-bound solitude after a long struggle to

remember what it feels like to embrace external things. Which leads me to ask how, over the same time period, the workings of my own inward and outward eye have changed, and in the end, who really inhabits that liminal space as I move through my own life's shifting landscape.

Lucy and I have relied on our deep bonds with land and landscape to hold us—as if cradled by stone and sky—through scary and vulnerable times when the peopled world or our own bodies have let us down. Often we seek the comfort of wilderness for its own sake and easily return to it by way of our shared affinities. Not surprisingly, the harder endeavor to reflect on my own creative journey and to grow and heal through it still remains bound up in Lucy's, or at least it feels that way. Some of that is friendship, of course; some of it is the intertwined nature of our respective healing processes, the return routes we've cleared to art and to life. The hard letting go of one purpose in order to fly forward to another. The return of my literal voice and the release of a writerly one. My concomitant appreciation of silence. These paths travel straight through Alces and remain linked to its earthen walled village, its piñon-lined canyons, its rough quilt of pastures, its bald-peaked massif towering over fir-clothed foothills, its historic and cultural underbelly, its religion of water rights, its sometimes-uneasy association of artists and the descendants of Spanish land-grant recipients.

I believe the lessons we take away from the soul searching that has informed our experiences as fellow travelers, as well as our roundabout routes to and from art, help us understand the process of remaking ourselves and the essential role art has played in these incarnative acts. Out of that belief comes the hope that this rendering of Lucy's story does justice, not only to her journey, but to her capacity to move beyond her uneasy encounters with love and to move, more decidedly than ever, toward the kind she's searching for, the kind she once referred to as "deep and hard-held love."

And so, looking back before I train my eye on the next phase of my own creative journey, I see that I have finally managed to relinquish my previously held sense of what it means to tell someone's story and what it means to tell one's own. Exploring the shadow and light that have animated Lucy's life shook me out of the narrow view I arrived with and freed me enough to see into and grow more comfortable knocking around in the often unfixed space of interior landscape.

That part of the journey has taught me a different form of perspective, one that comes from embracing self-interpretation from multiple directions. It has taught me to pause, to allow the inner eye to adjust its aperture to sometimes dim conditions, sometimes garish or blinding ones, in order to find form. I think I can say now that the art of it happens when that inner eye is turned outward again, working to reconfigure the shapes and colors of emotion—of lives being lived—so that another can experience them as truth.

CHILD OF DARKNESS

STORM OVER THE JEMEZ

RED WILLOW

LLANO VISTA

BEYOND DIMENSIONALITY:
AN EPILOGUE OF SIX WORKS

WHAT FOLLOWS IS A SERIES of six narratives that emerged out of the experience of walking around inside a set of paintings that mark a singular part of Lucy's artistic and personal journey. The works represent a time during which her struggle to move through great emotional pain led to a new way of interpreting the world around her, the people in it, and herself. While examining my own ability to speak for someone else's process of surviving trauma, I decided to give the paintings a chance to speak for themselves through my interpretive lens. I wanted to let the play of light, color, and form on these canvases do a little storytelling work, hoping the renderings might fill in or enhance some of the negative space created by my own. These *painting pieces* are meant as an invitation to step inside the images and trace the hand, eye, and heart that created them.

J-M

ZION

MALORIE

LESLIE

CHEYENNE

DAYNA

1

J-M — Full color on page 278

IT'S LATE MORNING. THE CANVAS is a freeze frame but far from static. The sun has risen high enough to shorten the shadows of the elderly walkers to rounded pools of dark ocean blue-green pouring from the contact points of a heel or toe in mid-step on the sidewalk. The man's mahogany cane swings forward as he moves toward the curb, which he will meet no more than two strides ahead. His right arm brings the cane forward. Sun skims past the brim of his white baseball cap, glancing his gray bristled chin and the nubbed wool of his burgundy sweatered shoulder. Clean cement squares and broad bars of white road paint mark the crosswalk beyond, awash in sun. The stiff creasing of khaki behind the flexed knee of the woman be-

side him draws energy up from the raised sole of her sneaker, through her heel, and up the back of her leg. Her toe has just pulled away from her shadow, which merges with a spread of dark lace across the cement in front of her, the rough shape of a leafy tree otherwise beyond the canvas frame, standing somewhere between the sidewalk and the sun.

A line of trees revealed by only the green of their leaves shades the next block straight ahead, though the sun's angle is high enough and the pink-white globe lights stand tall enough on their dark iron arms to catch it like a diminishing parade of bright bereted heads leading to where the horizon—if it were visible—would meet the pale strip of sky behind the treetops. The blue-white vertical wedge of sky appearing through a fil-igree of green drives the scene's perspective, further defining the street's angular path beyond what can be seen, as a jumble of activity loads the space between the couple and a horizon that is at once completely blocked from view yet as present as the two figures dominating the foreground.

The traffic light signals lucent green against the living green of leaves. The strolling couple head toward the shadier next block, where a dense mass of shapes and patches of light pack the sidewalk, above which the old-fashioned turquoise and pale red neon J-M Hotel sign makes promi-nent display of the location. A white café umbrella and a potted plant catch and spread the sun beneath the sign where the bustle of activity converg-es. A waiter or perhaps a patron standing in that same bright sun bends toward two seated patrons, one of whom is about to sip something from a glass. Ivy seeks the sun, creeping upward along the face of a red brick building, where bay window frames, façade decorations, hand-painted and commercial signs fill but somehow don't overwhelm the middle ground. People, sky, lamp posts, traffic lights, painted railings, slices of parked cars and brownstone buildings poking through in the haphazardness of a mo-ment, carry the eye toward a distinct center point and draw the motion of the street scene forward, finding a symmetry there in liquid light and deep-sea shadow, at once soft and clean-edged, crisp with the high contrast of approaching noon.

2

Zion — Full color on page 279

THEY WALK BRISKLY TOWARD THE lodge, the lowering sun so bright the young woman in front has raised her hand, palm forward, to shield her eyes. Her stride is strong—perhaps rushed, yet relaxed—and angular. She pushes ahead, facing away at a three-quarter angle. A line runs from her raised hand straight through the core of her body and down her left leg, her right arm stiff and straight along the same downward diagonal and ending with an ice-blue plastic water bottle that she grasps by its neck. Its angle and the slosh of water it holds suggest the swing of her arm as it begins to drive forward with the movement of her broad step and the opposing movement of her raised arm, which is entirely hidden behind her head. Her right leg swings straight

forward. Her ankle, exposed beneath the hem of her dark-as-midnight athletic stretch pants, carries the shift in movement, a tension visible in its front tendons.

The composition of her body, highlighted by the white and dull rust stripe along the outer seam of her right pant leg, forms an upside-down *y*, or a lambda in reverse, its shorter leg pointing forward rather than back. The backlit edges of her thick dark hair and raised hand, the side of a fleshed cheek suggesting a squint that is not in view, the top plane of a bare shoulder, the tank-top–covered breast and tor-so, and the stretchy athletic material covering her thigh and lower leg tingle with the bright heat of the day. Though her slack blue-black daypack with pale blueish piping is in full shadow of her body, its volume—its moderate weight held fast but not too tightly against her body—moves with her form while it pulls downward against it.

Her partner, a step behind her, is also hustling ahead toward the lodge. A red bandana knotted at the back of her head, she holds something, perhaps a map, in her left hand and looks down to study it as she walks. Her deep storm green shadow strikes transparently behind her. The newish cut-off jeans she wears rolled to the knee. That shadow dives dramatically off the bottom left edge of the canvas, distorted by the angle of the sun hitting her body full on but only visible where it reflects off the paper in her hand or pours over the top of her head, the contour of her barely revealed brow, the smooth outline of a bending arm. The shadow chases her along by the tip of a deeply treaded toe that's just pushing off and manages, through the double illusion of its own two-dimensionality, to define the three-dimensional space around her as she unselfconsciously reaches back over her right shoulder to adjust her black tank top strap or to scratch an itch on the back of her neck. Her bare arms, shoulder blades, and lower legs move with sturdy youthful energy while the sum total of her stance conveys a hint of tentativeness or distraction.

They're about to step into a slice of deep shade as the sun moves behind the low flat stone and wood frame building, its picture window entryway ahead of the walkers but reflecting soft greenery and more red stone con-tours behind our vantage point, conjuring even more tangible space outside the canvas. Sap-green leaves and pale rose-gray roof tiles convey complemen-tary patterns of orderliness. The blurring of an arrowhead shaped national park sign hanging deep in the shadow of the building's inverted corner is intensified by the almost blinding white light flooding the foreground, just as the contrast challenged eye would perceive it. We almost want to raise a hand to block the glare, as the lead park visitor is doing. But in the distance, behind the roof of the lodge, in the upper left corner of the canvas, a single triangular patch of pale blue and violet haze suggests a vertical slice of a dis-tant rock face, now out of the sun's direct rays and entirely abstracted by the deepening atmosphere of a late afternoon.

3

....

Malorie — Full color on page 280

SHE MIGHT BE SIXTEEN OR seventeen, sitting with a stiffness that could be an expression of shy discomfort at being photographed. Her face and torso fill more than two thirds of the canvas, her slender shoulders slouched a little forward as if she's leaning her wrists on her knees. She sits against a backdrop of lush prickly pear cactus lobes that, spineless as they are, seem to embrace her and appear close enough to brush against her, were she to lean just a little farther backward. Perhaps she's sitting on a garden wall that's out of view, as is everything else below the waist, including her forearms. She wears a simple turquoise tank top that neither hides nor reveals. A delicate silver-beaded chain holds a small pink flower shaped charm that falls slightly askance, resting lightly on the flat of her upper sternum. The necklace leaves a perfect beaded shadow along her skin following the contour of her collarbone.

She faces us, but her startlingly dark eyes are fixed slightly askance. It could be the bright sun or a shadow of sadness, but she doesn't quite meet the onlooking lens. Or does she? A barely perceptible tension around her mouth suggests an effort, perhaps to hide a smile, perhaps to appear more at ease than she is.

Her brown, glossy hair is very straight, pulled back so casually that copper and umber strands fly out lopsidedly from one side. It wasn't combed or brushed back but pulled haphazardly into a ponytail, as if she was driven by the intensity of the midday sun or a sudden need to simply get it out of her way. So rather than lying smoothly against her head, her hair remains unevenly ribboned and a little unruly. A few dark strands she missed peek out from behind the slope of her right shoulder; two more dance over an unassuming white stud earring on the left.

A dark red shape begins about halfway up the right edge of the canvas, follows loosely the diagonal line of the girl's shoulder, disappears behind her, and emerges just under her right ear, continuing to the top left of the canvas and dividing the image nearly in half. It's the profile of Mad Mountain's sloping shoulder, not painted with meticulous precision like the shape of the girl's face or the sun falling across her forehead, arms, neck, those rebellious strands of hair, or the green planes of prickly pear fanning out behind her. The mountain's contours are suggested by loose bold strokes of carmine, scarlet, and magenta with patches of violet peering through, streaks of black shadows marking ridges. If not for the mountain's signature outline against an improbably convincing beige sky, it might have hung there, a curtain of bright and dark red brush strokes distracting the eye from the tightly rendered figure in the foreground. But somehow this abstracted mound of rock living behind the figure provides depth and texture without stealing anything from the smooth face and glowing flesh of the reticent, almost-smiling girl. The mountain is raw and willful in precisely the ways she is not, though the tensions captured in her body and expression—the honest brush strokes that convey the sun streaking life into her wayward hair—also connect them on a deeper level. Perhaps she too seeks some kind of freedom.

4

....

Leslie — Full color on page 281

HER HEAD AT AN ALMOST perfect three-quarters view and the spheres of her gently tanned shoulders take up most of the canvas. The vantage point angle falls from slightly above and to her right. Her temple, just above the fine-framed arm of her eyeglasses, marks the absolute center of the nearly square canvas; the light traveling through the lens below directs the eye of the viewer to the painting's focal point. The woman leans slightly forward, looking down at a 45-degree angle toward something she's doing. Her focused gaze, the tension across the tops of her shoulders—all that is visible of them—and the taut vertical muscles that just catch the sun along the right side of her neck establish a unity between what is seen and what is not. She's busy with a task in front of her, pleasingly absorbed, alert, engaged.

Her mouth is moving either to or from a relaxed smile, her bottom lip drawing ever so slightly toward her orderly rounded teeth. She could be in the process of taking a breath, singing to herself, or speaking through her work to the person taking the photograph from less than an arm's length away. The tone of her skin shows faint signs of age, but only around the outer corner of her eye and in a slight gathering softness where the corner of her mouth meets and draws in the fullness of her cheek.

It's early morning, the sun low and bright, strong but as soft as it will be at any other time along its diurnal arc. The woman's chin-length hair falls light and straight, partially shading the side of her face, framing it with a white-gold curtain and texturing her cheek with a feathery shadow where the light passing through it leaves delicate striations against her skin. Perhaps it's late summer or early fall, still warm enough to wear an ice-pale blue tank top and matching overalls or a jumper whose flat metal cinch rings rest snugly against the cottony fabric of her shirt, sum-

mery but serviceable for long seasons of reliably warm and sunny weather. Slicing across the double layers of her shoulder straps, the jet black neck sash of an artist's smock forms an X against the faded cloud-blue material over her right shoulder and wraps behind her neck—under the shimmering blunt-cut of her hair—and back down the left side of her neck.

Bright sunlight falling at an extreme angle from above and behind us just manages to catch a backdrop of dracaena fronds emerging from a well of deep green-umber shade behind the woman. In the foreground it hits her cheekbone directly, while reflected light floods up from the space below her, highlighting the contours of her face. A perfect line leading from the center point along her eyeglasses frame toward the bottom right corner follows the downward angle of her head and reinforces the direction and calm intensity of her gaze.

The curved surfaces of her lenses are implied in the oval shapes that frame her eyes. But the light bending and warping as it travels through the lens closest to us becomes tangible in its effect: complex patterns created by light traveling through curved glass hitting the fleshy side of her nose and the bony slope where the bridge and eye socket meet. These patterns, rendered so faithfully and with such meticulous fascination, capture a marvelous trick the sun played that morning as it passed both toward us and away from us, marking a path in rounded fragments of light and shadow that happened to fall on both sides of the glass at once.

5

....

Cheyenne — Full color on page 282

HER FORM ACTS AS BOTH a centerpiece and a detail. She sits, facing forward and away, looking out from a perch of loosely painted red rock forms— across a torrent of flowers, a clump of twisted vertical stalks, and a patch of thorn-crowned cacti—to an expanse of pink and violet desert swales that give way to a distant sawtoothed ridge of lavender peaks. She wears a tightly rendered gambler style straw hat with a black bow and narrow black piping around the inside edge of the neatly upturned brim. A shock of summer-streaked straw- and copper-blonde hair juts out from below the brim and rides the side of her neck, just reaching the back of her left shoulder. She wears a crisp, sleeveless western shirt with a center pleat down the back and a pair of tan linen shorts rolled to the top of her one visible thigh and held high on her waist with a stylish dark leather concho belt. Her shorts have a comfortable looseness that gathers, softly tucking across the sacrum and buttocks, suggesting her modestly trim shape.

She balances on her sit bones, her left hip slightly higher than the right, her left knee raised to her chest and leaning gently to the outside, hooked in place with a cantilevered arm that wraps around just at the knee. Her back is entirely in shadow, fooling the eye into registering the fabric of her shirt as something between pale blue and violet, an echo of the distant hills and mountains and sky. But the top edge of her left shoulder, the right side of her torso, and the top slope of her right shoulder receive direct sun from a high frontal angle, revealing the clean whiteness of her light cotton blouse. A narrow bead of light follows the upper contour of her left shoulder and upper arm, out to the knob of her elbow; another catches the smooth inner line of her left thigh.

Part of the helix of her left ear emerging from below the hat brim, along with a small silver hoop earring that wraps closely around the lobe: these are all we see of her face. She appears at ease, suggesting deep reverie, despite her angular pose. The lines of her straight back and left knee tucked into the crook of her bent arm form a triangle—a vertical down her spine, a diagonal up and out from her hip to where her knee is braced behind her arm, and a horizontal from the elbow across to her shoulder—like a tea kettle with a sharply pointed handle. Clearly she has found her balance there in that particular spot. Her body communicates strongly that she is relaxed, vital, awake.

Her expression speaks through the mood of the landscape into which she is subsumed, a comfortable meeting of serenity and intensity, beginning with fiery, flat streaks of red and brown applied with broad abstracted strokes in the foreground and moving all the way out to a faded azure sky that whitens with soft but distinct brush marks where it diminishes into a violet line of mountains sinking into pink mistiness in the middle ground. There, a few desert foothills swell like waves surging gently in a dark magenta sea. We see through the back of the woman's head what her eyes see, out beyond swaths of yellow, gold, and pink flowers that dance around her.

Fearless impressionistic brushstrokes loosely illuminate yellow bells and desert sunflower petals, wafting masses of beige and gold playing against spiny brownish prickly pear needles, the furry silver coats of wooly torches, spear-like shapes—perhaps pink beardtongue and desert paintbrush—bordering a thin stand of ocotillo canes. Translucent as watercolor, the bed of Santa Rita prickly pear turned aqua blue and teal cascades around the woman's right side, picking up bold hues of cerulean. The cacti's negative space is blocked in with burnt red earth tones and an occasional bright wash of violet, somehow balanced and not brought to garishness either by the contrast between lava red and glassy blue or by the yellow daubs that form a textured floral border between the cactus bed and the rounded corner of a red mud house. The structure blocks nearly half of the horizon but provides an anchor and an opening, a single window reflecting the whitened azure sky.

Though the back of the woman's head faces the viewer, the conspicuous black rear bow of her hatband calling attention to itself, there is no doubt her eyes are fixed on the deep cool of that horizon as she takes in the sun and the energy and the luster of the garden that spreads before the rocky place she has chosen as her contemplation spot. She is out of her body, fully absorbed in the landscape's splendors and paradoxes, loading her imagination with color, filling it with possibility.

$$6$$

Dayna — Full color on page 283

SKY AND LAND ARE AFLAME, a primordial lava flow of color, of heat broken by looming blue-black mountains, dragonbacks slumping into shadow, a reddened black mesa cutting through a river of blood red, orange, and violet. Black too, but warmer, is a line of trees that anchors the near-ground edge of a deep scarlet valley, suggesting the flat bottom of a canyon where water must have run and might occasionally return, though the village it would have once sustained has been gone for centuries. Dark ridges of land in the distance wear sharp edges defined by outlines of magenta and light blue, a streak of yellow along a distant turquoise swell standing out but somehow not drawing attention to itself. Though out of direct view, the sun throws its light back up to a jagged diagonal slash of more pale blue, a long smudge of reflective cloud like an icicle piercing a blaze of orange, yellow, pink, and red that streaks the sky. Between the lumbering darkness of the mountains and the stern ridge of black rock along the right mid-ground, a deep field of cobalt and violet runs like a cool ocean through the middle of the canvas and fades into horizontal slivers of primary yellow, pink, orange-red, and manganese blue, a desert flowing into itself, holding back nothing.

A young girl, eight or nine years old, stands near the edge of a massive, muted, Naples yellow slab of rock illuminated by the sinking sun, the hidden master of ceremonies, making its magic from somewhere outside the frame, off to the girl's front left. Her form in the foreground is small in the midst of the deep and empty landscape, the roiling sky, the opposing bands of darkness and color beyond the platform upon which she stands. But she is not lost in that space because her body casts a looming wine red shadow that both dwarfs and announces her. The shadow, which links her equally to the arc of the sun

and to the earth, plunges from her diminutive feet—parallel to that long pale blue cloud that slices the sky in half—straight through the bottom left corner of the canvas. Given the sun's low angle, the little girl's shadow would stretch as wide as the sky, if only the canvas could encompass it.

The child stands facing straight ahead and to our right, her arms lightly folded and resting across her middle. Her gaze, focused beyond the canvas, draws her presence off in the direction of her quiet daydream, conspiring with her enormous shadow to reach far into the north and south we cannot see. The late-day rays, direct but beginning to gentle, highlight the edge of her face and the entire front of her body from the crown of her head down to a black high-top sneaker and set her compact shape off from the layers of space beyond her, out toward the mountains that could just as well represent the surface of the Red Planet as the desert of southern Utah.

The girl wears a red sun visor, a streaky blonde ponytail tied just above the band, a red T-shirt, and long navy blue pants. Her stance, with a slightly swayed back and the gentle swell of a child's belly, captures a little girl's innocence, her face the wide openness and vulnerability of a child beholding something terribly vast, stark, striking, mysterious. If her perch, just one giant step from the cliff edge, seems precarious, she stands steady, fast, cautious but calm and still in her thoughts on the edge of the world, wondering, perhaps, at the measurelessness of the land stretching around and below her, the spectacle of fading light yonder and above, and everywhere the fleeting colors that flare into almost impossible brilliance before shadows take over and the day folds into night.